Solving Systems
of Polynomial Equations

Conference Board of the Mathematical Sciences

CBMS

Regional Conference Series in Mathematics

Number 97

Solving Systems of Polynomial Equations

Bernd Sturmfels

Published for the
Conference Board of the Mathematical Sciences
by the
American Mathematical Society
Providence, Rhode Island
with support from the
National Science Foundation

CBMS Conference on Solving Polynomial Equations held at
Texas A&M University, College Station, Texas
May 20–24, 2002

Partially supported by the National Science Foundation

2000 *Mathematics Subject Classification*. Primary 13P10, 14Q99, 65H10;
Secondary 12D10, 14P10, 35E20, 52B20, 62J12, 68W30, 90C22, 91A06.

Maple® – Waterloo Maple, Inc., Ontario, Canada

MATLAB® – The MathWorks, Inc., Natick, MA

Library of Congress Cataloging-in-Publication Data

CBMS Conference on Solving Polynomial Equations (2002 : Texas A&M University)
    Solving systems of polynomial equations / Bernd Sturmfels.
        p. cm. — (Conference Board of the Mathematical Sciences regional conference series in
mathematics, ISSN 0160-7642 ; no. 97)
    Includes bibliographical references and index.
    ISBN 0-8218-3251-4 (alk. paper)
    1. Equations–Numerical solutions–Congresses.   2. Polynomials–Congresses.   I. Sturmfels, Bernd,
1962–   II. Title   III. Regional conference series in mathematics ; no. 97.

QA1.R33 no. 97
[QA214]
510 s–dc21   2002027951
[512.9′42]

Contents

Preface

This book grew out of the notes for ten lectures given by the author at the CBMS Conference at Texas A&M University, College Station, during the week of May 20-24, 2002. Paulo Lima Filho, J. Maurice Rojas and Hal Schenck did a fantastic job of organizing this conference and taking care of more than 80 participants, many of them graduate students working in a wide range of mathematical fields. We were fortunate to be able to listen to the excellent invited lectures delivered by the following twelve leading experts: Saugata Basu, Eduardo Cattani, Karin Gatermann, Craig Huneke, Tien-Yien Li, Gregorio Malajovich, Pablo Parrilo*, Maurice Rojas, Frank Sottile, Mike Stillman*, Thorsten Theobald, and Jan Verschelde*.

Systems of polynomial equations are for everyone: from graduate students in computer science, engineering, or economics to experts in algebraic geometry. This book aims to provide a bridge between mathematical levels and to expose as many facets of the subject as possible. It covers a wide spectrum of mathematical techniques and algorithms, both symbolic and numerical. There are two chapters on applications. The one about statistics is motivated by the author's current research interests, and the one about economics (Nash equilibria) recognizes Dave Bayer's role in the making of the movie *A Beautiful Mind*. (Many thanks, Dave, for introducing me to the stars at their kick-off party in NYC on March 16, 2001.)

At the end of each chapter there are about ten exercises. These exercises vary greatly in their difficulty. Some are straightforward applications of material presented in the text while other "exercises" are quite hard and ought to be renamed "suggested research directions". The reader may decide which is which.

We had an inspiring software session at the CBMS conference, and the joy of computing is reflected in this book as well. Sprinkled throughout the text, the reader finds short computer sessions involving polynomial equations. These involve the commercial packages `Maple`® and `MATLAB`® as well as the freely available packages `Singular`[1], `Macaulay 2`[2], `PHCpack`[3], and `SOSTools`[4]. Developers of the last three programs spoke at the CBMS conference. Their names are marked with a star above.

There are many fine computer programs for solving polynomial systems other than the ones listed above. Sadly, I did not have time to discuss them all. One

---

[1]Singular is a free software distributed under the GNU license. © Department of Mathematics and Centre for Computer Algebra, University of Kaiserslautern, Germany

[2]Macaulay 2: © Daniel R. Grayson and Michael E. Stillman (1993-2001) and is distributed free under the GNU license

[3]PHCpack: © 1998, Katholieke Universiteit Leuven, Department of Computer Science, Heverlee, Belgium

[4]SOSTools is a MATLAB® toolbox and freely available under the GNU license at: http://www.cds.caltech.edu/sostools or http://www.aut.ee.ethz.ch/~parrilo/sostools

such program is CoCoA[5] which is comparable to Singular and Macaulay 2. The
textbook by Kreuzer and Robbiano [**KR00**] does a wonderful job introducing the
basics of Computational Commutative Algebra together with examples in CoCoA.

Software is necessarily ephemeral. While the mathematics of solving polynomial
systems continues to live for centuries, the computer code presented in this book
will become obsolete much sooner. I tested it all in May 2002, and it worked well
at that time, on our departmental computer system at UC Berkeley. And if you
would like to find out more, each of these programs has excellent documentation.

I am grateful to the students in my graduate course, *Math 275: Topics in Applied Mathematics*, for listening to my ten lectures at home in Berkeley while I
first assembled them in the spring of 2002. Their spontaneous comments proved
to be extremely valuable for improving my performance later on in Texas. After
the CBMS conference, the following people provided very helpful comments on my
manuscript: John Dalbec, Jesus De Loera, Mike Develin, Alicia Dickenstein, Ian
Dinwoodie, Bahman Engheta, Stephen Fulling, Karin Gatermann, Raymond Hem-
mecke, Serkan Hoşten, Robert Lewis, Gregorio Malajovich, Pablo Parrilo, Francisco
Santos, Frank Sottile, Seth Sullivant, Caleb Walther, and Dongsheng Wu.

Special thanks go to Amit Khetan and Ruchira Datta for helping me while
in Texas and for contributing to Sections 4.5 and 6.2 respectively. Ruchira also
assisted me in the hard work of preparing the final version of this book. It was her
help that made the rapid completion of this project possible.

Last but not least, I wish to dedicate this book to the best team of all: my
daughter Nina, my son Pascal, and my wife Hyungsook. A million thanks for being
patient with your papa and putting up with his crazy early-morning work hours.

Bernd Sturmfels*
Berkeley, June 2002

---

[5]A. Capani, G. Niesi, L. Robbiano, CoCoA, a system for doing Computations in Commutative
Algebra, available via anonymous ftp from: http://cocoa.dima.unige.it

*The author was supported in part by the U.S. National Science Foundation, grants #DMS-
0200729 and #DMS-0138323

CHAPTER 1

Polynomials in One Variable

The study of systems of polynomial equations in many variables requires a good understanding of what can be said about one polynomial equation in one variable. The purpose of this chapter is to provide some basic tools for this problem. We shall consider the problem of how to compute and how to represent the zeros of a general polynomial of degree d in one variable x:

$$(1.1) \qquad p(x) \quad = \quad a_d x^d + a_{d-1} x^{d-1} + \cdots + a_2 x^2 + a_1 x + a_0.$$

1.1. The Fundamental Theorem of Algebra

We begin by assuming that the coefficients a_i lie in the field $\mathbb{Q}$ of rational numbers, with $a_d \neq 0$, where the variable x ranges over the field $\mathbb{C}$ of complex numbers. Our starting point is the fact that $\mathbb{C}$ is algebraically closed.

THEOREM 1.1. (**Fundamental Theorem of Algebra**) *The polynomial $p(x)$ has d roots, counting multiplicities, in the field $\mathbb{C}$ of complex numbers.*

If the degree d is four or less, then the roots are functions of the coefficients which can be expressed in terms of radicals. Here is how we can produce these familiar expressions in the computer algebra system `maple`. Readers more familiar with `mathematica`, or `reduce`, or other systems will find it equally easy to perform computations in those computer algebra systems.

```
> solve( a2 * x^2 + a1 * x + a0, x );
```

```
            2            1/2                    2            1/2
   -a1 + (a1   - 4 a2 a0)              -a1 - (a1   - 4 a2 a0)
1/2 ---------------------- , 1/2 ----------------------
            a2                            a2
```

The following expression is one of the three roots of the general cubic:

```
> lprint( solve( a3 * x^3 + a2 * x^2 +  a1 * x + a0, x )[1] );
```

```
1/6/a3*(36*a1*a2*a3-108*a0*a3^2-8*a2^3+12*3^(1/2)*(4*a1^3*a3
-a1^2*a2^2-18*a1*a2*a3*a0+27*a0^2*a3^2+4*a0*a2^3)^(1/2)*a3)
^(1/3)+2/3*(-3*a1*a3+a2^2)/a3/(36*a1*a2*a3-108*a0*a3^2-8*a2^3
+12*3^(1/2)*(4*a1^3*a3-a1^2*a2^2-18*a1*a2*a3*a0+27*a0^2*a3^2
+4*a0*a2^3)^(1/2)*a3)^(1/3)-1/3*a2/a3
```

The polynomial $p(x)$ has d distinct roots if and only if its *discriminant* is nonzero. The discriminant of $p(x)$ is the product of the squares of all pairwise differences of the roots of $p(x)$. Can you spot the discriminant of the cubic equation in the previous `maple` output? The discriminant can always be expressed as a polynomial in the coefficients $a_0, a_1, \ldots, a_d$. More precisely, it can be computed from the resultant (denoted Res_x and discussed in Chapter 4) of the polynomial $p(x)$ and its first derivative $p'(x)$ as follows:

$$\mathrm{discr}_x(p(x)) \quad = \quad \frac{1}{a_d} \cdot \mathrm{Res}_x(p(x), p'(x)).$$

This is an irreducible polynomial in the coefficients $a_0, a_1, \ldots, a_d$. It follows from Sylvester's matrix formula for the resultant that the discriminant is a homogeneous polynomial of degree $2d - 2$. Here is the discriminant of a quartic:

```
> f  :=  a4 * x^4 +  a3 * x^3 +  a2 * x^2 +  a1 * x +  a0 :
> lprint(resultant(f,diff(f,x),x)/a4);
```

```
-192*a4^2*a0^2*a3*a1-6*a4*a0*a3^2*a1^2+144*a4*a0^2*a2*a3^2
+144*a4^2*a0*a2*a1^2+18*a4*a3*a1^3*a2+a2^2*a3^2*a1^2
-4*a2^3*a3^2*a0+256*a4^3*a0^3-27*a4^2*a1^4-128*a4^2*a0^2*a2^2
-4*a3^3*a1^3+16*a4*a2^4*a0-4*a4*a2^3*a1^2-27*a3^4*a0^2
-80*a4*a3*a1*a2^2*a0+18*a3^3*a1*a2*a0
```

This sextic is the determinant of the following 7×7-matrix divided by a4:

```
> with(linalg):
> sylvester(f,diff(f,x),x);
```

[a4	a3	a2	a1	a0	0	0]
[0	a4	a3	a2	a1	a0	0]
[0	0	a4	a3	a2	a1	a0]
[4 a4	3 a3	2 a2	a1	0	0	0]
[0	4 a4	3 a3	2 a2	a1	0	0]
[0	0	4 a4	3 a3	2 a2	a1	0]
[0	0	0	4 a4	3 a3	2 a2	a1]

Galois theory tells us that there is no general formula which expresses the roots of $p(x)$ in radicals if $d \geq 5$. For specific instances with d not too big, say $d \leq 10$, it is possible to compute the Galois group of $p(x)$ over $\mathbb{Q}$. Occasionally, one is lucky and the Galois group is solvable, in which case maple has a chance of finding the solution of $p(x) = 0$ in terms of radicals.

```
> f  :=  x^6 + 3*x^5 + 6*x^4 + 7*x^3 + 5*x^2 + 2*x + 1:
> galois(f);
```

```
"6T11", {"[2^3]S(3)", "2 wr S(3)", "2S_4(6)"}, "-", 48,

   {"(2 4 6)(1 3 5)", "(1 5)(2 4)", "(3 6)"}
```

```
> solve(f,x)[1];
                1/2 1/3
1/12 (-6 (108 + 12 69    )
```

```
                    1/2 2/3       1/2                    1/2 1/3 1/2
  + 6 I (3 (108 + 12 69   )  + 8 69  + 8 (108 + 12 69   )   )


                     /              1/2 1/3
  + 72 )        /   (108 + 12 69   )
                /
```

The number 48 is the order of the Galois group and its name is "6T11". Of course, the user now has to consult help(galois) in order to learn more.

1.2. Numerical Root Finding

In symbolic computation, we frequently consider a polynomial problem as solved if it has been reduced to finding the roots of one polynomial in one variable. Naturally, the latter problem can still be very interesting and challenging from the perspective of numerical analysis, especially if d gets very large or if the a_i are given by floating point approximations. In the problems studied in this book, however, the a_i are usually exact rational numbers with reasonably small numerators and denominators, and the degree d rarely exceeds 100. For numerically solving univariate polynomials in this range, it has been the author's experience that maple does reasonably well and matlab has no difficulty whatsoever.

```
> Digits := 6:
> f := x^200 - x^157 + 8 * x^101 - 23 * x^61 + 1:
> fsolve(f,x);
                          .950624, 1.01796
```

This polynomial has only two real roots. To list the complex roots, we say:

```
> fsolve(f,x,complex);

-1.02820-.0686972 I, -1.02820+.0686972 I, -1.01767-.0190398 I,
-1.01767+.0190398 I, -1.01745-.118366 I, -1.01745 + .118366 I,
-1.00698-.204423 I, -1.00698+.204423 I, -1.00028 - .160348 I,
-1.00028+.160348 I, -.996734-.252681 I, -.996734 + .252681 I,
-.970912-.299748 I, -.970912+.299748 I, -.964269 - .336097 I,
ETC...ETC..
```

Our polynomial $p(x)$ is represented in matlab as the row vector of its coefficients $[a_d \, a_{d-1} \, \ldots \, a_2 \, a_1 \, a_0]$. For instance, the following two commands compute the three roots of the dense cubic $p(x) = 31x^3 + 23x^2 + 19x + 11$.

```
>> p = [31 23 19 11];
>> roots(p)
ans =
  -0.0486 + 0.7402i
  -0.0486 - 0.7402i
  -0.6448
```

Representing the sparse polynomial $p(x) = x^{200} - x^{157} + 8x^{101} - 23x^{61} + 1$ considered above requires introducing lots of zero coefficients:

```
>> p=[1 zeros(1,42) -1 zeros(1,55) 8 zeros(1,39) -23 zeros(1,60) 1]
>> roots(p)
ans =
```

```
    -1.0282 + 0.0687i
    -1.0282 - 0.0687i
    -1.0177 + 0.0190i
    -1.0177 - 0.0190i
    -1.0174 + 0.1184i
    -1.0174 - 0.1184i
ETC...ETC..
```

We note that convenient facilities are available for calling `matlab` inside of `maple` and for calling `maple` inside of `matlab`. We encourage our readers to experiment with the passage of data between these two programs.

Some numerical methods for solving a univariate polynomial equation $p(x) = 0$ work by reducing this problem to computing the eigenvalues of the companion matrix of $p(x)$, which is defined as follows. Let V denote the quotient of the polynomial ring modulo the ideal $\langle p(x) \rangle$ generated by the polynomial $p(x)$. The resulting quotient ring $V = \mathbb{Q}[x]/\langle p(x) \rangle$ is a d-dimensional $\mathbb{Q}$-vector space. Multiplication by the variable x defines a linear map from this vector space to itself.

$$(1.2) \qquad \mathrm{Times}_x \; : \; V \to V \, , \, f(x) \mapsto x \cdot f(x).$$

The *companion matrix* is the $d \times d$-matrix which represents the endomorphism Times_x with respect to the distinguished monomial basis $\{1, x, x^2, \ldots, x^{d-1}\}$ of V. Explicitly, the companion matrix of $p(x)$ looks like this:

$$(1.3) \qquad \mathrm{Times}_x \quad = \quad \begin{pmatrix} 0 & 0 & \cdots & 0 & -a_0/a_d \\ 1 & 0 & \cdots & 0 & -a_1/a_d \\ 0 & 1 & \cdots & 0 & -a_2/a_d \\ \vdots & \vdots & \ddots & \vdots & \vdots \\ 0 & 0 & \cdots & 1 & -a_{d-1}/a_d \end{pmatrix}$$

PROPOSITION 1.2. *The zeros of $p(x)$ are the eigenvalues of the matrix* Times_x.

PROOF. Suppose that $f(x)$ is a polynomial in $\mathbb{C}[x]$ whose image in $V \otimes \mathbb{C} = \mathbb{C}[x]/\langle p(x) \rangle$ is an eigenvector of (1.2) with eigenvalue λ. Then $x \cdot f(x) = \lambda \cdot f(x)$ in the quotient ring, which means that $(x - \lambda) \cdot f(x)$ is a multiple of $p(x)$. Since $f(x)$ is not a multiple of $p(x)$, we conclude that λ is a root of $p(x)$ as desired. Conversely, if μ is any root of $p(x)$ then the polynomial $f(x) = p(x)/(x - \mu)$ represents an eigenvector of (1.2) with eigenvalue μ. $\square$

COROLLARY 1.3. *The following statements about $p(x) \in \mathbb{Q}[x]$ are equivalent:*

- *The polynomial $p(x)$ is square-free, i.e., it has no multiple roots in $\mathbb{C}$.*
- *The companion matrix Times_x is diagonalizable.*
- *The ideal $\langle p(x) \rangle$ is a radical ideal in $\mathbb{Q}[x]$.*

We note that the set of multiple roots of $p(x)$ can be computed symbolically by forming the greatest common divisor of $p(x)$ and its derivative:

$$(1.4) \qquad q(x) \quad = \quad \gcd(p(x), p'(x))$$

Thus the three conditions in the Corollary are equivalent to $q(x) = 1$.

Every ideal in the univariate polynomial ring $\mathbb{Q}[x]$ is principal. Writing $p(x)$ for the ideal generator and computing $q(x)$ from $p(x)$ as in (1.4), we get the following general formula for computing the radical of any ideal in $\mathbb{Q}[x]$:

(1.5) $$\text{Rad}(\langle p(x) \rangle) \quad = \quad \langle p(x)/q(x) \rangle$$

1.3. Real Roots

In this section we describe symbolic methods for computing information about the real roots of a univariate polynomial $p(x)$. The *Sturm sequence* of $p(x)$ is the following sequence of polynomials of decreasing degree:

$$p_0(x) := p(x), \ p_1(x) := p'(x), \ p_i(x) := -\text{rem}(p_{i-2}(x), p_{i-1}(x)) \ \text{for} \ i \geq 2.$$

Thus $p_i(x)$ is the negative of the remainder on division of $p_{i-2}(x)$ by $p_{i-1}(x)$. Let $p_m(x)$ be the last non-zero polynomial in this sequence.

THEOREM 1.4. (**Sturm's Theorem**) *If $a < b$ in $\mathbb{R}$ and neither is a zero of $p(x)$ then the number of real zeros of $p(x)$ in the interval $[a, b]$ is the number of sign changes in the sequence $p_0(a), p_1(a), p_2(a), \ldots, p_m(a)$ minus the number of sign changes in the sequence $p_0(b), p_1(b), p_2(b), \ldots, p_m(b)$.*

We note that any zeros are ignored when counting the number of sign changes in a sequence of real numbers. For instance, a sequence of twelve numbers with signs $+, +, 0, +, -, -, 0, +, -, 0, -, 0$ has three sign changes.

If we wish to count all real roots of a polynomial $p(x)$ then we can apply Sturm's Theorem to $a = -\infty$ and $b = \infty$, which amounts to looking at the signs of the leading coefficients of the polynomials p_i in the Sturm sequence. Using bisection, one gets a procedure for isolating the real roots by rational intervals. This method is conveniently implemented in `maple`:

```
> p := x^11-20*x^10+99*x^9-247*x^8+210*x^7-99*x^2+247*x-210:
> sturm(p,x,-INFINITY, INFINITY);
                                    3
> sturm(p,x,0,10);
                                    2
> sturm(p,x,5,10);
                                    0

> realroot(p,1/1000);
                1101   551     1465   733      14509   7255
               [[----, ---],  [----, ---],  [-----,  ----]]
                1024   512     1024   512      1024    512

> fsolve(p);
            1.075787072, 1.431630905, 14.16961992
```

Another important classical result on real roots is the following:

THEOREM 1.5. (Déscartes's Rule of Signs) *The number of positive real roots of a polynomial is at most the number of sign changes in its coefficient sequence.*

For instance, the polynomial $p(x) = x^{200} - x^{157} + 8x^{101} - 23x^{61} + 1$, which was featured in Section 1.2, has four sign changes in its coefficient sequence. Hence it has at most four positive real roots. The true number is two.

If we replace x by $-x$ in Descartes's Rule then we get a bound on the number of negative real roots. It is a basic fact that both bounds are tight when all roots of $p(x)$ are real. In general, we have the following corollary to Descartes's Rule.

COROLLARY 1.6. *A polynomial with m terms has at most $2m-1$ real zeros.*

The bound in this corollary is optimal as the following example shows:

$$x \cdot \prod_{j=1}^{m-1} (x^2 - j)$$

All $2m-1$ zeros of this polynomial are real, and its expansion has m terms.

1.4. Puiseux Series

Suppose now that the coefficients a_i of our given polynomial are not rational numbers but are rational functions $a_i(t)$ in another parameter t. Hence we wish to determine the zeros of a polynomial in $K[x]$ where $K = \mathbb{Q}(t)$.

$$(1.6) \qquad p(t;x) \quad = \quad a_d(t)x^d + a_{d-1}(t)x^{d-1} + \cdots + a_2(t)x^2 + a_1(t)x + a_0(t).$$

The role of the ambient algebraically closed field containing K is now played by the field $\mathbb{C}\{\{t\}\}$ of *Puiseux series*. The elements of $\mathbb{C}\{\{t\}\}$ are formal power series in t with coefficients in $\mathbb{C}$ and having rational exponents, subject to the condition that the set of exponents which appear is bounded below and has a common denominator. Equivalently,

$$\mathbb{C}\{\{t\}\} \quad = \quad \bigcup_{N=1}^{\infty} \mathbb{C}((t^{\frac{1}{N}})),$$

where $\mathbb{C}((y))$ abbreviates the field of Laurent series in y with coefficients in $\mathbb{C}$. A classical theorem in algebraic geometry states that $\mathbb{C}\{\{t\}\}$ is algebraically closed. For a modern treatment see [**Eis95**, Corollary 13.15].

THEOREM 1.7. (**Puiseux's Theorem**) *The polynomial $p(t;x)$ has d roots, counting multiplicities, in the field of Puiseux series $\mathbb{C}\{\{t\}\}$.*

The proof of Puiseux's theorem is algorithmic, and, lucky for us, there is an implementation of this algorithm in `maple`. Here is how it works:

```
> with(algcurves):  p :=  x^2 +  x - t^3;
                           2        3
                    p := x  + x - t
> puiseux(p,t=0,x,20);
     18        15      12     9     6    3
{-42 t   + 14 t   - 5 t  + 2 t  - t  + t ,
         18        15      12     9     6    3
     + 42 t   - 14 t   + 5 t  - 2 t  + t  - t  - 1 }
```

We note that this implementation generally does not compute all Puiseux series solutions but only enough to generate the splitting field of $p(t;x)$ over K.

```
> with(algcurves):  q :=  x^2 + t^4 * x - t:
> puiseux(q,t=0,x,20);
                    29/2           15/2         4     1/2
              {- 1/128 t     + 1/8 t     - 1/2 t  + t    }
> S := solve(q,x):
```

FIGURE 1.1. The lower boundary of the Newton polygon

```
> series(S[1],t,20);
            1/2            4              15/2             29/2         43/2
           t       - 1/2 t   + 1/8 t         - 1/128 t       + O(t      )
> series(S[2],t,20);
            1/2            4              15/2             29/2         43/2
          -t       - 1/2 t   - 1/8 t         + 1/128 t       + O(t      )
```

We shall explain how to compute the first term (lowest order in t) in each of the d Puiseux series solutions $x(t)$ to our equation $p(t;x) = 0$. Suppose that the ith coefficient in (1.6) has the Laurent series expansion:

$$a_i(t) \quad = \quad c_i \cdot t^{A_i} + \text{higher terms in } t.$$

Each Puiseux series looks like

$$x(t) \quad = \quad \gamma \cdot t^\tau + \text{higher terms in } t.$$

We wish to characterize the possible pairs of numbers (τ, γ) in $\mathbb{Q} \times \mathbb{C}$ which allow the identity $p(t; x(t)) = 0$ to hold. This is done by first finding the possible values of τ. We ignore all higher terms and consider the equation

$$(1.7) \qquad c_d \cdot t^{A_d + d\tau} + \cdots + c_1 \cdot t^{A_1 + \tau} + c_0 \cdot t^{A_0} + \cdots \quad = \quad 0.$$

This equation imposes the following piecewise-linear condition on τ:

$$(1.8) \ \min\{A_d + d\tau, A_{d-1} + (d-1)\tau, \ldots, A_2 + 2\tau, A_1 + \tau, A_0\} \quad \text{is attained twice.}$$

The crucial condition (1.8) will reappear in Chapters 3 and 9. Throughout this book, the phrase "is attained twice" will always mean "is attained at least twice". As an illustration consider the example $p(t; x) = x^2 + x - t^3$. For this polynomial, the condition (1.8) reads

$$\min\{0 + 2\tau, \, 0 + \tau, \, 3\} \quad \text{is attained twice.}$$

That sentence means the following disjunction of linear inequality systems:

$$2\tau = \tau \le 3 \quad \text{or} \quad 2\tau = 3 \le \tau \quad \text{or} \quad 3 = \tau \le 2\tau.$$

This disjunction is equivalent to

$$\tau = 0 \quad \text{or} \quad \tau = 3,$$

which gives us the lowest terms in the two Puiseux series produced by `maple`.

It is customary to phrase the procedure described above in terms of the *Newton polygon* of $p(t; x)$. This polygon is the convex hull in $\mathbb{R}^2$ of the points (i, A_i) for $i = 0, 1, \ldots, d$. The condition (1.8) is equivalent to saying that $-\tau$ equals the slope of an edge on the lower boundary of the Newton polygon. Figure 1.1 shows a picture of the Newton polygon of the equation $p(t; x) = x^2 + x - t^3$.

1.5. Hypergeometric Series

The method of Puiseux series can be extended to the case when the coefficients a_i are rational functions in several variables $t_1, \ldots, t_m$. The case $m = 1$ was discussed in the last section. An excellent reference on Puiseux series solutions for general m is the work of John McDonald [**McD95**], [**McD02**].

In this section we examine the generic case when all $d+1$ coefficients $a_0, \ldots, a_d$ in (1.1) are indeterminates. Each zero X of the polynomial in (1.1) is an algebraic function of $d+1$ variables, written $X = X(a_0, \ldots, a_d)$. The following theorem due to Karl Mayer [**May37**] characterizes these functions by the differential equations which they satisfy.

THEOREM 1.8. *The roots of the general equation of degree d are a basis for the solution space of the following system of linear partial differential equations:*

$$(1.9) \qquad \frac{\partial^2 X}{\partial a_i \partial a_j} = \frac{\partial^2 X}{\partial a_k \partial a_l} \qquad whenever \quad i + j = k + l,$$

$$(1.10) \qquad \sum_{i=0}^d i a_i \frac{\partial X}{\partial a_i} = -X \qquad and \qquad \sum_{i=0}^d a_i \frac{\partial X}{\partial a_i} = 0.$$

The meaning of the phrase "are a basis for the solution space of" will be explained at the end of this section. Let us first replace this phrase by "are solutions of" and prove the resulting weaker version of the theorem.

PROOF. The two Euler equations (1.10) express the scaling invariance of the roots. They are obtained by applying the operator d/dt to the identities

$$X(a_0, ta_1, t^2 a_2, \ldots, t^{d-1} a_{d-1}, t^d a_d) = \tfrac{1}{t} \cdot X(a_0, a_1, a_2, \ldots, a_{d-1}, a_d),$$
$$X(ta_0, ta_1, ta_2, \ldots, ta_{d-1}, ta_d) = X(a_0, a_1, a_2, \ldots, a_{d-1}, a_d).$$

To derive (1.9), we consider the first derivative $f'(x) = \sum_{i=1}^d i a_i x^{i-1}$ and the second derivative $f''(x) = \sum_{i=2}^d i(i-1) a_i x^{i-2}$. Note that $f'(X) \neq 0$, since $a_0, \ldots, a_d$ are indeterminates. Differentiating the defining identity $\sum_{i=0}^d a_i X(a_0, a_1, \ldots, a_d)^i = 0$ with respect to a_j, we get

$$(1.11) \qquad X^j + f'(X) \cdot \frac{\partial X}{\partial a_j} = 0.$$

From this we derive

$$(1.12) \qquad \frac{\partial f'(X)}{\partial a_i} = -\frac{f''(X)}{f'(X)} \cdot X^i + i X^{i-1}.$$

We next differentiate $\partial X / \partial a_j$ with respect to the indeterminate a_i:

$$(1.13) \quad \frac{\partial^2 X}{\partial a_i \partial a_j} = \frac{\partial}{\partial a_i}\left(-\frac{X^j}{f'(X)}\right) = \frac{\partial f'(X)}{\partial a_i} X^j f'(X)^{-2} - j X^{j-1} \frac{\partial X}{\partial a_i} f'(X)^{-1}.$$

Using (1.11) and (1.12), we can rewrite (1.13) as follows:

$$\frac{\partial^2 X}{\partial a_i \partial a_j} = -f''(X) X^{i+j} f'(X)^{-3} + (i+j) X^{i+j-1} f'(X)^{-2}.$$

This expression depends only on the sum of indices $i + j$. This proves (1.9). $\qquad \square$

We check the validity of our differential system for the case $d = 2$ and we note that it characterizes the series expansions of the quadratic formula.

```
> X := solve(a0 + a1 * x + a2 * x^2, x)[1];
```
$$X := 1/2 \; \frac{-a1 + (a1^2 - 4\,a2\,a0)^{1/2}}{a2}$$

```
> simplify(diff(diff(X,a0),a2) - diff(diff(X,a1),a1));
                                0
> simplify( a1*diff(X,a1) + 2*a2*diff(X,a2) + X );
                                0
> simplify(a0*diff(X,a0)+a1*diff(X,a1)+a2*diff(X,a2));
                                0
> series(X,a1,4);
```
$$\frac{(-a2\,a0)^{1/2}}{a2} - 1/2\,\frac{1}{a2}\,a1 - 1/8\,\frac{(-a2\,a0)^{1/2}}{a2^2\,a0}\,a1^2 + O(a1^4)$$

What do you get when you now type `series(X,a0,4)` or `series(X,a2,4)`?

Writing series expansions for the solutions to the general equation of degree d has a long tradition in mathematics. In 1757 Johann Lambert expressed the roots of the trinomial equation $x^p + x + r$ as a *Gauss hypergeometric function* in the parameter r. Series expansions of more general algebraic functions were subsequently given by Euler, Chebyshev and Eisenstein, among others. The widely known poster "Solving the Quintic with Mathematica" published by Wolfram Research in 1994 gives a nice historical introduction to series solutions of the general equation of degree five:

$$(1.14) \qquad a_5 x^5 + a_4 x^4 + a_3 x^3 + a_2 x^2 + a_1 x + a_0 \;\; = \;\; 0.$$

Mayer's Theorem 1.8 can be used to write down all possible Puiseux series solutions to the general quintic (1.14). There are $16 = 2^{5-1}$ distinct expansions. For instance, here is one of the 16 expansions of the five roots:

$$X_1 = -\left[\frac{a_0}{a_1}\right], \qquad X_2 = -\left[\frac{a_1}{a_2}\right] + \left[\frac{a_0}{a_1}\right], \qquad X_3 = -\left[\frac{a_2}{a_3}\right] + \left[\frac{a_1}{a_2}\right],$$
$$X_4 = -\left[\frac{a_3}{a_4}\right] + \left[\frac{a_2}{a_3}\right], \qquad X_5 = -\left[\frac{a_4}{a_5}\right] + \left[\frac{a_3}{a_4}\right].$$

Each bracket is a series having the monomial in the bracket as its first term:

$$\left[\frac{a_0}{a_1}\right] = \frac{a_0}{a_1} + \frac{a_0^2 a_2}{a_1^3} - \frac{a_0^3 a_3}{a_1^4} + 2\frac{a_0^3 a_2^2}{a_1^5} + \frac{a_0^4 a_4}{a_1^5} - 5\frac{a_0^4 a_2 a_3}{a_1^6} - \frac{a_0^5 a_5}{a_1^6} + \cdots$$

$$\left[\frac{a_1}{a_2}\right] = \frac{a_1}{a_2} + \frac{a_1^2 a_3}{a_2^3} - \frac{a_1^3 a_4}{a_2^4} - 3\frac{a_0 a_1^2 a_5}{a_2^4} + 2\frac{a_1^3 a_3^2}{a_2^5} + \frac{a_1^4 a_5}{a_2^5} - 5\frac{a_1^4 a_3 a_4}{a_2^6} + \cdots$$

$$\left[\frac{a_2}{a_3}\right] = \frac{a_2}{a_3} - \frac{a_0 a_5}{a_3^2} - \frac{a_1 a_4}{a_3^2} + 2\frac{a_1 a_2 a_5}{a_3^3} + \frac{a_2^2 a_4}{a_3^3} - \frac{a_2^3 a_5}{a_3^4} + 2\frac{a_2^3 a_4^2}{a_3^3} + \cdots$$

$$\left[\frac{a_3}{a_4}\right] = \frac{a_3}{a_4} - \frac{a_2 a_5}{a_4^2} + \frac{a_3^2 a_5}{a_4^3} + \frac{a_1 a_5^2}{a_4^3} - 3\frac{a_2 a_3 a_5^2}{a_4^4} - \frac{a_0 a_5^3}{a_4^4} + 4\frac{a_1 a_3 a_5^3}{a_4^5} + \cdots$$

$$\left[\frac{a_4}{a_5}\right] = \frac{a_4}{a_5}$$

The last bracket is just a single Laurent monomial. The other four brackets $\left[\frac{a_{i-1}}{a_i}\right]$ can easily be written as an explicit sum over $\mathbb{N}^4$. For instance,

$$\left[\frac{a_0}{a_1}\right] \;=\; \sum_{i,j,k,l\geq 0} \frac{(-1)^{2i+3j+4k+5l}\,(2i+3j+4k+5l)!}{i!\,j!\,k!\,l!\,(i+2j+3k+4l+1)!}\cdot\frac{a_0^{i+2j+3k+4l+1}\,a_2^i a_3^j a_4^k a_5^l}{a_1^{2i+3j+4k+5l+1}}$$

Each coefficient appearing in one of these series is integral. Therefore these five formulas for the roots work in any characteristic. The situation is different for the other 15 series expansions of the roots of the quintic (1.14). For instance, consider the expansions into positive powers in a_1, a_2, a_3, a_4. They are

$$X_\xi \;=\; \xi\cdot\left[\frac{a_0^{1/5}}{a_5^{1/5}}\right] + \frac{1}{5}\cdot\left(\xi^2\left[\frac{a_1}{a_0^{3/5}a_5^{2/5}}\right] + \xi^3\left[\frac{a_2}{a_0^{2/5}a_5^{3/5}}\right] + \xi^4\left[\frac{a_3}{a_0^{1/5}a_5^{4/5}}\right] - \left[\frac{a_4}{a_5}\right]\right)$$

where ξ runs over the five complex roots of the equation $\xi^5 = -1$, and

$$\left[\frac{a_0^{1/5}}{a_5^{1/5}}\right] = \frac{a_0^{1/5}}{a_5^{1/5}} - \frac{1}{25}\frac{a_1 a_4}{a_0^{4/5}a_5^{6/5}} - \frac{1}{25}\frac{a_2 a_3}{a_0^{4/5}a_5^{6/5}} + \frac{2}{125}\frac{a_1^2 a_3}{a_0^{9/5}a_5^{6/5}} + \frac{3}{125}\frac{a_2 a_4^2}{a_0^{4/5}a_5^{11/5}} + \cdots$$

$$\left[\frac{a_1}{a_0^{3/5}a_5^{2/5}}\right] = \frac{a_1}{a_0^{3/5}a_5^{2/5}} - \frac{1}{5}\frac{a_3^2}{a_0^{3/5}a_5^{7/5}} - \frac{2}{5}\frac{a_2 a_4}{a_0^{3/5}a_5^{7/5}} + \frac{7}{25}\frac{a_3 a_4^2}{a_0^{3/5}a_5^{12/5}} + \frac{6}{25}\frac{a_1 a_2 a_3}{a_0^{8/5}a_5^{7/5}} + \cdots$$

$$\left[\frac{a_2}{a_0^{2/5}a_5^{3/5}}\right] = \frac{a_2}{a_0^{2/5}a_5^{3/5}} - \frac{1}{5}\frac{a_1^2}{a_0^{7/5}a_5^{3/5}} - \frac{3}{5}\frac{a_3 a_4}{a_0^{2/5}a_5^{8/5}} + \frac{6}{25}\frac{a_1 a_2 a_4}{a_0^{7/5}a_5^{8/5}} + \frac{3}{25}\frac{a_1 a_3^2}{a_0^{7/5}a_5^{8/5}} + \cdots$$

$$\left[\frac{a_3}{a_0^{1/5}a_5^{4/5}}\right] = \frac{a_3}{a_0^{1/5}a_5^{4/5}} - \frac{1}{5}\frac{a_1 a_2}{a_0^{6/5}a_5^{4/5}} - \frac{2}{5}\frac{a_4^2}{a_0^{1/5}a_5^{9/5}} + \frac{1}{25}\frac{a_1^3}{a_0^{11/5}a_5^{4/5}} + \frac{4}{25}\frac{a_1 a_3 a_4}{a_0^{6/5}a_5^{9/5}} + \cdots$$

Each of these four series can be expressed as an explicit sum over the lattice points in a 4-dimensional polyhedron. The general formula can be found in [**Stu00**, Theorem 3.2]. That reference gives all 2^{d-1} distinct Puiseux series expansions of the solution of the general equation of degree d.

The system (1.9)-(1.10) is a special case of the hypergeometric differential equations discussed in [**SST99**]. More precisely, it is the Gel'fand-Kapranov-Zelevinsky system with parameters $\binom{-1}{0}$ associated with the integer matrix

$$\mathcal{A} \;=\; \begin{pmatrix} 0 & 1 & 2 & 3 & \cdots & n-1 & n \\ 1 & 1 & 1 & 1 & \cdots & 1 & 1 \end{pmatrix}.$$

We abbreviate the derivation $\frac{\partial}{\partial a_i}$ by the symbol ∂_i and we consider the ideal generated by the operators (1.10) in the commutative polynomial ring $\mathbb{Q}[\partial_0, \partial_1, \ldots, \partial_d]$. This is the ideal of the 2×2-minors of the matrix

$$\begin{pmatrix} \partial_0 & \partial_1 & \partial_2 & \cdots & \partial_{d-1} \\ \partial_1 & \partial_2 & \partial_3 & \cdots & \partial_d \end{pmatrix}.$$

This ideal defines a projective curve of degree d, namely, the *rational normal curve*, and from this it follows that our system (1.9)-(1.10) is *holonomic of rank d*. This means the following: Let $(a_0, \ldots, a_d)$ be any point in $\mathbb{C}^{d+1}$ such that the discriminant of $p(x)$ is non-zero, and let $\mathcal{U}$ be a small open ball around that point. Then the set of holomorphic functions on $\mathcal{U}$ which are solutions to (1.9)-(1.10) is a complex vector space of dimension d. Theorem 1.8 states that the d roots of $p(x) = 0$ form a distinguished basis for that vector space.

1.6. Exercises

(1) Describe the Jordan canonical form of the companion matrix Times_x. What are the generalized eigenvectors of the endomorphism (1.2)?

(2) We define a unique cubic polynomial $p(x)$ by four interpolation conditions $p(x_i) = y_i$ for $i = 0, 1, 2, 3$. The discriminant of $p(x)$ is a rational function in $x_0, x_1, x_2, x_3, y_0, y_1, y_2, y_3$. What is the denominator of this rational function, and how many terms does the numerator have?

(3) Create a symmetric 50×50-matrix whose entries are random integers between -10 and 10 and compute the eigenvalues of your matrix.

(4) For which complex parameters α is the following system solvable?

$$x^d - \alpha \quad = \quad x^3 - x + 1 \quad = \quad 0.$$

Give a formula for the resultant in terms of α and d.

(5) Consider the set of all $65,536$ polynomials of degree 15 whose coefficients are $+1$ or -1. Answer the following questions about this set:
   (a) Which polynomial has largest discriminant?
   (b) Which polynomial has the smallest number of complex roots?
   (c) Which polynomial has the complex root of largest absolute value?
   (d) Which polynomial has the most real roots?

(6) Give a necessary and sufficient condition for the quartic equation

$$a_4 x^4 + a_3 x^3 + a_2 x^2 + a_1 x + a_0 \quad = \quad 0$$

to have exactly two real roots. We expect a condition which is a Boolean combination of polynomial inequalities involving a_0, a_1, a_2, a_3, a_4.

(7) Describe an algebraic algorithm for deciding whether a polynomial $p(x)$ has a complex root of absolute value one.

(8) Compute all five Puiseux series solutions $x(t)$ of the quintic equation

$$x^5 + t \cdot x^4 + t^3 \cdot x^3 + t^6 \cdot x^2 + t^{10} \cdot x + t^{15} \quad = \quad 0$$

What is the coefficient of t^n in each of the five series?

(9) Fix two real symmetric $n \times n$-matrices A and B. Consider the set of points (x, y) in the plane $\mathbb{R}^2$ such that all eigenvalues of the matrix $xA + yB$ are non-negative. Show that this set is closed and convex. Does every closed convex semi-algebraic subset of $\mathbb{R}^2$ arise in this way?

(10) Let α and β be integers and consider the following system of linear partial differential equations for an unknown function $X(a_0, a_1, a_2)$:

$$\partial^2 X / \partial a_0 \partial a_2 = \partial^2 X / \partial a_1^2$$
$$a_1 \tfrac{\partial X}{\partial a_1} + 2a_2 \tfrac{\partial X}{\partial a_1} = \alpha \cdot X$$
$$a_0 \tfrac{\partial X}{\partial a_0} + a_1 \tfrac{\partial X}{\partial a_1} + a_2 \tfrac{\partial X}{\partial a_2} = \beta \cdot X$$

For which values of α and β do (non-zero) polynomial solutions exist? Same question for rational solutions and algebraic solutions.

CHAPTER 2

Gröbner Bases of Zero-Dimensional Ideals

Suppose we are given polynomials $f_1, \ldots, f_m$ in $\mathbb{Q}[x_1, \ldots, x_n]$ which are known to have only finitely many common zeros in $\mathbb{C}^n$. Then $I = \langle f_1, \ldots, f_m \rangle$, the ideal generated by these polynomials, is zero-dimensional. In this section we demonstrate how Gröbner bases can be used to compute the zeros of I.

2.1. Computing Standard Monomials and the Radical

Let $\prec$ be a term order on the polynomial ring $S = \mathbb{Q}[x_1, \ldots, x_n]$. Every ideal I in S has a unique reduced Gröbner basis $\mathcal{G}$ with respect to $\prec$. The leading terms of the polynomials in $\mathcal{G}$ generate the initial monomial ideal $\mathrm{in}_\prec(I)$. Let $\mathcal{B} = \mathcal{B}_\prec(I)$ denote the set of all monomials $x^u = x_1^{u_1} x_2^{u_2} \cdots x_n^{u_n}$ which do not lie in $\mathrm{in}_\prec(I)$. These are the *standard monomials* of I with respect to $\prec$. Every polynomial f in S can be written uniquely as a $\mathbb{Q}$-linear combination of $\mathcal{B}$ modulo I, using the division algorithm with respect to the Gröbner basis $\mathcal{G}$. We write $\mathcal{V}(I) \subset \mathbb{C}^n$ for the complex variety defined by the ideal I.

PROPOSITION 2.1. *The variety $\mathcal{V}(I)$ is finite if and only if the set $\mathcal{B}$ is finite, and the cardinality of $\mathcal{B}$ equals the cardinality of $\mathcal{V}(I)$, counting multiplicities.*

Consider an example with three variables, namely, the ideal

(2.1) $I \quad = \quad \langle \, (x-y)^3 - z^2, \, (z-x)^3 - y^2, \, (y-z)^3 - x^2 \, \rangle$

in $S = \mathbb{Q}[x, y, z]$. The following `Macaulay 2` computation verifies that I is zero-dimensional:

```
i1 : S = QQ[x,y,z];

i2 : I = ideal( (x-y)^3-z^2, (z-x)^3-y^2, (y-z)^3-x^2 );

o2 : Ideal of S

i3 : dim I, degree I
o3 = (0, 14)

i4 : gb I

o4 = | y2z-1/2xz2-yz2+1/2z3+13/60x2-1/12y2+7/60z2
       x2z-xz2-1/2yz2+1/2z3+1/12x2-13/60y2-7/60z2
       y3-3y2z+3yz2-z3-x2
       xy2-2x2z-3y2z+3xz2+4yz2-3z3-7/6x2+5/6y2-1/6z2
       x2y-xy2-x2z+y2z+xz2-yz2+1/3x2+1/3y2+1/3z2
       x3-3x2y+3xy2-3y2z+3yz2-z3-x2-z2
       z4+1/5xz2-1/5yz2+2/25z2
       yz3-z4-13/20xz2-3/20yz2+3/10z3+2/75x2-4/75y2-7/300z2
```

13

```
    xz3-2yz3+z4+29/20xz2+19/20yz2-9/10z3-8/75x2+2/15y2+7/300z2
    xyz2-3/2y2z2+xz3+yz3-3/2z4+y2z-1/2xz2
                 -7/10yz2+1/5z3+13/60x2-1/12y2-1/12z2|

i5 : toString (x^10 % I)

o5 = -4/15625*x*z^2+4/15625*z^3-559/1171875*x^2
     -94/1171875*y^2+26/1171875*z^2

i6 : R = S/I;   basis R

o7 = | 1 x x2 xy xyz xz xz2 y y2 yz yz2 z z2 z3 |
             1              14
o7 : Matrix R   <--- R
```

The output o4 gives the reduced Gröbner basis for I with respect to the reverse lexicographic term order with $x > y > z$. In o5 we compute the expansion of x^{10} in this basis of S/I. We see in o7 that there are 14 standard monomials. We conclude that the number of complex zeros of I is at most 14.

If I is a zero-dimensional ideal in $S = \mathbb{Q}[x_1, \ldots, x_n]$ then the elimination ideal $I \cap \mathbb{Q}[x_i]$ is non-zero for all $i = 1, 2, \ldots, n$. Let $p_i(x_i)$ denote the generator of $I \cap \mathbb{Q}[x_i]$. The univariate polynomial p_i can be gotten from a Gröbner basis for I with respect to an elimination term order. Another method is to use an arbitrary Gröbner basis to compute the normal form of successive powers of x_i until they first become linearly dependent.

We denote the square-free part of the polynomial $p_i(x_i)$ by

$$p_{i,red}(x_i) \quad = \quad p_i(x_i)/\gcd(p_i(x_i), p_i'(x_i)).$$

The following result is proved in Proposition (2.7) of [**CLO98**].

THEOREM 2.2. *A zero-dimensional ideal I is radical if and only if the n elimination ideals $I \cap \mathbb{Q}[x_i]$ are radical. Moreover, the radical of I equals*

$$\mathrm{Rad}(I) \quad = \quad I + \langle p_{1,red}, p_{2,red}, \cdots, p_{n,red} \rangle.$$

Our example in (2.1) is symmetric with respect to the variables, so that

$$I \cap \mathbb{Q}[x] = \langle p(x) \rangle, \quad I \cap \mathbb{Q}[y] = \langle p(y) \rangle, \quad I \cap \mathbb{Q}[z] = \langle p(z) \rangle.$$

The common generator of the elimination ideals is a polynomial of degree 8:

$$p(x) \quad = \quad x^8 + \frac{6}{25}x^6 + \frac{17}{625}x^4 + \frac{8}{15625}x^2$$

This polynomial is not square-free. Its square-free part equals

$$p_{red}(x) \quad = \quad x^7 + \frac{6}{25}x^5 + \frac{17}{625}x^3 + \frac{8}{15625}x.$$

Hence our ideal I is not radical. Using Theorem 2.2, we compute its radical:

$$\mathrm{Rad}(I) \quad = \quad I + \langle p_{red}(x), p_{red}(y), p_{red}(z) \rangle$$
$$= \quad \langle \underline{x} - 5/2y^2 - 1/2y + 5/2z^2 - 1/2z,$$
$$\underline{y} + 3125/8z^6 + 625/4z^5 + 375/4z^4 + 125/4z^3 + 65/8z^2 + 3z,$$
$$\underline{z^7} + 6/25z^5 + 17/625z^3 + 8/15625z \rangle.$$

The three given generators form a lexicographic Gröbner basis. We see that $\mathcal{V}(I)$ has cardinality seven. The only real root is the origin. The other six zeros of I in $\mathbb{C}^3$ are not real. They are gotten by cyclically shifting

$$(x, y, z) \; = \; \left(-0.14233 - 0.35878i,\, 0.14233 - 0.35878i,\, 0.15188i \right)$$

and $\quad (x, y, z) \; = \; \left(-0.14233 + 0.35878i,\, 0.14233 + 0.35878i,\, -0.15188i \right).$

Note that the coordinates of these vectors also can be written in terms of radicals since $p_{red}(x)/x$ is a cubic polynomial in x^2.

If I is a zero-dimensional radical ideal in $S = \mathbb{Q}[x_1, \ldots, x_n]$ then, possibly after a linear change of variables, the ring S/I is always isomorphic to the univariate quotient ring $\mathbb{Q}[x_i]/(I \cap \mathbb{Q}[x_i])$. This is the content of the following result.

PROPOSITION 2.3. **(Shape Lemma)** *Let I be a zero-dimensional radical ideal in $\mathbb{Q}[x_1, \ldots, x_n]$ such that all d complex roots of I have distinct x_n-coordinates. Then the reduced Gröbner basis of I in the lexicographic term order has the shape*

$$\mathcal{G} \;\; = \;\; \left\{ x_1 - q_1(x_n),\, x_2 - q_2(x_n),\, \ldots,\, x_{n-1} - q_{n-1}(x_n),\, r(x_n) \right\}$$

where r is a polynomial of degree d and the q_i are polynomials of degree $\leq d - 1$.

For polynomial systems of moderate size, `Singular` is really fast in computing the lexicographically Gröbner basis $\mathcal{G}$. It is well known that the coefficients of the univariate polynomial $r(x_n)$ are rational numbers with very large numerators and denominators. But, if I is a prime ideal over $\mathbb{Q}$, which is frequently the case, there is nothing we can do because the irreducible polynomial $r(x_n) = p_n(x_n)$ is intrinsic to the problem and not an artifact of any particular solution method.

Perhaps surprisingly, the coefficients of the polynomials $q_i(x_n)$ are often even worse than those of $r(x_n)$. But these terrible integers are not intrinsic to the problem. They are an artifact of the method used. Roullier [**Rou99**] has proposed the method of *rational univariate representations* to circumvent the coefficient growth in the q_i. The key idea is to replace $x_i - q_i(x_n)$ by a polynomial $a_i(x_n) \cdot x_i - b_i(x_n)$ where a_i and b_i are also univariate polynomials of degree $\leq d - 1$, but their coefficients are much nicer than those of q_i. For details see [**Rou99**].

2.2. Localizing and Removing Known Zeros

In our running example, the origin is a zero of multiplicity eight, and it would have made sense to remove this distinguished zero right from the beginning. In this section we explain how to do this and how the number 8 could have been derived a priori. Let I be a zero-dimensional ideal in $S = \mathbb{Q}[x_1, \ldots, x_n]$ and $p = (p_1, \ldots, p_n)$ any point with coordinates in $\mathbb{Q}$. We consider the associated *maximal ideal*

$$M \;\; = \;\; \langle x_1 - p_1, x_2 - p_2, \ldots, x_n - p_n \rangle \;\; \subset \;\; S.$$

The *ideal quotient* of I by M is defined as

$$(I : M) \;\; = \;\; \{ f \in S \; : \; f \cdot M \subseteq I \}.$$

We can iterate this process to get the increasing sequence of ideals

$$I \subseteq (I : M) \subseteq (I : M^2) \subseteq (I : M^3) \subseteq \cdots$$

This sequence stabilizes with an ideal called the *saturation*

$$(I : M^\infty) \;\; = \;\; \{ f \in S \; : \; \exists m \in \mathbb{N} \; : \; f \cdot M^m \subseteq I \}.$$

PROPOSITION 2.4. *The variety of $(I : M^\infty)$ equals $\mathcal{V}(I) \backslash \{p\}$.*

Here is how we compute the ideal quotient and the saturation in `Macaulay 2`. We demonstrate this for the ideal in the previous section and $p = (0, 0, 0)$:

```
i1 : R = QQ[x,y,z];
i2 : I = ideal( (x-y)^3-z^2, (z-x)^3-y^2, (y-z)^3-x^2 );
i3 : M = ideal( x , y , z );

i4 : gb (I : M)

o4 = | y2z-1/2xz2-yz2+1/2z3+13/60x2-1/12y2+7/60z2
       xyz+3/4xz2+3/4yz2+1/20x2-1/20y2 x2z-xz2-1/2yz2+ ....

i5 : gb saturate(I,M)

o5 = | z2+1/5x-1/5y+2/25 y2-1/5x+1/5z+2/25
       xy+xz+yz+1/25 x2+1/5y-1/5z+2/25 |

i6 :   degree I, degree (I:M), degree (I:M^2), degree(I:M^3)

o6 = (14, 13, 10, 7)

i7 : degree (I : M^4), degree (I : M^5), degree (I : M^6)

o7 = (6, 6, 6)
```

In this example, the fourth ideal quotient $(I : M^4)$ equals the saturation $(I : M^\infty) =$ `saturate(I,M)`. Since $p = (0, 0, 0)$ is a zero of high multiplicity, namely eight, it would be interesting to further explore the local ring S_p/I_p. This is an 8-dimensional $\mathbb{Q}$-vector space which tells the *scheme structure* at p, meaning the manner in which those eight points pile on top of one another. The reader need not be alarmed if he or she has not yet fully digested the notion of schemes in algebraic geometry [EH00]. An elementary but useful perspective on schemes will be provided in Chapter 10 where we discuss linear partial differential equations with constant coefficients.

The following general method can be used to compute the local ring at an isolated zero of any polynomial system. Form the ideal quotient

$$(2.2) \qquad\qquad J = \big(I : (I : M^\infty)\big).$$

PROPOSITION 2.5. *The ring S/J is isomorphic to the local ring S_p/I_p under the natural map $x_i \mapsto x_i$. In particular, the multiplicity of p as a zero of I equals the number of standard monomials for any Gröbner basis of J.*

In our example, the local ideal J is particularly simple and the multiplicity eight is obvious. Here is how the `Macaulay 2` session continues:

```
i8 : J = ( I : saturate(I,M) )

            2   2   2
o8 = ideal (z , y , x )

i9 : degree J

o9 = 8
```

We note that `Singular` is fine-tuned for efficient computations in local rings via the techniques in Chapter 4 of [**CLO98**].

Propositions 2.4 and 2.5 provide a decomposition of the given ideal:

$$(2.3) \qquad\qquad I \;=\; J \;\cap\; (I : M^{\infty}).$$

Here J is the iterated ideal quotient in (2.2). This ideal is primary to the maximal ideal M, that is, $\mathrm{Rad}(J) = M$. We can now iterate by applying this process to the ideal $(I : M^{\infty})$, and this will eventually lead to the *primary decomposition* of I. We shall return to this topic in Chapter 5.

For the ideal in our example, the decomposition (2.3) is already the primary decomposition when working over the field of rational numbers. It equals

$$\langle\, (x-y)^3 - z^2,\ (z-x)^3 - y^2,\ (y-z)^3 - x^2 \,\rangle \;=$$
$$\langle\, x^2,\ y^2,\ z^2 \,\rangle \;\cap\; \langle\, \underline{z^2} + \tfrac{1}{5}x - \tfrac{1}{5}y + \tfrac{2}{25},\ \underline{y^2} - \tfrac{1}{5}x + \tfrac{1}{5}z + \tfrac{2}{25},$$
$$\underline{x^2} + \tfrac{1}{5}y - \tfrac{1}{5}z + \tfrac{2}{25},\ \underline{xy} + xz + yz + \tfrac{1}{25} \,\rangle$$

Note that the second ideal is maximal and hence prime in $\mathbb{Q}[x,y,z]$. The given generators are a Gröbner basis with leading terms underlined.

2.3. Companion Matrices

Let I be a zero-dimensional ideal in $S = \mathbb{Q}[x_1, \ldots, x_n]$, and suppose that the $\mathbb{Q}$-vector space S/I has dimension d. In this section we assume that some Gröbner basis of I is known. Let $\mathcal{B}$ denote the associated monomial basis for S/I. Multiplication by any of the variables x_i defines an endomorphism

$$(2.4) \qquad\qquad S/I \to S/I,\ f \mapsto x_i \cdot f$$

We write T_i for the $d \times d$-matrix over $\mathbb{Q}$ which represents the linear map (2.4) with respect to the basis $\mathcal{B}$. The rows and columns of T_i are indexed by the monomials in $\mathcal{B}$. If $x^u, x^v \in \mathcal{B}$ then the entry of T_i in row x^u and column x^v is the coefficient of x^u in the normal form of $x_i \cdot x^v$.

We call T_i the *ith companion matrix* of the ideal I. It follows directly from the definition that the companion matrices commute pairwise:

$$T_i \cdot T_j \;=\; T_j \cdot T_i \qquad \text{for } 1 \le i < j \le n.$$

The matrices T_i generate a commutative subalgebra of the non-commutative ring of $d \times d$-matrices, and this subalgebra is isomorphic to our ring

$$\mathbb{Q}[T_1, \ldots, T_n] \;\simeq\; S/I,\qquad T_i \mapsto x_i.$$

THEOREM 2.6. (**Stickelberger's Theorem**) *The complex zeros of the ideal I are the vectors of joint eigenvalues of the companion matrices $T_1, \ldots, T_n$, that is,*

$$(2.5)\qquad \mathcal{V}(I) \;=\; \big\{\, (\lambda_1, \ldots, \lambda_n) \in \mathbb{C}^n \;:\; \exists\, v \in \mathbb{C}^n\ \forall i\ :\ T_i \cdot v = \lambda_i \cdot v \,\big\}.$$

PROOF. Suppose that v is a non-zero complex vector such that $T_i \cdot v = \lambda_i \cdot v$ for all i. Then, for any polynomial $p \in S$,

$$p(T_1, \ldots, T_n) \cdot v \;=\; p(\lambda_1, \ldots, \lambda_n) \cdot v.$$

If p is in the ideal I then $p(T_1, \ldots, T_n)$ is the zero matrix and we conclude that $p(\lambda_1, \ldots, \lambda_n) = 0$. Hence the left hand side of (2.5) contains the right hand side of (2.5).

We prove the converse under the hypothesis that I is a radical ideal. (The general case is left to the reader). Let $\lambda = (\lambda_1, \ldots, \lambda_n) \in \mathbb{C}^n$ be any zero of I. There exists a polynomial $q \in S \otimes \mathbb{C}$ such that $q(\lambda) = 1$ and q vanishes at all points in $\mathcal{V}(I) \backslash \{\lambda\}$. Then $x_i \cdot q = \lambda_i \cdot q$ holds on $\mathcal{V}(I)$, hence $(x_i - \lambda_i) \cdot q$ lies in the radical ideal I. Let v be the non-zero vector representing the element q of $S/I \otimes \mathbb{C}$. Then v is a joint eigenvector with joint eigenvalue λ.   □

Suppose that I is a zero-dimensional radical ideal. We can form a square invertible matrix V whose columns are the eigenvectors v described above. Then $V^{-1} \cdot T_i \cdot V$ is a diagonal matrix whose entries are the ith coordinates of all the zeros of I. This proves the if-direction in the following corollary. The only-if-direction is also true but we omit its proof.

COROLLARY 2.7. *The companion matrices* $T_1, \ldots, T_n$ *can be simultaneously diagonalized if and only if* I *is a radical ideal.*

As an example consider the Gröbner basis given at the end of the last section. The given ideal is a prime ideal in $\mathbb{Q}[x, y, z]$ having degree $d = 6$. We determine the three companion matrices Tx, Ty and Tz.

```
> with(Groebner):

> GB := [z^2+1/5*x-1/5*y+2/25, y^2-1/5*x+1/5*z+2/25,
>        x*y+x*z+y*z+1/25, x^2+1/5*y-1/5*z+2/25]:

> B := [1, x, y, z, x*z, y*z]:

> for v in [x,y,z] do
>   T := array([],1..6,1..6):
>   for j from 1 to 6 do
>     p := normalf( v*B[j], GB, tdeg(x,y,z)):
>     for i from 1 to 6 do
>       T[i,j] := coeff(coeff(coeff(p,x,degree(B[i],x)),y,
>               degree(B[i],y)),z,degree(B[i],z)):
>   od:
> od:

> print(cat(T,v),T);
> od:
```

$$
\text{Tx, }\begin{bmatrix}
\dfrac{-2}{25} & \dfrac{-1}{25} & 0 & \dfrac{-2}{125} & 0 \\
 & & & & \\
1 & 0 & 0 & 0 & \dfrac{-1}{25} & 1/25 \\
 & & & & \\
0 & -1/5 & 0 & 0 & 1/25 & 1/25 \\
 & & & & \\
\end{bmatrix}
$$

```
    [                           -2        ]
    [0    1/5    0    0         --    1/25 ]
    [                           25        ]
    [                                     ]
    [0    0     -1    1          0     0   ]
    [                                     ]
    [0    0     -1    0        -1/5    0   ]
```

```
         [   -1    -2                          ]
         [0   --    --    0     0       2/125  ]
         [    25    25                         ]
         [                                     ]
         [0    0    1/5   0    1/25     1/25   ]
         [                                     ]
         [                              -1     ]
         [1    0    0     0    1/25      --    ]
Ty,      [                              25     ]
         [                                     ]
         [                              -2     ]
         [0    0   -1/5   0    1/25      --    ]
         [                              25     ]
         [                                     ]
         [0   -1    0     0     0       1/5    ]
         [                                     ]
         [0   -1    0     1     0        0     ]
```

```
         [                 -2            -1    ]
         [0    0    0      --    1/125   ---   ]
         [                 25           125    ]
         [                                     ]
         [                 -2                  ]
         [0    0    0     -1/5    --    1/25   ]
         [                 25                  ]
         [                                     ]
         [                              -2     ]
Tz,      [0    0    0     1/5    1/25    --    ]
         [                              25     ]
         [                                     ]
         [                 -1           -1     ]
         [1    0    0      0     --      --    ]
         [                 25           25     ]
         [                                     ]
         [0    1    0      0    -1/5    1/5    ]
         [                                     ]
         [0    0    1      0    -1/5    1/5    ]
```

The matrices Tx, Ty and Tz commute pairwise and they can be simultaneously diagonalized. The entries on the diagonal are the six complex zeros. We invite the reader to compute the common basis of eigenvectors using matlab.

2.4. The Trace Form

In this section we explain how to compute the number of real roots of a zero-dimensional ideal which is presented to us by a Gröbner basis as before. Fix any other polynomial $h \in S$ and consider the following bilinear form on our vector space $S/I \simeq \mathbb{Q}^d$. This is called the *trace form for h*:

$$B_h \; : \; S/I \times S/I \to \mathbb{Q}, \quad (f,g) \; \mapsto \; \mathrm{trace}\big((f \cdot g \cdot h)(T_1, T_2, \ldots, T_n)\big).$$

This formula means the following: first multiply f, g and h to get a polynomial in $x_1, \ldots, x_n$, then substitute $x_1 \mapsto T_1, \ldots, x_n \mapsto T_n$ to get an $n \times n$-matrix, and finally sum up the diagonal entries of that $n \times n$-matrix.

We represent the quadratic form B_h by a symmetric $d \times d$-matrix over $\mathbb{Q}$ with respect to the basis $\mathcal{B}$. If $x^u, x^v \in \mathcal{B}$ then the entry of B_h in row x^u and column x^v is the sum of the diagonal entries in the $d \times d$-matrix gotten by substituting the companion matrices T_i for the variables x_i in the polynomial $x^{u+v} \cdot h$. This rational number can be computed by summing, over all $x^w \in \mathcal{B}$, the coefficient of x^w in the normal form of $x^{u+v+w} \cdot h$ modulo I.

Since the matrix B_h is symmetric, all of its eigenvalues are real numbers. The *signature* of B_h is the number of positive eigenvalues of B_h minus the number of negative eigenvalues of B_h. It turns out that this number is always non-negative for symmetric matrices of the special form B_h. In the following theorem, real zeros of I with multiplicities are counted only once.

THEOREM 2.8. *The signature of the trace form B_h equals the number of real roots p of I with $h(p) > 0$ minus the number of real roots p of I with $h(p) < 0$.*

The special case when $h = 1$ is used to count all real roots:

COROLLARY 2.9. *The number of real roots of I equals the signature of B_1.*

We compute the symmetric 6×6-matrix B_1 for the case of the polynomial system whose companion matrices were determined in the previous section.

```
> with(linalg): with(Groebner):

> GB := [z^2+1/5*x-1/5*y+2/25, y^2-1/5*x+1/5*z+2/25,
>        x*y+x*z+y*z+1/25, x^2+1/5*y-1/5*z+2/25]:
> B :=  [1, x, y, z, x*z, y*z]:

> B1 := array([ ],1..6,1..6):
> for j from 1 to 6 do
> for i from 1 to 6 do
> B1[i,j] :=  0:
> for k from 1 to 6 do
> B1[i,j] := B1[i,j] +  coeff(coeff(coeff(
> normalf(B[i]*B[j]*B[k], GB, tdeg(x,y,z)),x,
> degree(B[k],x)), y, degree(B[k],y)),z, degree(B[k],z)):
> od:
> od:
```

```
> od:

> print(B1);
                    [                                   -2        -2 ]
                    [6       0        0        0        --        -- ]
                    [                                   25        25 ]
                    [                                                ]
                    [        -12      -2       -2       -2           ]
                    [0       ---      --       --       --        0  ]
                    [        25       25       25       25           ]
                    [                                                ]
                    [        -2       -12      -2                    ]
                    [0       --       ---      --       0        2/25]
                    [        25       25       25                    ]
                    [                                                ]
                    [        -2       -2       -12               -2  ]
                    [0       --       --       ---      2/25      -- ]
                    [        25       25       25               25   ]
                    [                                                ]
                    [-2      -2                         34       -16 ]
                    [--      --       0       2/25      ---      --- ]
                    [25      25                         625      625 ]
                    [                                                ]
                    [-2                        -2       -16      34  ]
                    [--      0       2/25      --       ---      --- ]
                    [25                        25       625      625 ]

> charpoly(B1,z);

  6    2918  5    117312  4    1157248  3    625664   2
z  -  ---- z  -  ------ z  -  ------- z  -  ------- z
       625          15625         390625       9765625

         4380672          32768
    + -------- z  -  ------
       48828125         9765625

> fsolve(%);

-.6400000, -.4371281, -.4145023, .04115916, .1171281, 6.002143
```

Here the matrix B_1 has three positive eigenvalues and three negative eigenvalues, so the trace form has signature zero. This confirms our earlier finding that these equations have no real zeros. We note that we can read off the signature of B_1 directly from the characteristic polynomial. Namely, the characteristic polynomial has three sign changes in its coefficient sequence. Using the following result, which appears in Exercise 5 on page 67 of [**CLO98**], we infer that there are three positive real eigenvalues and this implies that the signature of B_1 is zero.

LEMMA 2.10. *The number of positive eigenvalues of a real symmetric matrix equals the number of sign changes in the coefficient sequence of its characteristic polynomial.*

It is instructive to examine the trace form for the case of one polynomial in one variable. Consider the principal ideal

$$I \quad = \quad \langle\, a_d x^d + a_{d-1} x^{d-1} + \cdots + a_2 x^2 + a_1 x + a_0 \,\rangle \quad \subset \quad S = \mathbb{Q}[x].$$

We consider the traces of successive powers of the companion matrix:

$$b_i \quad := \quad \mathrm{trace}\big(\mathrm{Times}_x^i\big) \quad = \quad \sum_{u \in \mathcal{V}(I)} u^i.$$

Thus b_i is a Laurent polynomial of degree zero in $a_0, \dots, a_d$, which is essentially the familiar Newton relation between elementary symmetric polynomials and power sum symmetric polynomials. The trace form is given by the matrix

$$(2.6) \qquad B_1 \quad = \quad \begin{pmatrix} b_0 & b_1 & b_2 & \cdots & b_{d-1} \\ b_1 & b_2 & b_3 & \cdots & b_d \\ b_2 & b_3 & b_4 & \cdots & b_{d+1} \\ \vdots & \vdots & \vdots & \ddots & \vdots \\ b_{d-1} & b_d & b_{d+1} & \cdots & b_{2d-2} \end{pmatrix}$$

Thus the number of real zeros of I is the signature of this Hankel matrix. For instance, for $d = 4$ the entries in the 4×4-Hankel matrix B_1 are

$$b_0 = 4$$
$$b_1 = \frac{-a_3}{a_4}$$
$$b_2 = \frac{-2a_4 a_2 + a_3^2}{a_4^2}$$
$$b_3 = \frac{-3a_4^2 a_1 + 3a_4 a_3 a_2 - a_3^3}{a_4^3}$$
$$b_4 = \frac{-4a_4^3 a_0 + 4a_4^2 a_3 a_1 + 2a_4^2 a_2^2 - 4a_4 a_3^2 a_2 + a_3^4}{a_4^4}$$
$$b_5 = \frac{-5a_4^3 a_3 a_0 - 5a_4^3 a_2 a_1 + 5a_4^2 a_3^2 a_1 + 5a_4^2 a_3 a_2^2 - 5a_4 a_3^3 a_2 + a_3^5}{a_4^5}$$
$$b_6 = \frac{-6a_4^4 a_2 a_0 - 3a_4^4 a_1^2 + 6a_4^3 a_3^2 a_0 + 12a_4^3 a_3 a_2 a_1 + 2a_4^3 a_2^3 - 6a_4^2 a_3^3 a_1 - 9a_4^2 a_3^2 a_2^2 + 6a_4 a_3^4 a_2 - a_3^6}{a_4^6},$$

and the characteristic polynomial of the 4×4-matrix B_1 equals

$$\begin{aligned}
x^4 \quad &+ \quad (-b_0 - b_2 - b_4 - b_6) \cdot x^3 \\
+ \quad & (b_0 b_2 + b_0 b_4 + b_0 b_6 - b_5^2 - b_1^2 - b_2^2 + b_2 b_4 + b_2 b_6 - 2b_3^2 - b_4^2 + b_4 b_6) \cdot x^2 \\
+ \quad & (b_0 b_5^2 - b_0 b_2 b_4 - b_0 b_2 b_6 + b_0 b_3^2 + b_0 b_4^2 - b_0 b_4 b_6 + b_5^2 b_2 - 2b_5 b_2 b_3 - 2b_5 b_3 b_4 + b_1^2 b_4 \\
& + b_1^2 b_6 - 2b_1 b_2 b_3 - 2b_1 b_3 b_4 + b_2^3 + b_2^2 b_6 + b_2 b_3^2 - b_2 b_4 b_6 + b_3^2 b_4 + b_3^2 b_6 + b_4^3) \cdot x \\
- \quad & b_0 b_5^2 b_2 + 2b_0 b_5 b_3 b_4 + b_0 b_2 b_4 b_6 - b_0 b_3^2 b_6 - b_0 b_4^3 + b_5^2 b_1^2 - 2b_5 b_1 b_2 b_4 - 2b_5 b_1 b_3^2 \\
& + 2b_5 b_2^2 b_3 - b_1^2 b_4 b_6 + 2b_1 b_2 b_3 b_6 + 2b_1 b_3 b_4^2 - b_2^3 b_6 + b_2^2 b_4^2 - 3b_2 b_3^2 b_4 + b_3^4
\end{aligned}$$

By considering sign alternations among these expressions in $b_0, b_1, \dots, b_6$, we get explicit conditions for the general quartic to have zero, one, two, three, or four real roots respectively. These are *semialgebraic conditions*. This means the conditions are Boolean combinations of polynomial inequalities in the five indeterminates a_0, a_1, a_2, a_3, a_4. In particular, all four zeros of the general quartic are real if and only if the trace form is positive definite. Recall that a symmetric matrix is positive definite if and only if its principal minors are positive. Hence the quartic has four real roots if and only if

$$b_0 > 0 \text{ and } b_0b_2 - b_1^2 > 0 \text{ and } b_0b_2b_4 - b_0b_3^2 - b_1^2b_4 + 2b_1b_2b_3 - b_2^3 > 0 \text{ and }$$

$$2b_0b_5b_3b_4 - b_0b_5^2b_2 + b_0b_2b_4b_6 - b_0b_3^2b_6 - b_0b_4^3 + b_5^2b_1^2 - 2b_5b_1b_2b_4 - 2b_5b_1b_3^2$$

$$+2b_5b_2^2b_3 - b_1^2b_4b_6 + 2b_1b_2b_3b_6 + 2b_1b_3b_4^2 - b_2^3b_6 + b_2^2b_4^2 - 3b_2b_3^2b_4 + b_3^4 > 0.$$

The last polynomial is the determinant of B_1. It equals the discriminant of the quartic (displayed in maple at the beginning of Chapter 1) divided by a_4^6.

2.5. Solving Polynomial Equations in Singular

The computer algebra system Singular [**GPS01**] performs well in Gröbner basis computations for zero-dimensional systems. Moreover, there now exists a Singular library for numerically solving such systems. In this section we give a brief demonstration how this works. For many more details see [**GP02**].

Let us start with our small running example:

```
ring R = 0, (x,y,z), dp;
ideal I = ( (x-y)^3-z^2, (z-x)^3-y^2, (y-z)^3-x^2 );
ideal G = groebner(I);
G;
```

These four lines produce the reduced Gröbner basis in the total degree term order "dp":

```
G[1]=60y2z-30xz2-60yz2+30z3+13x2-5y2+7z2
G[2]=60x2z-60xz2-30yz2+30z3+5x2-13y2-7z2
G[3]=y3-3y2z+3yz2-z3-x2
G[4]=6xy2-12x2z-18y2z+18xz2+24yz2-18z3-7x2+5y2-z2
G[5]=3x2y-3xy2-3x2z+3y2z+3xz2-3yz2+x2+y2+z2
G[6]=x3-3x2z+3xz2-z3+y2
G[7]=25z4+5xz2-5yz2+2z2
G[8]=300yz3-300z4-195xz2-45yz2+90z3+8x2-16y2-7z2
G[9]=600xz3-300yz3-300z4+285xz2+435yz2-270z3-40x2+32y2-7z2
G[10]=100xyz2-200xz3+100yz3-105xz2-135yz2+90z3+16x2-8y2-13z2
```

We next run the numerical solver in Singular:

```
LIB "solve.lib";
solve(G,6);
```

This computes floating point approximations to our solutions, truncated to six digits:

```
[1]:
   [1]:        (-0.142332+i*0.358782)
   [2]:        (0.142332+i*0.358782)
   [3]:        (-i*0.151879)
[2]:
   [1]:        (-0.142332-i*0.358782)
   [2]:        (0.142332-i*0.358782)
   [3]:        (i*0.151879)
[3]:
   [1]:        (0.142332-i*0.358782)
   [2]:        (i*0.151879)
```

```
    [3]:          (-0.142332-i*0.358782)
[4]:
    [1]:          (-i*0.151879)
    [2]:          (-0.142332+i*0.358782)
    [3]:          (0.142332+i*0.358782)
[5]:
    [1]:          (i*0.151879)
    [2]:          (-0.142332-i*0.358782)
    [3]:          (0.142332-i*0.358782)
[6]:
    [1]:          (0.142332+i*0.358782)
    [2]:          (-i*0.151879)
    [3]:          (-0.142332+i*0.358782)
[7]:
    [1]:          0
    [2]:          0
    [3]:          0
```

We next present a more realistic example. It arises from the following question due to Olivier Mathieu: *Does there exist a Laurent polynomial*

$$f(x) \;=\; x^{-n} + a_{n-1}x^{-n+1} + \cdots + a_1 x^{-1} + b_1 x + \cdots + b_{n-1}x^{n-1} + x^n$$

with complex coefficients all of whose powers have zero constant term?

This question can be phrased as a polynomial solving problem. For any integer $i \geq 2$, let $[f^i]$ denote the constant coefficient of the ith power of f. Thus $[f^i]$ is a polynomial of degree i in $S = \mathbb{Q}[a_1, \dots, a_{n-1}, b_1, \dots, b_{n-1}]$. In view of Hilbert's Nullstellensatz, the answer to Mathieu's question is "no" if and only if $\langle [f^2], [f^3], [f^4], \dots \rangle$ is the unit ideal in S. This answer "no" was proved by Duistermaat and van der Kallen [**DvK98**]. In fact, in this remarkable paper, they establish the analogous theorem for Laurent polynomials in any number of variables. We propose the following effective version of Mathieu's question.

PROBLEM 2.11. *Is* $\left\langle [f^2], [f^3], [f^4], \dots, [f^{2n-1}] \right\rangle$ *the unit ideal in S?*

The answer is known to be "yes" for $n \leq 4$. Assuming that the answer is always "yes", it makes sense to consider the zero-dimensional ideal

$$I_n \;=\; \left\langle [f^2], [f^3], [f^4], \dots, [f^{2n-2}] \right\rangle.$$

The zeros of I_n are precisely those Laurent polynomials $f \in \mathbb{C}[x, x^{-1}]$ which have the longest possible sequence of powers with zero constant terms. We shall compute all solutions for $n = 3$. Consider the Laurent polynomial

$$(2.7) \qquad f(x) \;=\; x^{-3} + a_2 x^{-2} + a_1 x^{-1} + b_1 x + b_2 x^2 + x^3.$$

We take its successive powers to get our input for `Singular`:

```
ring R = 0,(a1,a2,b1,b2), lp;
ideal I3 =
2*a1*b1+2*a2*b2+2,
3*a1^2*b2+3*a2*b1^2+6*a1*a2+6*b1*b2,
6*a1^2*b1^2+24*a1*a2*b1*b2+6*a2^2*b2^2+4*a1^3
 +12*a1*b2^2+12*a2^2*b1+4*b1^3+24*a1*b1+24*a2*b2+6,
20*a1^3*b1*b2+30*a1^2*a2*b2^2+20*a1*a2*b1^3+30*a2^2*b1^2*b2
```

```
 +60*a1^2*a2*b1+60*a1*a2^2*b2+60*a1*b1^2*b2+60*a2*b1*b2^2
 +60*a1^2*b2+10*a2^3+60*a2*b1^2+10*b2^3+60*a1*a2+60*b1*b2;
ideal G = groebner(I3);
dim(G), vdim(G);
   0  66
```

The output 0 66 tells us that I_3 is a zero-dimensional ideal of degree $d = 66$. We next check that I_3 is a radical ideal in $\mathbb{Q}[a_1, a_2, b_1, b_2]$:

```
LIB "primdec.lib";
ideal J = radical(I3);
ideal H = groebner(J);
dim(H), vdim(H);
   0  66
```

We now know that I_3 has exactly 66 distinct complex solutions, i.e., there are 66 Laurent polynomials (2.7) with $[f^2] = [f^3] = [f^4] = [f^5] = 0$. They are:

```
LIB "solve.lib";
solve(H,10,0,50);
   [1]:
      [1]:       -2.111645747
      [2]:       (-i*1.5063678639)
      [3]:       -0.9084318754
      [4]:       (-i*1.9372998961)
   [2]:
      [1]:       -0.9084318754
      [2]:       (-i*1.9372998961)
      [3]:       -2.111645747
      [4]:       (-i*1.5063678639)
         . . . . . . . . . . .

   [37]:
      [1]:        0.4916247383
      [2]:       -1.1143136378
      [3]:        0.4916247383
      [4]:        1.1143136378
         . . . . . . . . . . .

   [59]:
      [1]:        2.5222531827
      [2]:       -2.7132565522
      [3]:        2.5222531827
      [4]:        2.7132565522
         . . . . . . . . . . .
   [65]:
      [1]:        (0.3357455874-i*0.5815284157)
      [2]:       0
      [3]:        (-0.7446114243-i*1.2897048188)
      [4]:       0
   [66]:
      [1]:       -0.6714911747
```

```
[2]:        0
[3]:        1.4892228486
[4]:        0
```

The 66 solutions come in pairs with respect to the obvious symmetry

$$(a_1, a_2, b_1, b_2) \quad \longleftrightarrow \quad (b_1, b_2, a_1, a_2).$$

For instance, the first two solutions [1] and [2] are such a pair. There are precisely three pairs of real solutions. Representatives are the solutions [37], [59] and [66]. The latter one corresponds to the Laurent polynomial

$$f(x) \quad = \quad x^{-3} \ - \ 0.6714911747 \cdot x^{-1} \ + \ 1.4892228486 \cdot x \ + \ x^3.$$

The entire computation took about 30 seconds. Note that the lexicographic term order `lp` was used in defining the `ring R`. The Gröbner basis `H` has five elements and is hence not as in the Shape Lemma. In the command `solve(H,10,0,50)` we are telling `Singular` to use 50 digits of internal precision for the numerical computation. The roots are given with 10 digits.

This was a lot of fun, indeed. Time to say...

```
> exit;
Auf Wiedersehen.
```

2.6. Exercises

(1) Let $A = (a_{ij})$ be a non-singular $n \times n$-matrix whose entries are positive integers. How many complex solutions do the following equations have:

$$\prod_{j=1}^{n} x_j^{a_{1j}} \ = \ \prod_{j=1}^{n} x_j^{a_{2j}} \ = \ \cdots \ = \ \prod_{j=1}^{n} x_j^{a_{nj}} \ = \ 1.$$

(2) Pick a random homogeneous cubic polynomial in four variables. Compute the 27 lines on the cubic surface defined by your polynomial.

(3) Given d arbitrary rational numbers $a_0, a_1, \dots, a_{d-1}$, consider the system of d polynomial equations in d unknowns $z_1, z_2, \dots, z_d$ given by setting

$$x^d + a_{d-1}x^{d-1} \cdots + a_1 x + a_0 \ = \ (x - z_1)(x - z_2) \cdots (x - z_d).$$

Describe the primary decomposition of this ideal in $\mathbb{Q}[z_1, z_2, \dots, z_d]$. How can you use this to find the Galois group of the given polynomial?

(4) For any two positive integers m, n, find an explicit radical ideal I in $\mathbb{Q}[x_1, \dots, x_n]$ and a term order $\prec$ such that $in_\prec(I) = \langle x_1, x_2, \dots, x_n \rangle^m$.

(5) Fix the monomial ideal $M = \langle x, y \rangle^3 = \langle x^3, x^2 y, xy^2, y^3 \rangle$ and compute its companion matrices T_x, T_y. Describe all polynomial ideals in $\mathbb{Q}[x, y]$ which are within distance $\epsilon = 0.0001$ from M, in the sense that the companion matrices are ϵ-close to T_x, T_y in your favorite matrix norm.

(6) Does every zero-dimensional ideal in $\mathbb{Q}[x, y]$ have a radical ideal in all of its ϵ-neighborhoods? How about zero-dimensional ideals in $\mathbb{Q}[x, y, z]$? (Hint: The answer was given thirty years ago by Iarobbino [**Iar72**].)

(7) How many distinct real vectors $(x, y, z) \in \mathbb{R}^3$ satisfy the equations

$$x^3 + z = 2y^2, \quad y^3 + x = 2z^2, \quad z^3 + y = 2x^2 \quad ?$$

(8) Pick eight random points in the real projective plane. Compute the 12 nodal cubic curves passing through your points. Repeat the computation 100 times, recording the number of complex and real solutions. Can you find eight points such that all 12 solutions are real?

(9) Consider a quintic polynomial in two variables, for instance,

$$f \quad = \quad 5y^5 + 19y^4x + 36y^3x^2 + 34y^2x^3 + 16yx^4 + 3x^5$$
$$+6y^4 + 4y^3x + 6y^2x^2 + 4yx^3 + x^4 + 10y^3 + 10y^2 + 5y + 1.$$

Determine the irreducible factors of f in $\mathbb{R}[x, y]$, and also in $\mathbb{C}[x, y]$.

(10) Consider a polynomial system which has infinitely many complex zeros but only finitely many of them have all their coordinates distinct. How would you compute those zeros with distinct coordinates?

(11) The following system of equations appears in [**Rou99**]:

$$24xy - x^2 - y^2 - x^2y^2 \quad = \quad 13,$$
$$24xz - x^2 - z^2 - x^2z^2 \quad = \quad 13,$$
$$24yz - y^2 - z^2 - y^2z^2 \quad = \quad 13.$$

Solve these equations.

(12) A well-studied problem in number theory is to find rational points on elliptic curves. Given an ideal $I \subset \mathbb{Q}[x_1, \dots, x_n]$ how can you decide whether $\mathcal{V}(I)$ is an elliptic curve, and, in the affirmative case, which computer program would you use to look for points in $\mathcal{V}(I) \cap \mathbb{Q}^n$?

(13) The number of complex solutions of the ideals $I_2, I_3, I_4, \dots$ in Mathieu's problem appears to be $4, 66, 2416, \dots$. How does this sequence continue?

CHAPTER 3

Bernstein's Theorem and Fewnomials

The Gröbner basis methods described in the previous chapter apply to arbitrary systems of polynomial equations. They are so general that they are frequently not the best choice when dealing with specific classes of polynomial systems. A situation encountered in many applications is a system of n sparse polynomial equations in n variables which has finitely many roots. Algebraically, this situation is special because we are dealing with a complete intersection, and sparsity allows us to use polyhedral techniques for counting and computing the zeros. Here and throughout this book, a polynomial is called *sparse* if we know a priori which monomials appear with non-zero coefficients in that polynomial. This chapter gives an introduction to sparse polynomial systems by explaining some basic techniques for $n = 2$.

3.1. From Bézout's Theorem to Bernstein's Theorem

A polynomial in two unknowns looks like

$$(3.1) \qquad f(x,y) \quad = \quad a_1 x^{u_1} y^{v_1} + a_2 x^{u_2} y^{v_2} + \cdots + a_m x^{u_m} y^{v_m},$$

where the exponents u_i and v_i are non-negative integers and the coefficients a_i are non-zero rationals. Its *total degree* $deg(f)$ is the maximum of the numbers $u_1 + v_1, \ldots, u_m + v_m$. The following theorem gives an upper bound on the number of common complex zeros of two polynomials in two unknowns.

THEOREM 3.1. (**Bézout's Theorem**) *Consider two polynomial equations in two unknowns: $g(x,y) = h(x,y) = 0$. If this system has only finitely many zeros $(x,y) \in \mathbb{C}^2$, then the number of zeros is at most $deg(g) \cdot deg(h)$.*

Bézout's Theorem is the best possible in the sense that almost all polynomial systems have $deg(g) \cdot deg(h)$ distinct solutions. An explicit example is gotten by taking g and h as products of linear polynomials $\alpha_1 x + \alpha_2 y + \alpha_3$. More precisely, there exists a polynomial in the coefficients of g and h such that whenever this polynomial is non-zero then f and g have the expected number of zeros. The first exercise below concerns finding such a polynomial.

A drawback of Bézout's Theorem is that it yields little information for polynomials that are sparse. For example, consider the two polynomials

$$(3.2) \quad g(x,y) = a_1 + a_2 x + a_3 xy + a_4 y, \quad h(x,y) = b_1 + b_2 x^2 y + b_3 xy^2.$$

These two polynomials have precisely four distinct zeros $(x,y) \in \mathbb{C}^2$ for generic choices of coefficients a_i and b_j. Here "generic" means that a certain polynomial in the coefficients a_i, b_j, called the *discriminant*, should be non-zero. The discriminant of the system (3.2) is the following expression:

$$4a_1^7 a_3 b_2^3 b_3^3 + a_1^6 a_2^2 b_2^2 b_3^4 - 2a_1^6 a_2 a_4 b_2^3 b_3^3 + a_1^6 a_4^2 b_2^4 b_3^2 + 22a_1^5 a_2 a_3^2 b_1 b_2^2 b_3^3$$

$$+22a_1^5 a_3^2 a_4 b_1 b_2^3 b_3^2 + 22a_1^4 a_3^3 a_3 b_1 b_2 b_3^4 + 18a_1 a_2 a_3 a_4^5 b_1^2 b_2^4 - 30a_1^4 a_2 a_3 a_3 a_4^2 b_1 b_2^3 b_3^2$$

$$+a_1^4 a_3^4 b_1^2 b_2^2 b_3^2 + 22a_1^4 a_3 a_4^3 b_1 b_2^4 b_3 + 4a_1^3 a_2^5 b_1 b_3^5 - 14a_1^3 a_2^4 a_4 b_1 b_2 b_3^4$$

$$+10a_1^3 a_2^3 a_4^2 b_1 b_2^2 b_3^3 + 22a_1^3 a_2^2 a_3^3 b_1^2 b_2 b_3^3 + 10a_1^3 a_2^2 a_4^3 b_1 b_2^3 b_3^2 + 116a_1^3 a_2 a_3^2 a_4 b_1^2 b_2^2 b_3^2$$

$$-14a_1^3 a_2 a_4^4 b_1 b_2^4 b_3 + 22a_1^3 a_3^3 a_4^2 b_1^2 b_2^3 b_3 + 4a_1^3 a_4^5 b_1 b_2^5 + a_1^2 a_2^4 a_3^2 b_1^2 b_3^4$$

$$+94a_1^2 a_2^3 a_3^2 a_4 b_1^2 b_2 b_3^3 - 318a_1^2 a_2^2 a_3^2 a_4^2 b_1^2 b_2^2 b_3^2 + 396a_1 a_2^3 a_3 a_4^3 b_1^2 b_2^2 b_3^2 + a_1^2 a_3^3 a_4^4 b_1^2 b_2^4$$

$$+94a_1^2 a_2 a_3^2 a_4^3 b_1^2 b_2^3 b_3 + 4a_1^2 a_2 a_3^5 b_1^3 b_2 b_3^2 + 4a_1^2 a_3^5 a_4 b_1^3 b_2^2 b_3 + 18a_1 a_2^5 a_3 a_4 b_1^2 b_3^4$$

$$-216a_1 a_2^4 a_3 a_4^2 b_1^2 b_2^2 b_3^2 + 96a_1 a_2^2 a_3^4 a_4 b_1^3 b_2 b_3^2 - 216a_1 a_2^2 a_3 a_4^4 b_1^2 b_2^3 b_3 - 27a_2^6 a_4^2 b_1^2 b_3^4$$

$$-30a_1^4 a_2^2 a_3 a_4 b_1 b_2^2 b_3^3 + 96a_1 a_2 a_3^4 a_4^2 b_1^3 b_2^2 b_3 + 108a_2^5 a_4^3 b_1^2 b_2 b_3^3$$

$$+4a_2^4 a_3^3 a_4 b_1^3 b_3^3 - 162a_2^4 a_4^4 b_1^2 b_2^2 b_3^2 - 132a_2^3 a_3^3 a_4^2 b_1^3 b_2 b_3^2 + 108a_2^3 a_4^5 b_1^2 b_2^3 b_3$$

$$-132a_2^2 a_3^3 a_4^3 b_1^3 b_2^2 b_3 - 27a_2^2 a_4^6 b_1^2 b_2^4 + 16a_2 a_3^6 a_4 b_1^4 b_2 b_3 + 4a_2 a_3^3 a_4^4 b_1^3 b_2^3$$

If this polynomial of degree 14 is non-zero, then the system (3.2) has four distinct complex zeros. This discriminant is computed in `maple` as follows.

```
g := a1 + a2 * x + a3 * x*y + a4 * y;
h := b1 + b2 * x^2 * y + b3 * x * y^2;
R := resultant(g,h,x):
S := factor( resultant(R,diff(R,y),y) ):
discriminant := op( nops(S), S);
```

The last command extracts the last (and most important) factor of the expression S.

Bézout's Theorem would predict $deg(g) \cdot deg(h) = 6$ common complex zeros for the equations in (3.2). Indeed, in projective geometry we would expect the cubic curve $\{g = 0\}$ and the quadratic curve $\{h = 0\}$ to intersect in six points. But these particular curves never intersect in more than four points in $\mathbb{C}^2$. To understand why the number is four and not six, we need to associate convex polygons to our given polynomials.

Convex polytopes have been studied since the earliest days of mathematics. We shall see that they are very useful for analyzing and solving polynomial equations. A *polytope* is a subset of $\mathbb{R}^n$ which is the convex hull of a finite set of points. A familiar example is the convex hull of $\{(0,0,0), (0,1,0), (0,0,1), (0,1,1), (1,0,0), (1,1,0), (1,0,1), (1,1,1)\}$ in $\mathbb{R}^3$; this is the regular 3-cube. A d-dimensional polytope has many *faces*, which are again polytopes of various dimensions between 0 and $d - 1$. The 0-dimensional faces are called *vertices*, the 1-dimensional faces are called *edges*, and the $(d - 1)$-dimensional faces are called *facets*. For instance, the cube has 8 vertices, 12 edges and 6 facets. If $d = 2$ then the edges coincide with the facets. A 2-dimensional polytope is called a *polygon*.

Consider the polynomial $f(x, y)$ in (3.1). Each term $x^{u_i} y^{v_i}$ appearing in $f(x, y)$ can be regarded as a lattice point (u_i, v_i) in the plane $\mathbb{R}^2$. The convex hull of all these points is called the *Newton polygon* of $f(x, y)$. In symbols,

$$New(f) \quad := \quad \text{conv}\{ (u_1, v_1), (u_2, v_2), \ldots, (u_m, v_m) \}$$

This is a polygon in $\mathbb{R}^2$ having at most m vertices. More generally, every polynomial in n unknowns gives rise to a *Newton polytope* in $\mathbb{R}^n$.

FIGURE 3.1. Mixed subdivision

Our running example in this chapter is the pair of polynomials in (3.2). The Newton polygon of the polynomial $g(x, y)$ is a quadrangle, and the Newton polygon of $h(x, y)$ is a triangle. If P and Q are any two polygons in the plane, then their *Minkowski sum* is the polygon

$$P + Q \quad := \quad \{\, p + q : p \in P, q \in Q \,\}.$$

Note that each edge of $P + Q$ is parallel to an edge of P or an edge of Q.

The geometric operation of taking the Minkowski sum of polytopes mirrors the algebraic operation of multiplying polynomials. More precisely, the Newton polytope of a product of two polynomials equals the Minkowski sum of two given Newton polytopes:

$$New(g \cdot h) \quad = \quad New(g) + New(h).$$

If P and Q are any two polygons then we define their *mixed area* as

$$\mathcal{M}(P, Q) \quad := \quad area(P + Q) - area(P) - area(Q).$$

For instance, the mixed area of the two Newton polygons in (3.2) equals

$$\mathcal{M}(P, Q) \quad = \quad \mathcal{M}(New(g), New(h)) \quad = \quad \frac{13}{2} - 1 - \frac{3}{2} \quad = \quad 4.$$

The correctness of this computation can be seen in the following diagram:

This figure shows a subdivision of $P + Q$ into five pieces: a translate of P, a translate of Q and three parallelograms. The mixed area is the sum of the areas of the three parallelograms, which is four. This number coincides with the number of common zeros of g and h. This is not an accident, but is an instance of a general theorem due to David Bernstein [**Ber75**]. We abbreviate $\mathbb{C}^* := \mathbb{C} \backslash \{0\}$. The set $(\mathbb{C}^*)^2$ of pairs (x, y) with $x \neq 0$ and $y \neq 0$ is a group under multiplication, called the *two-dimensional algebraic torus*.

THEOREM 3.2. (**Bernstein's Theorem**)
If g and h are two generic bivariate polynomials, then the number of solutions of $g(x, y) = h(x, y) = 0$ in $(\mathbb{C}^*)^2$ equals the mixed area $\mathcal{M}(New(g), New(h))$.

Actually, this assertion is valid for *Laurent polynomials*, which means that the exponents in our polynomials (3.1) can be any integers, possibly negative. Bernstein's Theorem implies the following combinatorial fact about lattice polygons. If P and Q are lattice polygons (i.e., the vertices of P and Q have integer coordinates), then $\mathcal{M}(P, Q)$ is a non-negative integer.

We remark that Bézout's Theorem follows as a special case from Bernstein's Theorem. Namely, if g and h are general polynomials of degree d and e respectively, then their Newton polygons are the triangles

$$P := New(g) = \text{conv}\{(0,0),(0,d),(d,0)\},$$
$$Q := New(h) = \text{conv}\{(0,0),(0,e),(e,0)\},$$
$$P+Q := New(g \cdot h) = \text{conv}\{(0,0),(0,d+e),(d+e,0)\}.$$

The areas of these triangles are $d^2/2$, $e^2/2$, $(d+e)^2/2$, and hence

$$\mathcal{M}(P,Q) = \frac{(d+e)^2}{2} - \frac{d^2}{2} - \frac{e^2}{2} = d \cdot e.$$

Hence two general plane curves of degree d and e meet in $d \cdot e$ points.

We shall present a proof of Bernstein's Theorem. This proof is algorithmic in the sense that it tells us how to approximate all the zeros numerically. The steps in this proof form the foundation for the method of polyhedral homotopies for solving polynomial systems. This is an active area of research, with lots of progress in the last few years. For an introduction and many references see [**Li97**].

We proceed in three steps. The first deals with an easy special case.

3.2. Zero-dimensional Binomial Systems

A *binomial* is a polynomial with two terms. We first prove Theorem 1.1 in the case when g and h are binomials. After multiplying or dividing both binomials by suitable scalars and powers of the variables, we may assume that our given equations are

$$(3.3) \qquad g = x^{a_1} y^{b_1} - c_1 \qquad \text{and} \qquad h = x^{a_2} y^{b_2} - c_2,$$

where a_1, a_2, b_1, b_2 are integers (possibly negative) and c_1, c_2 are non-zero complex numbers. Note that multiplying the given equations by a (Laurent) monomial changes neither the number of zeros in $(\mathbb{C}^*)^2$ nor the mixed area of their Newton polygons

To solve the equations $g = h = 0$, we compute an invertible integer 2×2-matrix $U = (u_{ij}) \in SL_2(\mathbb{Z})$ such that

$$\begin{pmatrix} u_{11} & u_{12} \\ u_{21} & u_{22} \end{pmatrix} \cdot \begin{pmatrix} a_1 & b_1 \\ a_2 & b_2 \end{pmatrix} = \begin{pmatrix} r_1 & r_3 \\ 0 & r_2 \end{pmatrix}.$$

This is accomplished using the *Hermite normal form* algorithm of integer linear algebra. The invertible matrix U triangularizes our system of equations:

$$g = h = 0$$
$$\Longleftrightarrow \qquad x^{a_1} y^{b_1} = c_1 \quad \text{and} \quad x^{a_2} y^{b_2} = c_2$$
$$\Longleftrightarrow \quad (x^{a_1} y^{b_1})^{u_{11}} (x^{a_2} y^{b_2})^{u_{12}} = c_1^{u_{11}} c_2^{u_{12}} \text{ and } (x^{a_1} y^{b_1})^{u_{21}} (x^{a_2} y^{b_2})^{u_{22}} = c_1^{u_{21}} c_2^{u_{22}}$$
$$\Longleftrightarrow \qquad x^{r_1} y^{r_3} = c_1^{u_{11}} c_2^{u_{12}} \quad \text{and} \quad y^{r_2} = c_1^{u_{21}} c_2^{u_{22}}.$$

This triangularized system has precisely $r_1 r_2$ distinct non-zero complex solutions. These can be expressed in terms of radicals in the coefficients c_1 and c_2. The number of solutions equals

$$r_1 r_2 = \det \begin{pmatrix} r_1 & r_3 \\ 0 & r_2 \end{pmatrix} = \det \begin{pmatrix} a_1 & b_1 \\ a_2 & b_2 \end{pmatrix} = \text{area}(New(g) + New(h)).$$

This equals the mixed area $\mathcal{M}(New(g), New(h))$, since the two Newton polygons are just segments, so that $area(New(g)) = area(New(h)) = 0$. This proves Bernstein's Theorem for binomials. Moreover, it gives a simple algorithm for finding all zeros in this case.

The method described here clearly works also for n binomial equations in n variables, in which case we are to compute the Hermite normal form of an integer $n \times n$-matrix. We note that the Hermite normal form computation is similar but not identical to the computation of a lexicographic Gröbner basis. We illustrate this in `maple` for a system with $n = 3$ having 20 zeros:

```
> with(Groebner): with(linalg):
> gbasis([
>                x^3 * y^5  * z^7   -   c1,
>                x^11 * y^13 * z^17  -   c2,
>                x^19 * y^23 * z^29  -   c3],         plex(x,y,z));

      13  3      8  10     15   2  2     9  8     6  3        4  7
[-c2  c1  + c3  z  ,  c2   c1  y  - c3  z ,  c2 c1  x - c3  z  y]

> ihermite( array([
> [ 3,   5,   7 ],
> [ 11,  13,  17 ],
> [ 19,  23,  29 ] ]));
                                    [1   1    5]
                                    [          ]
                                    [0   2    2]
                                    [          ]
                                    [0   0   10]
```

3.3. Introducing a Toric Deformation

We introduce a new indeterminate t, and we multiply each monomial of g and each monomial of h by a power of t. What we want is the solutions to this system for $t = 1$, but what we will do instead is to analyze it for t in neighborhood of 0. For instance, our system (3.2) gets replaced by

$$g_t(x, y) = a_1 t^{\nu_1} + a_2 x t^{\nu_2} + a_3 xy t^{\nu_3} + a_4 y t^{\nu_4}$$
$$h_t(x, y) = b_1 t^{\omega_1} + b_2 x^2 y t^{\omega_2} + b_3 xy^2 t^{\omega_3}$$

We require that the integers ν_i and ω_j be "sufficiently generic" in a sense to be made precise below. The system $g_t = h_t = 0$ can be interpreted as a bivariate system which depends on a parameter t. Its zeros $(x(t), y(t))$ depend on that parameter. They define the branches of an *algebraic function* $t \mapsto (x(t), y(t))$. Our goal is to identify the branches.

In a neighborhood of the origin in the complex plane, each branch of our algebraic function can be written as follows:

$$x(t) = x_0 \cdot t^u + \text{higher order terms in } t,$$
$$y(t) = y_0 \cdot t^v + \text{higher order terms in } t,$$

where x_0, y_0 are non-zero complex numbers and u, v are rational numbers. To determine the exponents u and v we substitute $x = x(t)$ and $y = y(t)$ into the equations $g_t(x, y) = h_t(x, y) = 0$. In our example this gives

$$\begin{aligned}
g_t\big(x(t), y(t)\big) &= a_1 t^{\nu_1} + a_2 x_0 t^{u+\nu_2} + a_3 x_0 y_0 t^{u+v+\nu_3} + a_4 y_0 t^{v+\nu_4} + \cdots, \\
h_t\big(x(t), y(t)\big) &= b_1 t^{\omega_1} + b_2 x_0^2 y_0 t^{2u+v+\omega_2} + b_3 x_0 y_0^2 t^{u+2v+\omega_3} + \cdots.
\end{aligned}$$

In order for $\big(x(t), y(t)\big)$ to be a root, the term of lowest order must vanish in each of these two equations. Since x_0 and y_0 are chosen to be non-zero, this is possible only if the lowest order in t is attained by at least two different terms. This implies the following two piecewise-linear equations for the indeterminate vector $(u, v) \in \mathbb{Q}^2$:

$$\min\big\{\, \nu_1,\ u + \nu_2,\ u + v + \nu_3,\ v + \nu_4 \,\big\} \quad \text{is attained twice,}$$
$$\min\big\{\, \omega_1,\ 2u + v + \omega_2,\ u + 2v + \omega_3 \,\big\} \quad \text{is attained twice.}$$

As in Chapter 1, each of these translates into a disjunction of linear equations and inequalities. For instance, the second "min-equation" translates into

$$\begin{aligned}
& \omega_1 = 2u + v + \omega_2 \leq u + 2v + \omega_3 \\
\text{or} \quad & \omega_1 = u + 2v + \omega_3 \leq 2u + v + \omega_2 \\
\text{or} \quad & 2u + v + \omega_2 = u + 2v + \omega_3 \leq \omega_1
\end{aligned}$$

It is now easy to state what we mean by the ν_i and ω_j being *sufficiently generic*. It means that the minimum is attained twice but not thrice. More precisely, at every solution (u, v) of the two piecewise-linear equations, precisely two of the linear forms attain the minimum value in each of the two equations.

One issue in the algorithm for Bernstein's Theorem is to choose powers of t that are small but yet generic. In our example, the choice $\nu_1 = \nu_2 = \nu_3 = \nu_4 = \omega_3 = 0$, $\omega_1 = \omega_2 = 1$ is generic. Here the two polynomials are

$$g_t(x, y) = a_1 + a_2 x + a_3 xy + a_4 y, \qquad h_t(x, y) = b_1 t + b_2 x^2 yt + b_3 xy^2,$$

and the corresponding two piecewise-linear equations are

$$\min\big\{\, 0,\ u,\ u + v,\ v \,\big\} \quad \text{and} \quad \min\big\{\, 1,\ 2u + v + 1,\ u + 2v \,\big\} \quad \text{are attained twice.}$$

This system has precisely three solutions:

$$(u, v) \quad \in \quad \big\{\, (1, 0),\ (0, 1/2),\ (-1, 0) \,\big\}.$$

For each of these pairs (u, v), we now obtain a binomial system

$$\tilde{g}(x_0, y_0) = \tilde{h}(x_0, y_0) = 0$$

which expresses the fact that the lowest terms in $g_t\big(x(t), y(t)\big)$ and $h_t\big(x(t), y(t)\big)$ do indeed vanish. The three binomial systems are

- $\tilde{g}(x_0, y_0) = a_1 + a_4 y_0$ and $\tilde{h}(x_0, y_0) = b_1 + b_3 x_0 y_0^2$ for $(u, v) = (1, 0)$.
- $\tilde{g}(x_0, y_0) = a_1 + a_2 x_0$ and $\tilde{h}(x_0, y_0) = b_1 + b_3 x_0 y_0^2$ for $(u, v) = (0, 1/2)$.
- $\tilde{g}(0, y_0) = a_2 x_0 + a_3 x_0 y_0$ and $\tilde{h}(x_0, y_0) = b_2 x_0^2 y_0 + b_3 x_0 y_0^2$ for $(u, v) = (-1, 0)$.

These binomial systems have one, two and one roots respectively. For instance, the unique Puiseux series solution for $(u, v) = (1, 0)$ has

$$x_0 = -a_4^2 b_1 / a_1^2 b_3 \qquad \text{and} \qquad y_0 = -a_1 / a_4.$$

Hence our algebraic function has a total number of four branches. If one wishes more information about the four branches, one can now compute further terms in the Puiseux expansions of these branches. For instance,

$$x(t) \quad = \qquad\qquad -\frac{a_4^2 b_1}{a_1^2 b_3}\cdot t \quad + \quad 2\cdot\frac{a_4^3 b_1^2(a_1 a_3 - a_2 a_4)}{a_1^5 b_2^2}\cdot t^2$$

$$+ \quad \frac{a_4^4 b_1^2(a_1^3 a_4 b_2 - 5a_1^2 a_3^2 b_1 + 12 a_1 a_2 a_3 a_4 b_1 - 7a_2^2 a_4^2 b_1)}{a_1^8 b_3^8}\cdot t^3 \quad + \quad \cdots$$

$$y(t) \quad = \quad -\frac{a_1}{a_4} \quad + \quad \frac{b_1(a_1 a_3 - a_2 a_4)}{a_1^2 b_3}\cdot t \quad + \quad \frac{a_4 b_1^2(a_1 a_3 - a_2 a_4)(a_1 a_3 - 2a_2 a_4)}{a_1^5 b_3^2}\cdot t^2 + \cdots .$$

For details on computing multivariate Puiseux series see [**McD95**]. In [**McD02**] a method is given for finding all the Puiseux series solutions to a system of n polynomial equations in n unknowns and m parameters.

3.4. Mixed Subdivisions of Newton Polytopes

We fix a generic toric deformation $g_t = h_t = 0$ of our equations. In this section we introduce a polyhedral technique for solving the associated piecewise linear equation and, in order to prove Bernstein's Theorem, we show that the total number of branches equals the mixed area of the Newton polygons.

Let us now think of g_t and h_t as Laurent polynomials in three variables (x, y, t) whose zero set is a curve in $(\mathbb{C}^*)^3$. The *Newton polytopes* of these trivariate polynomials are the following two polytopes in $\mathbb{R}^3$:

$$P \quad := \qquad \mathrm{conv}\big\{(0, 0, \nu_1), (1, 0, \nu_2), (1, 1, \nu_3), (0, 1, \nu_4)\big\}$$

$$\text{and} \quad Q \quad := \qquad \mathrm{conv}\big\{(0, 0, \omega_1), (2, 1, \omega_2), (1, 2, \omega_3)\big\}.$$

The Minkowski sum $P + Q$ is a polytope in $\mathbb{R}^3$. By a *facet* of $P + Q$ we mean a two-dimensional face. A facet F of $P + Q$ is a *lower facet* if there is a vector $(u, v) \in \mathbb{R}^2$ such that $(u, v, 1)$ is an inward pointing normal vector to $P + Q$ at F. Our genericity conditions for the integers ν_i and ω_j is equivalent to:

(1) The Minkowski sum $P + Q$ is a 3-dimensional polytope.
(2) Every lower facet of $P + Q$ has the form $F_1 + F_2$ where either
    (a) F_1 is a vertex of P and F_2 is a facet of Q, or
    (b) F_1 is an edge of P and F_2 is an edge of Q, or
    (c) F_1 is a facet of P and F_2 is a vertex of Q.

As an example consider our lifting from before, $\nu_1 = \nu_2 = \nu_3 = \nu_4 = \omega_3 = 0$ and $\omega_1 = \omega_2 = 1$. It meets the requirements (1) and (2). The polytope P is a quadrangle and Q is triangle. But they lie in non-parallel planes in $\mathbb{R}^3$. Their Minkowski sum $P + Q$ is a 3-dimensional polytope with 10 vertices:

The union of all lower facets of $P + Q$ is called the *lower hull* of the polytope $P + Q$. Algebraically speaking, the lower hull is the subset of all points in $P + Q$ at which some linear functional of the form $(x_1, x_2, x_3) \mapsto ux_1 + vx_2 + x_3$ attains its minimum. Geometrically speaking, the lower hull is that part of the boundary of $P + Q$ which is visible from below. Let $\pi : \mathbb{R}^3 \to \mathbb{R}^2$ denote the projection onto the first two coordinates. Then

$$\pi(P) = New(g), \quad \pi(Q) = New(h), \quad \text{and} \quad \pi(P + Q) = New(g) + New(h).$$

The map π restricts to a bijection from the lower hull onto $New(g) + New(h)$. The set of polygons $\Delta := \{\pi(F) : F \text{ lower facet of } P + Q\}$ defines a subdivision of $New(g) + New(h)$. A subdivision Δ constructed by this process, for some choice of

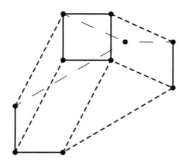

FIGURE 3.2. The 3-dimensional polytope P+Q

ν_i and ω_j, is called a *mixed subdivision* of the given Newton polygons. The polygons $\pi(F)$ are the *cells* of the mixed subdivision Δ.

Every cell of a mixed subdivision Δ has the form $F_1 + F_2$ where either

(a) $F_1 = \{(u_i, v_i)\}$ where $x^{u_i} y^{v_i}$ appears in g and F_2 is the projection of a facet of Q, or

(b) F_1 is the projection of an edge of P and F_2 is the projection of an edge of Q, or

(c) F_1 is the projection of a facet of P and $F_2 = \{(u_i, v_i)\}$ where $x^{u_i} y^{v_i}$ appears in h.

The cells of type (b) are called the *mixed cells* of Δ.

LEMMA 3.3. *Let Δ be any mixed subdivision for g and h. Then the sum of the areas of the mixed cells in Δ equals the mixed area $\mathcal{M}(New(g), New(h))$.*

PROOF. Let γ and δ be arbitrary positive real numbers and consider the polytope $\gamma P + \delta Q$ in $\mathbb{R}^3$. Its projection into the plane $\mathbb{R}^2$ equals

$$\pi(\gamma P + \delta Q) \quad = \quad \gamma \pi(P) + \delta \pi(Q) \quad = \quad \gamma \cdot New(g) + \delta \cdot New(h).$$

Let $A(\gamma, \delta)$ denote the area of this polygon. This polygon can be subdivided into cells $\gamma F_1 + \delta F_2$ where $F_1 + F_2$ runs over all cells of Δ. Note that $area(\gamma F_1 + \delta F_2)$ equals $\delta^2 \cdot area(F_1 + F_2)$ if $F_1 + F_2$ is a cell of type (a), $\gamma\delta \cdot area(F_1 + F_2)$ if it is a mixed cell, and $\gamma^2 \cdot area(F_1 + F_2)$ if it has type (c). The sum of these areas equals $A(\gamma, \delta)$. Therefore $A(\gamma, \delta) = A_{(a)} \cdot \delta^2 + A_{(b)} \cdot \gamma\delta + A_{(c)} \cdot \gamma^2$, where $A_{(b)}$ is the sum of the areas of the mixed cells in Δ. We conclude $A_{(b)} = A(1,1) - A(1,0) - A(0,1) = \mathcal{M}(New(g), New(h))$. $\qquad\square$

The following lemma makes the connection with the previous section.

LEMMA 3.4. *A pair $(u, v) \in \mathbb{Q}^2$ solves the piecewise-linear min-equations if and only if $(u, v, 1)$ is the normal vector to a mixed lower facet of $P + Q$.*

This implies that the valid choices of (u, v) are in bijection with the mixed cells in the mixed subdivision Δ. Each mixed cell of Δ is expressed uniquely as the Minkowski sum of a Newton segment $New(\tilde{g})$ and a Newton segment $New(\tilde{h})$, where $\tilde{g}$ is a binomial consisting of two terms of g, and $\tilde{h}$ is a binomial consisting of two terms of h. Thus each mixed cell in Δ can be identified with a system of two binomial equations $\tilde{g}(x, y) = \tilde{h}(x, y) = 0$. In this situation we can rewrite our system as follows:

$$g_t(x(t), y(t)) \quad = \quad \tilde{g}(x_0, y_0) \cdot t^a \; + \text{ higher order terms in } t,$$
$$h_t(x(t), y(t)) \quad = \quad \tilde{h}(x_0, y_0) \cdot t^b \; + \text{ higher order terms in } t,$$

where a and b are suitable rational numbers. This implies the following lemma.

LEMMA 3.5. *Let (u, v) be as in Lemma 3.4. The corresponding choices of $(x_0, y_0) \in (\mathbb{C}^*)^2$ are the non-zero solutions of the binomial system $\tilde{g}(x_0, y_0) = \tilde{h}(x_0, y_0) = 0$.*

We shall now complete the proof of Bernstein's Theorem. This is done by showing that the equations $g_t(x, y) = h_t(x, y) = 0$ have $\mathcal{M}(\text{New}(g), \text{New}(h))$ many distinct isolated solutions in $(K^*)^2$ where $K = \mathbb{C}\{\{t\}\}$ is the algebraically closed field of Puiseux series.

By Section 3.2, the number of roots $(x_0, y_0) \in (\mathbb{C}^*)^2$ of the binomial system in Lemma 3.5 coincides with the area of the mixed cell $\text{New}(\tilde{g}) + \text{New}(\tilde{h})$. Each of these roots provides the leading coefficients in a Puiseux series solution $(x(t), y(t))$ to our equations. Conversely, by Lemma 3.4 every series solution arises from some mixed cell of Δ. We conclude that the number of series solutions equals the sum of these areas over all mixed cells in Δ. By Lemma 3.3, this quantity coincides with the mixed area $\mathcal{M}(\text{New}(f), \text{New}(g))$. General facts from algebraic geometry guarantee that the same number of roots is attained for almost all choices of coefficients, and that we can descend from the field K to the complex numbers $\mathbb{C}$ under the substitution $t = 1$. $\square$

Our proof of Bernstein's Theorem gives rise to a numerical algorithm for finding all roots of a sparse system of polynomial equations. This algorithm belongs to the general class of *numerical continuation* methods, which are sometimes also called *homotopy methods*. Standard references include [**AG90**] and [**Li97**]. An exciting recent advance on homotopy methods is the work on numerical irreducible decomposition by Sommese, Verschelde and Wampler [**SVW01**]. In Section 6.5 the reader will find a hands-on demonstration of how to use homotopy methods for a concrete problem.

The idea of our homotopy is to trace each of the branches of the algebraic curve $(x(t), y(t))$ between $t = 0$ and $t = 1$. We have shown that the number of branches equals the mixed area. Our constructions give sufficient information about the Puiseux series so that we can approximate $(x(t), y(t))$ for any t in a small neighborhood of zero. Using numerical continuation, it is now possible to approximate $(x(1), y(1))$.

The statement of Bernstein's Theorem given above extends verbatim to higher dimensions: *The number of solutions in $(\mathbb{C}^*)^n$ of a sparse system of n Laurent polynomials in n unknowns with generic coefficients equals the mixed volume of the n Newton polytopes.* If $P_1, P_2, \dots, P_n$ are polytopes in $\mathbb{R}^n$ then their mixed volume can be defined by the inclusion-exclusion formula

$$\mathcal{M}(P_1, P_2, \dots, P_n) \quad = \quad \sum_{J \subseteq \{1, 2, \dots, n\}} (-1)^{n - \#(J)} \cdot \text{volume}\left(\sum_{j \in J} P_j \right).$$

Equivalently, $\mathcal{M}(P_1, P_2, \dots, P_n)$ is the coefficient of the monomial $\lambda_1 \lambda_2 \cdots \lambda_n$ in the expansion of the following homogeneous polynomial of degree n:

$$V(\lambda_1, \dots, \lambda_n) \quad = \quad \text{volume}\big(\lambda_1 P_1 + \lambda_2 P_2 + \cdots + \lambda_n P_n\big).$$

Here volume denotes the usual Euclidean volume in $\mathbb{R}^n$ and $\lambda_1, \dots, \lambda_n \geq 0$.

In any dimension, the mixed volume can be computed by the technique of mixed subdivisions. The currently fastest software for computing mixed volumes is due to T.Y. Li and his collaborators [**LL01**]. It is based on a highly optimized search procedure for finding the mixed cells in a mixed subdivision.

If our given polynomial system is *unmixed*, that is, if the n polynomials have the same Newton polytope, then the expected number of zeros is the *normalized volume* of the common Newton polytope $P = P_1 = \cdots = P_n$:

$$\mathcal{M}(P, P, \dots, P) \quad = \quad n! \cdot \text{volume}(P).$$

Two useful properties of the mixed volume operator $\mathcal{M}$ are its symmetry and its multilinearity. For instance, if we have three polytopes in $\mathbb{R}^3$, each of which is the sum of two other polytopes, then multilinearity says:

$$\mathcal{M}(P_1 + Q_1, P_2 + Q_2, P_3 + Q_3) \quad =$$
$$\mathcal{M}(P_1, P_2, P_3) + \mathcal{M}(P_1, P_2, Q_3) + \mathcal{M}(P_1, Q_2, P_3) + \mathcal{M}(P_1, Q_2, Q_3) +$$
$$\mathcal{M}(Q_1, P_2, P_3) + \mathcal{M}(Q_1, P_2, Q_3) + \mathcal{M}(Q_1, Q_2, P_3) + \mathcal{M}(Q_1, Q_2, Q_3).$$

This sum of eight smaller mixed volumes reflects the fact that the number of roots of system of equations is additive when each equation factors as in

$$
\begin{aligned}
f_1(x, y, z) \cdot g_1(x, y, z) &= 0, \\
f_2(x, y, z) \cdot g_2(x, y, z) &= 0, \\
f_3(x, y, z) \cdot g_3(x, y, z) &= 0.
\end{aligned}
$$

When we are given a system of equations which are multilinear (or, more general, multihomogeneous) then its mixed volume can be computed using multilinearity alone. This observation will be crucial in our discussion of Nash equilibria in Chapter 6. The mixed volume computation there involves a collection of polytopes all of which are faces of a product of simplices.

3.5. Khovanskii's Theorem on Fewnomials

Polynomial equations arise in many mathematical models in science and engineering. In such applications one is typically interested in solutions over the real numbers $\mathbb{R}$ instead of the complex numbers $\mathbb{C}$. This study of real roots of polynomial systems is considerably more difficult than the study of complex roots. Even the most basic questions remain unanswered to-date. Let us start out with a very concrete such question:

QUESTION 3.6. *What is the maximum number of isolated real roots of any system of two polynomial equations in two variables each having four terms?*

The polynomial equations considered here look like

$$
\begin{aligned}
f(x, y) &= a_1 x^{u_1} y^{v_1} + a_2 x^{u_2} y^{v_2} + a_3 x^{u_3} y^{v_3} + a_4 x^{u_4} y^{v_4}, \\
g(x, y) &= b_1 x^{\tilde{u}_1} y^{\tilde{v}_1} + b_2 x^{\tilde{u}_2} y^{\tilde{v}_2} + b_3 x^{\tilde{u}_3} y^{\tilde{v}_3} + b_4 x^{\tilde{u}_4} y^{\tilde{v}_4}.
\end{aligned}
$$

where a_i, b_j are arbitrary real numbers and $u_i, v_j, \tilde{u}_i, \tilde{v}_j$ are arbitrary integers. To stay consistent with our earlier discussion, we shall count only solutions (x, y) in $(\mathbb{R}^*)^2$, that is, we require that both x and y are non-zero real numbers.

There is an obvious lower bound for the number Question 3.6: *thirty-six*. It is easy to write down a system of the above form that has 36 real roots:

$$f(x) = (x^2 - 1)(x^2 - 2)(x^2 - 3) \quad \text{and} \quad g(y) = (y^2 - 1)(y^2 - 2)(y^2 - 3).$$

Each of the polynomials f and g depends on one variable only, and it has 6 non-zero real roots in that variable. Therefore the system $f(x) = g(y) = 0$ has 36 distinct isolated roots in $(\mathbb{R}^*)^2$. Note also that the expansions of f and g have exactly four terms each, as required.

A priori it is not clear whether Question 3.6 even makes sense: why should such a maximum exist? It certainly does not exist if we consider complex zeros, because one can get arbitrarily many complex zeros by increasing the degrees of the equations. The point is that such an unbounded increase of roots is impossible over the real numbers. This was proved by Khovanskii [Kho80]. He found a bound on the number of real roots which does not depend on the degrees of the given equations. We state the version for positive roots.

THEOREM 3.7. **(Khovanskii's Theorem)** *Consider n polynomials in n variables involving m distinct monomials in total. The number of isolated roots in the positive orthant $(\mathbb{R}_+)^n$ of any such system is at most $2^{\binom{m}{2}} \cdot (n+1)^m$.*

The basic idea behind the proof of Khovanskii's Theorem is to establish the following more general result. We consider systems of n equations which can be expressed as polynomial functions in at most m monomials in $\mathbf{x} = (x_1, \ldots, x_n)$. If we abbreviate the ith such monomial by $\mathbf{x}^{\mathbf{a}_i} := x_1^{a_{i1}} x_2^{a_{i2}} \cdots x_n^{a_{in}}$, then we can write our n polynomials as

$$F_i\big(\mathbf{x}^{\mathbf{a}_1}, \mathbf{x}^{\mathbf{a}_2}, \ldots, \mathbf{x}^{\mathbf{a}_m}\big) = 0 \qquad (i = 1, 2, \ldots, n)$$

We claim that the number of real zeros in the positive orthant is at most

$$2^{\binom{m}{2}} \cdot \Big(1 + \sum_{i=1}^{n} \deg(F_i)\Big)^m \cdot \prod_{i=1}^{d} \deg(F_i).$$

Theorem 3.7 concerns the case where $\deg(F_i) = 1$ for all i.

We proceed by induction on $m - n$. If $m = n$, then our system is expressed in n monomials in n unknowns. By a multiplicative change of variables

$$x_i \quad \mapsto \quad z_1^{u_{i1}} z_2^{u_{i2}} \cdots z_n^{u_{in}}$$

we can transform our d monomials into the n coordinate functions $z_1, \ldots, z_n$. (Here the u_{ij} can be rational numbers, since all roots under consideration are positive real numbers.) Our assertion follows from Bézout's Theorem, which states that the number of isolated complex roots is at most the product of the degrees of the equations.

Now suppose $m > n$. We introduce a new variable t, and we multiply one of the given monomials by t. For instance, we may do this to the first monomial and set

$$G_i(t, x_1, \ldots, x_n) := F_i\big(\mathbf{x}^{\mathbf{a}_1} \cdot t, \mathbf{x}^{\mathbf{a}_2}, \ldots, \mathbf{x}^{\mathbf{a}_m}\big) \qquad (i = 1, 2, \ldots, n)$$

This is a system of equations in $\mathbf{x}$ depending on the parameter t. We study the behavior of its positive real roots as t moves from 0 to 1. At $t = 0$ we have a system involving one monomial less, so the induction hypothesis provides a bound on the number of roots. Along our trail from 0 to 1 we encounter some bifurcation points at which two new roots are born. Hence the number of roots at $t = 1$ is at most twice the number of bifurcation points plus the number of roots of $t = 0$.

Each bifurcation point corresponds to a root $(\mathbf{x}, t)$ of the augmented system

$$J(t, \mathbf{x}) \;=\; G_1(t, \mathbf{x}) \;=\; \cdots \;=\; G_n(t, \mathbf{x}) \;=\; 0,$$

where $J(t, \mathbf{x})$ denotes the *toric Jacobian*:

$$J(t, x_1, \ldots, x_m) \;=\; det\left(x_i \cdot \frac{\partial}{\partial x_j} G_j(t, \mathbf{x}) \right)_{1 \le i, j \le m}.$$

Now, the punch line is that each of the $n + 1$ equations in the augmented system – including the Jacobian – can be expressed in terms of only m monomials $\mathbf{x^{a_1}} \cdot t, \mathbf{x^{a_2}}, \cdots, \mathbf{x^{a_m}}$. Therefore we can bound the number of bifurcation points by the induction hypothesis, and we are done.

This was only to give the flavor of how Theorem 3.7 is proved. There are combinatorial and topological fine points which need most careful attention. The reader will find the complete proof in [**Kho80**], in [**Kho91**] or in [**BR90**].

Khovanskii's Theorem implies an upper bound for the root count suggested in Question 3.6. After multiplying one of the given equations by a suitable monomial, we may assume that our system has seven distinct monomials. Substituting $n = 2$ and $m = 7$ into Khovanskii's formula, we see that there are at most $2^{\binom{7}{2}} \cdot (2 + 1)^7 = 4,586,471,424$ roots in the positive quadrant. By summing over all four quadrants, we conclude that the maximum in Question 3.6 lies between 36 and $18,345,885,696 = 2^2 \cdot 2^{\binom{7}{2}} \cdot (2 + 1)^7$. The gap between 36 and $18,345,885,696$ is frustratingly large. Experts agree that the truth should be closer to the lower bound than to the upper bound, but at the moment nobody knows the exact value. Could it be 36?

The original motivation for Khovanskii's work was the following conjecture from the 1970's due to Kouchnirenko. *Consider any system of n polynomial equations in n unknown, where the ith equation has at most m_i terms. The number of isolated real roots in $(\mathbb{R}_+)^n$ of such a system is at most $(m_1 - 1)(m_2 - 1) \cdots (m_d - 1)$.* This number is attained by equations in distinct variables, as was demonstrated by our example with $d = 2, m_1 = m_2 = 4$ which has $(m_1 - 1)(m_2 - 1) = 9$ positive real zeros.

Remarkably, Kouchnirenko's conjecture remained open for many years after Khovanskii had developed his theory of fewnomials which includes the above theorem. Only recently, Bertrand Haas [**Haa02**] found the following counterexample to Kouchnirenko's conjecture in the case $d = 2, m_1 = m_2 = 3$. Proving the following proposition from scratch is a nice challenge.

PROPOSITION 3.8. **(Haas)** *The two equations*

$$x^{108} + 1.1y^{54} - 1.1y \;=\; y^{108} + 1.1x^{54} - 1.1x \;=\; 0$$

have five distinct strictly positive solutions $(x, y) \in (\mathbb{R}_+)^2$.

It was proved by Li, Rojas and Wang [**LRW00**] that the lower bound provided by Haas' example coincides with the upper bound for two trinomials.

THEOREM 3.9. **(Li, Rojas and Wang)** *A system of two trinomials*

$$
\begin{aligned}
f(x, y) &= a_1 x^{u_1} y^{v_1} + a_2 x^{u_2} y^{v_2} + a_3 x^{u_3} y^{v_3}, \\
g(x, y) &= b_1 x^{\tilde{u}_1} y^{\tilde{v}_1} + b_2 x^{\tilde{u}_2} y^{\tilde{v}_2} + b_3 x^{\tilde{u}_3} y^{\tilde{v}_3},
\end{aligned}
$$

with $a_i, b_j \in \mathbb{R}$ and $u_i, v_j, \tilde{u}_i, \tilde{v}_j \in \mathbb{R}$ has at most five positive real zeros.

The exponents in this theorem are allowed to be real numbers not just integers. Li, Rojas and Wang [**LRW00**] proved a more general result for two equations in x and y where the first equation and the second equation has m terms. The number of positive real roots of such a system is at most $2^m - 2$. Note that this upper bound evaluates to 6 for $m = 3$, while the best possible bound is 5, as seen above.

Let us end this section with a light-hearted reference to [**LR97**]. In that paper, Lagarias and Richardson analyzed a particular sparse system in two variables, and the author of the present book lost a considerable amount of money along the way.

3.6. Exercises

(1) Consider the intersection of a general conic and a general cubic curve
$$a_1 x^2 + a_2 xy + a_3 y^2 + a_4 x + a_5 y + a_6 = 0$$
$$b_1 x^3 + b_2 x^2 y + b_3 xy^2 + b_4 y^3 + b_5 x^2 + b_6 xy + b_7 y^2 + b_8 x + b_9 y + b_{10} = 0$$
Compute an explicit polynomial in the unknowns a_i, b_j such that the equations have six distinct solutions whenever your polynomial is non-zero.

(2) Draw the Newton polytope of the following polynomial
$$f(x_1, x_2, x_3, x_4) = (x_1 - x_2)(x_1 - x_3)(x_1 - x_4)(x_2 - x_3)(x_2 - x_4)(x_3 - x_4).$$

(3) For general $\alpha_i, \beta_j \in \mathbb{Q}$, how many vectors $(x, y) \in (\mathbb{C}^*)^2$ satisfy
$$\alpha_1 x^3 y + \alpha_2 xy^3 = \alpha_3 x + \alpha_4 y \quad \text{and} \quad \beta_1 x^2 y^2 + \beta_2 xy = \beta_3 x^2 + \beta_4 y^2 \ ?$$
Can your bound be attained with all real vectors $(x, y) \in (\mathbb{R}^*)^2$?

(4) Find the first three terms in each of the four Puiseux series solutions $(x(t), y(t))$ of the two equations
$$t^2 x^2 + t^5 xy + t^{11} y^2 + t^{17} x + t^{23} y + t^{31} = 0$$
$$t^3 x^2 + t^7 xy + t^{13} y^2 + t^{19} x + t^{29} y + t^{37} = 0$$

(5) Prove Bernstein's Theorem for n equations in n variables.

(6) Bernstein's Theorem can be used in reverse, namely, we can calculate the mixed volume of n polytopes by counting the number of zeros in $(\mathbb{C}^*)^n$ of a sparse system of polynomial equations. Pick your favorite three distinct three-dimensional lattice polytopes in $\mathbb{R}^3$ and compute their mixed volume with this method using `Macaulay 2`.

(7) Show that Kouchnirenko's Conjecture is true for $d = 2$ and $m_1 = 2$.

(8) Prove Proposition 3.8. Please use any computer program of your choice.

(9) Can Haas's example be modified to show that the answer to Question 3.6 is strictly larger than 36?

(10) Determine the number of solutions of the following four equations in the four unknowns a, b, c, d:
$$(a - 1)(a - 2)(b - 7)(b - 8)(c - 7)(c - 8)(d - 3)(d - 4) = 0$$
$$(a - 3)(a - 4)(b - 1)(b - 2)(c - 5)(c - 6)(d - 5)(d - 6) = 0$$
$$(a - 5)(a - 6)(b - 3)(b - 4)(c - 1)(c - 2)(d - 7)(d - 8) = 0$$
$$(a - 7)(a - 8)(b - 5)(b - 6)(c - 3)(c - 4)(d - 1)(d - 2) = 0$$
State your answer as the result of a mixed volume computation.

CHAPTER 4

Resultants

Elimination theory deals with the problem of eliminating one or more variables from a system of polynomial equations, thus reducing the given problem to a smaller problem in fewer variables. For instance, if we wish to solve

$$a_0 + a_1 x + a_2 x^2 \;\; = \;\; b_0 + b_1 x + b_2 x^2 \;\; = \;\; 0,$$

with $a_2 \neq 0$ and $b_2 \neq 0$ then we can eliminate the variable x to get

$$(4.1) \quad a_0^2 b_2^2 - a_0 a_1 b_1 b_2 - 2 a_0 a_2 b_0 b_2 + a_0 a_2 b_1^2 + a_1^2 b_0 b_2 - a_1 a_2 b_0 b_1 + a_2^2 b_0^2 \;\; = \;\; 0.$$

This polynomial of degree 4 is the *resultant*. It vanishes if and only if the given quadratic polynomials have a common complex root x. The resultant (4.1) has the following three determinantal representations:

$$(4.2) \quad \begin{vmatrix} a_0 & a_1 & a_2 & 0 \\ 0 & a_0 & a_1 & a_2 \\ b_0 & b_1 & b_2 & 0 \\ 0 & b_0 & b_1 & b_2 \end{vmatrix} \;\; = \;\; - \begin{vmatrix} a_0 & a_1 & a_2 \\ b_0 & b_1 & b_2 \\ [01] & [02] & 0 \end{vmatrix} \;\; = \;\; - \begin{vmatrix} [01] & [02] \\ [02] & [12] \end{vmatrix}$$

where $[ij] = a_i b_j - a_j b_i$. Our aim in this section is to discuss such formulas.

The computation of resultants is an important tool for solving polynomial systems. It is particularly well suited for eliminating all but one variable from a system of n polynomials in n unknowns which has finitely many solutions.

4.1. The Univariate Resultant

Consider two general polynomials of degrees d and e in one variable:

$$\begin{aligned} f &= a_0 + a_1 x + a_2 x^2 + \cdots + a_{d-1} x^{d-1} + a_d x^d, \\ g &= b_0 + b_1 x + b_2 x^2 + \cdots + b_{e-1} x^{e-1} + b_e x^e. \end{aligned}$$

THEOREM 4.1. *There exists a unique (up to sign) irreducible polynomial* Res *in* $\mathbb{Z}[a_0, a_1, \ldots, a_d, b_0, b_1, \ldots, b_e]$ *which vanishes whenever the polynomials* $f(x)$ *and* $g(x)$ *have a common zero.*

Here and throughout this section "common zeros" may lie in any algebraically closed field (say, $\mathbb{C}$) which contains the field to which we specialize the coefficients a_i and b_j of the given polynomials (say, $\mathbb{Q}$). Note that a polynomial with integer coefficients being "irreducible" implies that the coefficients are relatively prime. The resultant Res $=$ Res$_x(f, g)$ can be expressed as the determinant of the *Sylvester matrix*

$$
(4.3) \qquad \mathrm{Res}_x(f,g) \;=\;
\begin{vmatrix}
a_0 & & & & b_0 & & \\
a_1 & a_0 & & & b_1 & b_0 & \\
 & a_1 & \ddots & & & b_1 & \ddots \\
\vdots & & \ddots & a_0 & \vdots & & \ddots & b_0 \\
\vdots & & & a_1 & \vdots & & & b_1 \\
a_d & & & & b_e & & \\
 & a_d & & \vdots & & b_e & & \vdots \\
 & & \ddots & & & & \ddots & \\
 & & & a_d & & & & b_e
\end{vmatrix}
$$

where the blank spaces are filled with zeroes. See the left formula in (4.2).

There are many other useful formulas for the resultant. For instance, suppose that the roots of f are $\xi_1, \ldots, \xi_d$ and the roots of g are $\eta_1, \ldots, \eta_e$. Then we have the following product formulas:

$$
\mathrm{Res}_x(f,g) \;=\; a_d^e b_e^d \prod_{i=1}^{d}\prod_{j=1}^{e}(\xi_i - \eta_j) \;=\; a_d^e \prod_{i=1}^{d} g(\xi_i) \;=\; (-1)^{de} b_e^d \prod_{j=1}^{e} f(\eta_j).
$$

From this we conclude the following proposition.

PROPOSITION 4.2. *If C_f and C_g are the companion matrices of f and g then*

$$
\mathrm{Res}_x(f,g) \;=\; a_d^e \cdot \det\bigl(g(C_f)\bigr) \;=\; (-1)^{de} b_e^d \cdot \det\bigl(f(C_g)\bigr).
$$

If f and g are polynomials of the same degree $d = e$, then the following method for computing the resultant is often used in practice. Compute the following polynomial in two variables, which is called the *Bézoutian*:

$$
B(x,y) \;=\; \frac{f(x)g(y) - f(y)g(x)}{x - y} \;=\; \sum_{i,j=0}^{d-1} c_{ij} x^i y^j.
$$

Form the symmetric $d \times d$-matrix $C = (c_{ij})$. Its entries c_{ij} are sums of brackets $[kl] = a_k b_l - a_l b_k$. The case $d = 2$ appears in (4.1) on the right.

THEOREM 4.3. (**Bézout's resultant**) *The determinant of C equals $\mathrm{Res}_x(f,g)$.*

PROOF. The resultant $Res_x(f,g)$ is an irreducible polynomial of degree $2d$ in $a_0, \ldots, a_d, b_0, \ldots, b_d$. The determinant of C is also a polynomial of degree $2d$. We will show that the zero set of $Res_x(f,g)$ is contained in the zero set of $det(C)$. This implies that the two polynomials are equal up to a constant. By examining the leading terms of both polynomials in the lexicographic term order, we find that the constant is either 1 or -1.

If $(a_0, \ldots, a_d, b_0, \ldots, b_d)$ is in the zero set of $Res_x(f,g)$ then the system $f = g = 0$ has a complex solution x_0. Then $B(x_0, y)$ is identically zero as a polynomial in y. This implies that the non-zero complex vector $(1, x_0, x_0^2, \ldots, x_0^{m-1})$ lies in the kernel of C, and therefore $det(C) = 0$. $\qquad\square$

The 3×3-determinant in the middle of (4.1) shows that one can also use mixtures of Bézout matrices and Sylvester matrices. Such hybrid formulas for resultants are very important in higher-dimensional problems as we shall see below. Let us first show three simple applications of the univariate resultant.

Example. (*Intersecting two algebraic curves in the real plane*)
Consider two polynomials in two variables, say,

$$f = x^4 + y^4 - 1 \quad \text{and} \quad g = x^5y^2 - 4x^3y^3 + x^2y^5 - 1.$$

We wish to compute the intersection of the curves $\{f = 0\}$ and $\{g = 0\}$ in the real plane $\mathbb{R}^2$, that is, all points $(x, y) \in \mathbb{R}^2$ with $f(x, y) = g(x, y) = 0$. To this end we evaluate the resultant with respect to one of the variables,

$$\begin{aligned}
\text{Res}_x(f, g) \quad = \quad & 2y^{28} - 16y^{27} + 32y^{26} + 249y^{24} + 48y^{23} - 128y^{22} + 4y^{21} \\
& -757y^{20} - 112y^{19} + 192y^{18} - 12y^{17} + 758y^{16} + 144y^{15} - 126y^{14} \\
& +28y^{13} - 251y^{12} - 64y^{11} + 30y^{10} - 36y^9 - y^8 + 16y^5 + 1.
\end{aligned}$$

This is an irreducible polynomial in $\mathbb{Q}[y]$. It has precisely four real roots

$$y = -0.9242097, \quad y = -0.5974290, \quad y = 0.7211134, \quad y = 0.9665063.$$

Hence the two curves have four intersection points, with these y-coordinates. By the symmetry in f and g, the same values are also the possible x-coordinates. By trying out (numerically) all 16 conceivable x-y-combinations, we find that the following four pairs are the real solutions to our equations:

$$\begin{aligned}
(x, y) = (-0.9242, 0.7211), \quad & (x, y) = (0.7211, -0.9242), \\
(x, y) = (-0.5974, 0.9665), \quad & (x, y) = (0.9665, -0.5974).
\end{aligned}$$

Example. (*Implicitization of a rational curve in the plane*)
Consider a plane curve which is given to us parametrically:

$$\mathcal{C} = \left\{ \left(\frac{a(t)}{b(t)}, \frac{c(t)}{d(t)} \right) \in \mathbb{R}^2 \; : \; t \in \mathbb{R} \right\},$$

where $a(t), b(t), c(t), d(t)$ are polynomials in $\mathbb{Q}[t]$. The goal is to find the unique irreducible polynomial $f \in \mathbb{Q}[x, y]$ which vanishes on $\mathcal{C}$. We may find f by the general Gröbner basis approach explained in [**CLO97**]. It is more efficient, however, to use the following formula:

$$f(x, y) = \text{Res}_t\big(b(t) \cdot x - a(t), d(t) \cdot y - c(t) \big).$$

Here is an explicit example in `maple` of a rational curve of degree six:

```
> a := t^3 - 1: b := t^2 - 5:
> c := t^4 - 3: d := t^3 - 7:
> f := resultant(b*x-a,d*y-c,t);
```

$$\begin{aligned}
f := \; & 26 - 16\,x - 162\,y + 18\,x\,y + 36\,x^2 - 704\,x^2\,y + 324\,y^2 \\
& + 378\,x\,y^2 + 870\,x^2\,y^2 - 226\,x^3\,y \\
& + 440\,x^3 - 484\,x^4 + 758\,x^3\,y^2 - 308\,x^4\,y^2 - 540\,x^3\,y \\
& - 450\,x^2\,y^3 - 76\,x^3\,y^3 + 76\,x^4\,y^2 - 216\,y^3
\end{aligned}$$

Example. *(Computation with algebraic numbers)*
Let α and β be algebraic numbers over $\mathbb{Q}$. They are represented by their *minimal polynomials* $f, g \in \mathbb{Q}[x]$. These are the unique (up to scaling) irreducible polynomials satisfying $f(\alpha) = 0$ and $g(\beta) = 0$. Our problem is to find the minimal polynomials p and q for their sum $\alpha + \beta$ and their product $\alpha \cdot \beta$ respectively. The answer is given by the following two formulas

$$p(z) = \mathrm{Res}_x\big(f(x), g(z-x)\big) \quad \text{and} \quad q(z) = \mathrm{Res}_x\big(f(x), g(z/x) \cdot x^{deg(g)}\big).$$

It is easy to check the identities $p(\alpha + \beta) = 0$ and $q(\alpha \cdot \beta) = 0$. It can happen, for special f and g, that the output polynomials p or q are not irreducible. In that event an appropriate factor of p or q will do the trick.

As an example consider two algebraic numbers given in terms of radicals:

$$\alpha = \sqrt[5]{2}, \qquad \beta = \sqrt[3]{-7/2 - 1/18\sqrt{3981}} + \sqrt[3]{-7/2 + 1/18\sqrt{3981}}.$$

Their minimal polynomials are $\alpha^5 - 2$ and $\beta^3 + \beta + 7$ respectively. Using the above formulas, we find that the minimal polynomial for their sum $\alpha + \beta$ is

$$\begin{aligned}
p(z) = \ & z^{15} + 5\, z^{13} + 35\, z^{12} + 10\, z^{11} + 134\, z^{10} + 500\, z^9 + 240\, z^8 + 2735\, z^7 \\
& + 3530 z^6 + 1273 z^5 - 6355 z^4 + 12695 z^3 + 1320 z^2 + 22405 z + 16167,
\end{aligned}$$

and the minimal polynomial for their product $\alpha \cdot \beta$ equals

$$q(z) = z^{15} - 70\, z^{10} + 984\, z^5 + 134456.$$

4.2. The Classical Multivariate Resultant

Consider a system of n homogeneous polynomials in n indeterminates

$$(4.4) \qquad f_1(x_1, \ldots, x_n) = \cdots = f_n(x_1, \ldots, x_n) = 0.$$

We assume that the ith equation is homogeneous of degree $d_i > 0$, that is,

$$f_i = \sum_{j_1 + \cdots + j_n = d_i} c^{(i)}_{j_1, \ldots, j_n} x_1^{j_1} \cdots x_n^{j_n},$$

where the sum is over all $\binom{n + d_i - 1}{d_i}$ monomials of degree d_i in $x_1, \ldots, x_n$. Note that the zero vector $(0, 0, \ldots, 0)$ is always a solution of (4.4). Our question is to determine under which condition there is a non-zero solution. In other words, in this section we are concerned with solutions in projective space $\mathbb{P}^{n-1}$, in contrast to the affine solutions considered in the previous section.

As a first example we consider three linear equations ($n = 3, d_1 = d_2 = d_3 = 1$):

$$\begin{aligned}
f_1 &= c^{(1)}_{100} x_1 + c^{(1)}_{010} x_2 + c^{(1)}_{001} x_3 = 0 \\
f_2 &= c^{(2)}_{100} x_1 + c^{(2)}_{010} x_2 + c^{(2)}_{001} x_3 = 0 \\
f_3 &= c^{(3)}_{100} x_1 + c^{(3)}_{010} x_2 + c^{(3)}_{001} x_3 = 0.
\end{aligned}$$

This system has a non-zero solution if and only if the determinant is zero:

$$\det \begin{pmatrix} c^{(1)}_{100} & c^{(1)}_{010} & c^{(1)}_{001} \\ c^{(2)}_{100} & c^{(2)}_{010} & c^{(2)}_{001} \\ c^{(3)}_{100} & c^{(3)}_{010} & c^{(3)}_{001} \end{pmatrix} = 0.$$

Returning to the general case, we regard each coefficient $c^{(i)}_{j_1,\ldots,j_n}$ of each polynomial f_i as an unknown, and we write $\mathbb{Z}[c]$ for the ring of polynomials with integer coefficients in these variables. The total number of variables in $\mathbb{Z}[c]$ equals $N = \sum_{i=1}^n \binom{n+d_i-1}{d_i}$. For instance, the 3×3-determinant in the example above may be regarded as a cubic polynomial in $\mathbb{Z}[c]$. The following theorem characterizes the classical multivariate resultant $\text{Res} = \text{Res}_{d_1 \cdots d_n}$.

THEOREM 4.4. *Fix positive degrees $d_1, \ldots, d_n$. There exists a unique (up to sign) irreducible polynomial $\text{Res} \in \mathbb{Z}[c]$ which has the following properties:*

(a) *Res vanishes under specializing the $c^{(i)}_{j_1\ldots,j_n}$ to rational numbers if and only if the corresponding equations (4.4) have a non-zero solution in $\mathbb{C}^n$.*
(b) *Res is irreducible, even when regarded as a polynomial in $\mathbb{C}[c]$.*
(c) *Res is homogeneous of degree $d_1 \cdots d_{i-1} \cdot d_{i+1} \cdots d_n$ in the coefficients $(c^{(i)}_a : |a| = d_i)$ of the polynomial f_i, for each fixed $i \in \{1, \ldots, n\}$.*

We sketch a proof of Theorem 4.4. It uses results from algebraic geometry.

PROOF. The elements of $\mathbb{C}[c]$ are polynomial functions on the affine space $\mathbb{C}^N$. We regard $x = (x_1, \ldots, x_n)$ as homogeneous coordinates for the complex projective space $\mathbb{P}^{n-1}$. Thus (c, x) are the coordinates on the product variety $\mathbb{C}^N \times \mathbb{P}^{n-1}$. Let $\mathcal{I}$ denote the subvariety of $\mathbb{C}^N \times \mathbb{P}^{n-1}$ defined by the equations

$$\sum_{j_1+\cdots+j_n=d_i} c^{(i)}_{j_1,\ldots,j_n} x_1^{j_1} \cdots x_n^{j_n} = 0 \qquad \text{for } i = 1, 2, \ldots, n.$$

Note that $\mathcal{I}$ is defined over $\mathbb{Q}$. Consider the projection

$$\phi : \mathbb{C}^N \times \mathbb{P}^{n-1} \to \mathbb{P}^{n-1}, \quad (c, x) \mapsto x.$$

Then $\phi(\mathcal{I}) = \mathbb{P}^{n-1}$. The preimage $\phi^{-1}(x)$ of any point $x \in \mathbb{P}^{n-1}$ can be identified with the set $\{c \in \mathbb{C}^N : (c, x) \in \mathcal{I}\}$. This is a linear subspace of codimension n in $\mathbb{C}^N$. To this situation we apply [**Sha94**, §I.6.3, Theorem 8] to conclude that the variety $\mathcal{I}$ is closed and irreducible of codimension n in $\mathbb{C}^N \times \mathbb{P}^{n-1}$. Hence $dim(\mathcal{I}) = N - 1$.

Consider the projection $\psi : \mathbb{C}^N \times \mathbb{P}^{n-1} \to \mathbb{C}^N$, $(c, x) \mapsto c$. It follows from the *Main Theorem of Elimination Theory*, [**Eis95**, Theorem 14.1] that $\psi(\mathcal{I})$ is an irreducible subvariety of $\mathbb{C}^N$ which is defined over $\mathbb{Q}$ as well. Every point c in $\mathbb{C}^N$ can be identified with a particular polynomial system $f_1 = \cdots = f_n = 0$. That system has a nonzero root if and only if c lies in the subvariety $\psi(\mathcal{I})$. For every such c we have

$$dim(\psi(\mathcal{I})) \quad \leq \quad dim(\mathcal{I}) = N - 1 \quad \leq \quad dim(\psi^{-1}(c)) + dim(\psi(\mathcal{I}))$$

The two inequalities follow respectively from parts (2) and (1) of Theorem 7 in Section I.6.3 of [**Sha94**]. We now choose c by choosing $(f_1, \ldots, f_n)$ as follows. Let $f_1, \ldots, f_{n-1}$ be any equations as in (4.4) which have only finitely many zeros in $\mathbb{P}^{n-1}$. Then choose f_n which vanishes at exactly one of these zeros, say $y \in \mathbb{P}^{n-1}$. Hence $\psi^{-1}(c) = \{(c, y)\}$, a zero-dimensional variety. For this particular choice of c both inequalities hold with equality. This implies $dim(\psi(\mathcal{I})) = N - 1$.

We have shown that the image of $\mathcal{I}$ under ψ is an irreducible hypersurface in $\mathbb{C}^N$, which is defined over $\mathbb{Z}$. Hence there exists an irreducible polynomial $\text{Res} \in \mathbb{Z}[c]$, unique up to sign, whose zero set equals $\psi(\mathcal{I})$. By construction, this polynomial $\text{Res}(c)$ satisfies properties (a) and (b) of Theorem 4.4.

Part (c) of the theorem is derived from Bézout's Theorem. $\qquad\qquad\square$

Various determinantal formulas are known for the multivariate resultant. The most useful formulas are mixtures of Bézout matrices and Sylvester matrices like the expression in the middle of (4.2). Exact division-free formulas of this kind are available when $n \leq 4$. We discuss such formulas for $n = 3$.

The first non-trivial case is $d_1 = d_2 = d_3 = 2$. Here the problem is to eliminate two variables x and y from a system of three quadratic forms

$$
\begin{aligned}
F &= a_0 x^2 + a_1 xy + a_2 y^2 + a_3 xz + a_4 yz + a_5 z^2, \\
G &= b_0 x^2 + b_1 xy + b_2 y^2 + b_3 xz + b_4 yz + b_5 z^2, \\
H &= c_0 x^2 + c_1 xy + c_2 y^2 + c_3 xz + c_4 yz + c_5 z^2.
\end{aligned}
$$

To do this, we first compute their *Jacobian determinant*

$$
J := \det \begin{pmatrix} \partial F/\partial x & \partial F/\partial y & \partial F/\partial z \\ \partial G/\partial x & \partial G/\partial y & \partial G/\partial z \\ \partial H/\partial x & \partial H/\partial y & \partial H/\partial z \end{pmatrix}.
$$

We next compute the partial derivatives of J. They are quadratic as well:

$$
\begin{aligned}
\partial J/\partial x &= u_0 x^2 + u_1 xy + u_2 y^2 + u_3 xz + u_4 yz + u_5 z^2, \\
\partial J/\partial y &= v_0 x^2 + v_1 xy + v_2 y^2 + v_3 xz + v_4 yz + v_5 z^2, \\
\partial J/\partial z &= w_0 x^2 + w_1 xy + w_2 y^2 + w_3 xz + w_4 yz + w_5 z^2.
\end{aligned}
$$

Each coefficient u_i, v_j or w_k is a polynomial of degree 3 in the original coefficients a_i, b_j, c_k. The resultant of F, G and H coincides with the following 6×6-determinant:

$$
(4.5) \qquad \mathrm{Res}_{2,2,2} = \det \begin{pmatrix} a_0 & b_0 & c_0 & u_0 & v_0 & w_0 \\ a_1 & b_1 & c_1 & u_1 & v_1 & w_1 \\ a_2 & b_2 & c_2 & u_2 & v_2 & w_2 \\ a_3 & b_3 & c_3 & u_3 & v_3 & w_3 \\ a_4 & b_4 & c_4 & u_4 & v_4 & w_4 \\ a_5 & b_5 & c_5 & u_5 & v_5 & w_5 \end{pmatrix}
$$

This is a homogeneous polynomial of degree 12 in the 18 unknowns $a_0, a_1, \ldots,$ $a_5, b_0, b_1, \ldots, b_5, c_0, c_1, \ldots, c_5$. The full expansion of Res has $21{,}894$ terms.

In a typical application of $\mathrm{Res}_{2,2,2}$, the coefficients a_i, b_j, c_k will themselves be polynomials in another variable t. Then the resultant is a polynomial in t which represents the projection of the desired solutions onto the t-axis.

Consider now the more general case of three ternary forms f, g, h of the same degree $d = d_1 = d_2 = d_3$. The following determinantal formula for their resultant was known to Sylvester. It is featured in Exercise 15 of Section 3.4 of [**CLO98**]. We know from part (c) of Theorem 4.4 that $\mathrm{Res}_{d,d,d}$ is a homogeneous polynomial of degree $3d^2$ in $3\binom{d+2}{2}$ unknowns. We shall express $\mathrm{Res}_{d,d,d}$ as the determinant of a square matrix of size

$$
\binom{2d}{2} = \binom{d}{2} + \binom{d}{2} + \binom{d}{2} + \binom{d+1}{2}.
$$

We write $S_e = \mathbb{Q}[x, y, z]_e$ for the $\binom{e+2}{2}$-dimensional vector space of ternary forms of degree e. Our matrix represents a linear map of the following form

$$
\begin{aligned}
S_{d-2} \oplus S_{d-2} \oplus S_{d-2} \oplus S_{d-1} &\rightarrow S_{2d-2} \\
(a, b, c, u) &\mapsto a \cdot f + b \cdot g + c \cdot h + \delta(u),
\end{aligned}
$$

where δ is a linear map from S_{d-1} to S_{2d-2} to be described next. We shall define δ by specifying its image on any monomial $x^i y^j z^k$ with $i + j + k = d - 1$. For any such monomial, we choose arbitrary representations

$$
\begin{aligned}
f &= x^{i+1} \cdot P_x + y^{j+1} \cdot P_y + z^{k+1} \cdot P_z \\
g &= x^{i+1} \cdot Q_x + y^{j+1} \cdot Q_y + z^{k+1} \cdot Q_z \\
h &= x^{i+1} \cdot R_x + y^{j+1} \cdot R_y + z^{k+1} \cdot R_z,
\end{aligned}
$$

where P_x, Q_x, R_x are homogeneous of degree $d - i - 1$, P_y, Q_y, R_y are homogeneous of degree $d - j - 1$, and P_z, Q_z, R_z are homogeneous of degree $d - k - 1$. Then we define

$$
\delta\bigl(x^i y^j z^k\bigr) = \det \begin{pmatrix} P_x & P_y & P_z \\ Q_x & Q_y & Q_z \\ R_x & R_y & R_z \end{pmatrix}.
$$

Note that this determinant is indeed a ternary form of degree

$$
(d - i - 1) + (d - j - 1) + (d - k - 1) = 3d - 3 - (i + j + k) = 2d - 2.
$$

4.3. The Sparse Resultant

Most systems of polynomial equations encountered in real world applications are *sparse* in the sense that only few monomials appear with non-zero coefficient. The classical multivariate resultant is not well suited to this situation. As an example consider the following system of three quadratic equations:

$$
f = a_0 x + a_1 y + a_2 xy, \quad g = b_0 + b_1 xy + b_2 y^2, \quad h = c_0 + c_1 xy + c_2 y^2.
$$

If we substitute the coefficients of f, g and h into the resultant $\mathrm{Res}_{2,2,2}$ in (4.5) then the resulting expression vanishes identically. This is consistent with Theorem 4.4 because the corresponding system of homogeneous equations

$$
F = a_0 xz + a_1 yz + a_2 xy, \quad G = b_0 z^2 + b_1 xy + b_2 y^2, \quad H = c_0 z^2 + c_1 xy + c_2 y^2
$$

always have the common root $(1 : 0 : 0)$, regardless of what the coefficients a_i, b_j, c_k are. In other words, the three given quadrics always intersect in the projective plane. But they generally do not intersect in the affine plane $\mathbb{C}^2$. In order for this to happen, the following polynomial in the coefficients must vanish:

$$
\begin{aligned}
& a_1^2 b_2 b_1^2 c_0^2 c_1 - 2a_1^2 b_2 b_1 b_0 c_0 c_1^2 + a_1^2 b_2 b_0^2 c_1^3 - a_1^2 b_1^3 c_0^2 c_2 + 2a_1^2 b_1^2 b_0 c_0 c_1 c_2 \\
& -a_1^2 b_1 b_0^2 c_1^2 c_2 - 2a_1 a_0 b_2^2 b_1 c_0^2 c_1 + 2a_1 a_0 b_2^2 b_0 c_0 c_1^2 + 2a_1 a_0 b_2 b_1^2 c_0^2 c_2 \\
& -2a_1 a_0 b_2 b_0^2 c_1^2 c_2 - 2a_1 a_0 b_1^2 b_0 c_0 c_2^2 + 2a_1 a_0 b_1 b_0^2 c_1 c_2^2 + a_0^2 b_2^2 c_0^2 c_1 - a_0^2 b_2^2 b_1 c_0 c_2^2 \\
& -2a_0^2 b_2^2 b_0 c_0 c_1 c_2 + 2a_0^2 b_2 b_1 b_0 c_0 c_2^2 + a_0^2 b_2 b_0^2 c_1 c_2^2 - a_0^2 b_1 b_0^2 c_2^3 - a_2^2 b_2^2 b_1 c_0^3 \\
& +a_2^2 b_2^2 b_0 c_0^2 c_1 + 2a_2^2 b_2 b_1 b_0 c_0^2 c_2 - 2a_2^2 b_2 b_0^2 c_0 c_1 c_2 - a_2^2 b_1 b_0^2 c_0 c_2^2 + a_2^2 b_0^3 c_1 c_2^2.
\end{aligned}
$$

The expression is the *sparse resultant* of f, g and h. This resultant is custom-tailored to the specific monomials appearing in the given input equations.

In this section we introduce the set-up of "sparse elimination theory". In particular, we present the precise definition of the sparse resultant. Let $\mathcal{A}_0, \mathcal{A}_1, \ldots, \mathcal{A}_n$ be finite subsets of $\mathbb{Z}^n$. Set $m_i := \#(\mathcal{A}_i)$. Consider a system of $n + 1$ Laurent polynomials in n variables $x = (x_1, \ldots, x_n)$ of the form

$$
f_i(x) = \sum_{a \in \mathcal{A}_i} c_{ia} x^a \qquad (i = 0, 1, \ldots, n).
$$

Here $x^a = x_1^{a_1} \cdots x_n^{a_n}$ for $a = (a_1, \dots, a_n) \in \mathbb{Z}^n$. We say that $\mathcal{A}_i$ is the *support* of the polynomial $f_i(x)$. In the example above, $n = 2$, $m_1 = m_2 = m_3 = 3$, $\mathcal{A}_0 = \{(1,0), (0,1), (1,1)\}$ and $\mathcal{A}_1 = \mathcal{A}_2 = \{(0,0), (1,1), (0,2)\}$. For any subset $J \subseteq \{0, \dots, n\}$ consider the affine lattice spanned by $\sum_{j \in J} \mathcal{A}_j$,

$$\mathcal{L}_J := \{ \sum_{j \in J} \lambda_j a^{(j)} \mid a^{(j)} \in \mathcal{A}_j, \, \lambda_j \in \mathbb{Z} \text{ for all } j \in J \text{ and } \sum_{j \in J} \lambda_j = 1 \}.$$

We may assume that $\mathcal{L}_{\{0,1,\dots,n\}} = \mathbb{Z}^n$. Let $rank(J)$ denote the rank of the lattice $\mathcal{L}_J$. A subcollection of supports $\{\mathcal{A}_i\}_{i \in I}$ is said to be *essential* if

$$rank(I) = \#(I) - 1 \quad \text{and} \quad rank(J) \geq \#(J) \quad \text{for each proper subset } J \text{ of } I.$$

The vector of all coefficients c_{ia} appearing in $f_0, f_1, \dots, f_n$ represents a point in the product of complex projective spaces $\mathbb{P}^{m_0-1} \times \cdots \times \mathbb{P}^{m_n-1}$. Let Z denote the subset of those systems (4.3) which have a solution x in $(\mathbb{C}^*)^n$, where $\mathbb{C}^* := \mathbb{C} \backslash \{0\}$. Let $\bar{Z}$ be the closure of Z in $\mathbb{P}^{m_0-1} \times \cdots \times \mathbb{P}^{m_n-1}$.

LEMMA 4.5. *The projective variety $\bar{Z}$ is irreducible and defined over $\mathbb{Q}$.*

It is possible that $\bar{Z}$ is not a hypersurface but has codimension ≥ 2. This is where the condition that the supports be essential comes in. It is known that the codimension of $\bar{Z}$ in $\mathbb{P}^{m_0-1} \times \cdots \times \mathbb{P}^{m_n-1}$ equals the maximum of the numbers $\#(I) - rank(I)$, where I runs over all subsets of $\{0, 1, \dots, n\}$.

We now define the *sparse resultant* Res. If $codim(\bar{Z}) = 1$ then Res is the unique (up to sign) irreducible polynomial in $\mathbb{Z}[\dots, c_{ia}, \dots]$ which vanishes on the hypersurface $\bar{Z}$. We have the following result, Theorem 4.6, which is a generalization of Theorem 4.4 in the same way that Bernstein's Theorem generalizes Bézout's Theorem.

THEOREM 4.6. *Suppose that $\{\mathcal{A}_0, \mathcal{A}_1, \dots, \mathcal{A}_n\}$ is essential, and let Q_i denote the convex hull of $\mathcal{A}_i$. For all $i \in \{0, \dots, n\}$ the degree of Res in the ith group of variables $\{c_{ia}, a \in \mathcal{A}_i\}$ is a positive integer, equal to the mixed volume*

$$\mathcal{M}(Q_0, \dots, Q_{i-1}, Q_{i+1} \dots, Q_n) = \sum_{J \subseteq \{0, \dots, i-1, i+1 \dots, n\}} (-1)^{\#(J)} \cdot \text{vol}\left(\sum_{j \in J} Q_j\right).$$

We refer to [**GKZ94**] and [**PeS93**] for proofs and details. The latter paper contains the following combinatorial criterion for the existence of a non-trivial sparse resultant. Note that, if each $\mathcal{A}_i$ is n-dimensional, then $I = \{0, 1, \dots, n\}$ is essential.

COROLLARY 4.7. *The variety $\bar{Z}$ has codimension 1 if and only if there exists a unique subset $\{\mathcal{A}_i\}_{i \in I}$ which is essential. In this case the sparse resultant Res coincides with the sparse resultant of the equations $\{f_i : i \in I\}$.*

Here is a small example. For the linear system

$$c_{00}x + c_{01}y = c_{10}x + c_{11}y = c_{20}x + c_{21}y + c_{22} = 0.$$

the variety $\bar{Z}$ has codimension 1 in the coefficient space $\mathbb{P}^1 \times \mathbb{P}^1 \times \mathbb{P}^2$. The unique essential subset consists of the first two equations. Hence the sparse resultant of this system is *not* the 3×3-determinant (which would be reducible). The sparse resultant is the 2×2-determinant Res $= c_{00}c_{11} - c_{10}c_{01}$.

We illustrate Theorem 4.6 for our little system $\{f, g, h\}$. Clearly, the triple of support sets $\{\mathcal{A}_1, \mathcal{A}_2, \mathcal{A}_3\}$ is essential, since all three *Newton polygons* $Q_i = conv(\mathcal{A}_i)$ are triangles. The mixed volume of two polygons equals

$$\mathcal{M}(Q_i, Q_j) \quad = \quad area(Q_i + Q_j) - area(Q_i) - area(Q_j).$$

In our example the triangles Q_2 and Q_3 coincide, and we have

$$area(Q_1) = 1/2, \ area(Q_2) = 1, \ area(Q_1 + Q_2) = 9/2, \ area(Q_2 + Q_3) = 4.$$

This implies

$$\mathcal{M}(Q_1, Q_2) \ = \ \mathcal{M}(Q_1, Q_3) \ = \ 3 \quad \text{and} \quad \mathcal{M}(Q_2, Q_3) \ = \ 2.$$

This explains why the sparse resultant above is quadratic in (a_0, a_1, a_2) and homogeneous of degree 3 in (b_0, b_1, b_2) and in (c_0, c_1, c_2) respectively.

One of the central problems in elimination theory is to find "nice" determinantal formulas for resultants. The best one can hope for, at least if the $\mathcal{A}_i$ are all distinct, is a *Sylvester-type formula*, that is, a square matrix whose non-zero entries are the coefficients of the given equation and whose determinant equals precisely the resultant. The archetypical example of such a formula is (4.3). Sylvester-type formulas do not exist in general, even for the classical multivariate resultant.

If a Sylvester-type formula is not available or too hard to find, the next best thing is to construct a "reasonably small" square matrix whose determinant is a non-zero multiple of the resultant under consideration. For the sparse resultant such a construction was given by Canny and Emiris [**CE00**]. See also [**Stu94**] for a more algebraic discussion. A Canny-Emiris matrix for our example is

	y^2	y^3	xy^3	y^4	xy^4	xy^2	x^2y^2	x^2y^3	y	xy
yf	a_1	0	0	0	0	a_2	0	0	0	a_0
y^2f	0	a_1	a_2	0	0	a_0	0	0	0	0
xy^2f	0	0	a_1	0	0	0	a_0	a_2	0	0
y^2g	b_0	0	b_1	b_2	0	0	0	0	0	0
xy^2g	0	0	0	0	b_2	b_0	0	b_1	0	0
yg	0	b_2	0	0	0	b_1	0	0	b_0	0
xyg	0	0	b_2	0	0	0	b_1	0	0	b_0
xy^2h	0	0	0	0	c_2	c_0	0	c_1	0	0
yh	0	c_2	0	0	0	c_1	0	0	c_0	0
xyh	0	0	c_2	0	0	0	c_1	0	0	c_0

The determinant of this matrix equals $a_1 b_2$ times the sparse resultant.

The structure of this 10×10-matrix can be understood as follows. Form the product fgh and expand it into monomials in x and y. A certain combinatorial rule selects 10 out of the 15 monomials appearing in fgh. The columns are indexed by these 10 monomials. Say the ith column is indexed by the monomial $x^j y^k$. Next there is a second combinatorial rule which selects a monomial multiple of one of the input equations f, g or h such that this multiple contains $x^i y^j$ in its expansion. The ith row is indexed by that polynomial. Finally the (i, j)-entry contains the coefficient of the jth column monomial in the ith row polynomial. This construction implies that the matrix has non-zero entries along the main diagonal. The two combinatorial rules mentioned in the previous paragraph are based on the geometric construction of a *mixed subdivision of the Newton polytopes* as described in Section 3.4.

The main difficulty overcome by the Canny-Emiris formula is this: If one sets up a matrix like the one above just by "playing around" then most likely its determinant will vanish (try it), unless there is a good reason why it shouldn't vanish. Now the key idea is this: a big unknown polynomial (such as Res) will be non-zero if one can ensure that its initial monomial (with respect to some term order) is non-zero.

Consider the lexicographic term order induced by the variable ordering $a_1 > a_0 > a_2 > b_2 > b_1 > b_0 > c_0 > c_1 > c_2$. The 24 monomials of Res are listed in this order above. All $10!$ permutations contribute a (possible) non-zero term to the expansion of the determinant of the Canny-Emiris matrix. There will undoubtedly be some cancellation. However, the unique largest monomial (in the above term order) appears only once, namely, on the main diagonal. This guarantees that the determinant is a non-zero polynomial. Note that the product of the diagonal elements in the 10×10-matrix equals $a_1 b_2$ times the underlined leading monomial.

An explicit combinatorial construction for all possible initial monomials (with respect to any term order) of the sparse resultant is given in [**Stu94**]. It is shown there that for any such initial monomial there exists a Canny-Emiris matrix which has that monomial on its main diagonal.

4.4. The Unmixed Sparse Resultant

In this section we consider the important special case when the given Laurent polynomials $f_0, f_1, \ldots, f_n$ all have the same support:

$$\mathcal{A} \quad := \quad \mathcal{A}_0 = \mathcal{A}_1 = \cdots = \mathcal{A}_n \quad \subset \quad \mathbb{Z}^n.$$

In this situation, the sparse resultant Res is the *Chow form* of the projective toric variety $X_{\mathcal{A}}$ which is given parametrically by the vector of monomials $(x^a : a \in \mathcal{A})$. For an introduction to Chow forms see [**GKZ94**, Section 3.2.B]. Chow forms play a central role in elimination theory, and it is of great importance to find determinantal formulas for Chow forms of projective varieties which appear frequently. Significant progress in this direction has been made in the recent work of Eisenbud and Schreyer [**ES02**] on exterior syzygies and the Bernstein-Gel'fand-Gel'fand correspondence. Khetan [**Khe02**] has applied these techniques to give an explicit determinantal formula of mixed Bézout-Sylvester type for the Chow form of any toric surface or toric threefold. This provides a very practical technique for eliminating two variables from three equations or three variables from four equations.

We describe Khetan's formula for an example. Consider the following unmixed system of three equations in two unknowns:

$$
\begin{aligned}
f &= a_1 + a_2 x + a_3 y + a_4 xy + a_5 x^2 y + a_6 xy^2, \\
g &= b_1 + b_2 x + b_3 y + b_4 xy + b_5 x^2 y + b_6 xy^2, \\
h &= c_1 + c_2 x + c_3 y + c_4 xy + c_5 x^2 y + c_6 xy^2.
\end{aligned}
$$

The common Newton polygon of f, g and h is a pentagon of normalized area 5. It defines a toric surface of degree 5 in projective 5-space. The sparse unmixed resultant $\mathrm{Res} = \mathrm{Res}(f, g, h)$ is the Chow form of this surface. It can be written as a homogeneous polynomial of degree 5 in the brackets

$$
[ijk] \quad = \quad \begin{pmatrix} a_i & a_j & a_k \\ b_i & b_j & b_k \\ c_i & c_j & c_k \end{pmatrix}.
$$

Hence Res is a polynomial of degree 15 in the 18 unknowns $a_1, a_2, \ldots, c_6$. It equals the determinant of the following 9×9-matrix

$$
\begin{pmatrix}
0 & -[124] & 0 & [234] & [235] & [236] & a_1 & b_1 & c_1 \\
0 & -[125] & 0 & 0 & 0 & 0 & a_2 & b_2 & c_2 \\
0 & -[126] & 0 & -[146] & -[156]-[345] & -[346] & a_3 & b_3 & c_3 \\
0 & 0 & 0 & [345]-[156]-[246] & -[256] & -[356] & a_4 & b_4 & c_4 \\
0 & 0 & 0 & -[256] & 0 & 0 & a_5 & b_5 & c_5 \\
0 & 0 & 0 & -[356] & -[456] & 0 & a_6 & b_6 & c_6 \\
a_1 & a_2 & a_3 & a_4 & a_5 & a_6 & 0 & 0 & 0 \\
b_1 & b_2 & b_3 & b_4 & b_5 & b_6 & 0 & 0 & 0 \\
c_1 & c_2 & c_3 & c_4 & c_5 & c_6 & 0 & 0 & 0
\end{pmatrix}
$$

The reader may wonder what is the use of this for solving polynomial equations. How can one apply such determinantal formulas for resultants? We will now try to answer this question by presenting a concrete example. Consider the following innocent polynomial optimization problem in three unknowns:

$$\text{Maximize} \quad z \quad \text{subject to}$$
$$8 + 5\,z^3 x - 4\,z^8 y + 3\,x^2 y - xy^2 \;=\; 0,$$
$$1 - z^9 - z^3 x + y + 3\,z^5 xy + 7\,x^2 y + 2\,xy^2 \;=\; 0,$$
$$-1 - 5\,z - 5\,z^9 x - 5\,z^8 y - 2\,z^9 xy + x^2 y + 4\,xy^2 \;=\; 0.$$

We wish to find the largest z-coordinate among the real zeros of these three equations. The three polynomials generate a radical ideal of degree 85 in $\mathbb{Q}[x, y, z]$. It takes about 20 seconds in $\mathtt{Singular}$ get a Gröbner basis for that ideal.

We shall use the above unmixed resultant to solve our optimization problem. We regard the three polynomials as polynomials in x and y whose coefficients are polynomials in z. Then the three polynomials have the same Newton polygon, namely, it is the pentagon discussed above. We can thus identify our system with the equations $f = g = h = 0$ by setting $a_1 = 8, a_2 = 5z^3, \ldots, c_6 = 4$. We then substitute these coefficients into the above 9×9-matrix. Taking the determinant gives the following polynomial in z:

$$-22164480\,z^{88} + 15475200\,z^{87} + 122137600\,z^{86} + 2529280\,z^{85}$$
$$-127449920\,z^{84} + 32229600\,z^{83} + 602821440\,z^{82} + 82392960\,z^{81}$$
$$+346487960\,z^{80} - 185665480\,z^{79} - 826226960\,z^{78} - 1109723680\,z^{77}$$
$$+11127639562\,z^{76} + 463378760\,z^{75} + 501611630\,z^{74} - 381982588\,z^{73}$$
$$-2652411801\,z^{72} - 1262356225\,z^{71} + 41327276770\,z^{70} - 1851079789\,z^{69}$$
$$+20177395368\,z^{68} - 12234532687\,z^{67} + 2917319158\,z^{66} + 5550379172\,z^{65}$$
$$+55290733641\,z^{64} - 7157109518\,z^{63} + 22594171392\,z^{62} - 59668817247\,z^{61}$$
$$+9284745119\,z^{60} - 24457258566\,z^{59} + 11916256872\,z^{58} - 48972229683\,z^{57}$$
$$-10708963850\,z^{56} + 14930224972\,z^{55} + 11945104288\,z^{54} - 67351685674\,z^{53}$$
$$+30076150819\,z^{52} - 183771841266\,z^{51} - 67110924959\,z^{50} + 128326366727\,z^{49}$$
$$+82566055130\,z^{48} + 67047977503\,z^{47} + 79814883590\,z^{46} - 11384678903\,z^{45}$$
$$-167471148156\,z^{44} - 84019239967\,z^{43} - 302711927414\,z^{42} - 637289913117 z^{41}$$

$$+28678967096\,z^{40} - 16099713942\,z^{39} + 95010313255\,z^{38} - 95142265127\,z^{37}$$
$$+140514519496\,z^{36} + 30751712914\,z^{35} + 101472313202\,z^{34} - 232022638120\,z^{33}$$
$$+169474847373\,z^{32} + 194154012741\,z^{31} - 55498446549\,z^{30} - 136708130533\,z^{29}$$
$$-19227547495\,z^{28} - 32503148691\,z^{27} + 77588325009\,z^{26} + 215265703718\,z^{25}$$
$$+66072328920\,z^{24} + 48410904568\,z^{23} + 89707435519\,z^{22} + 6091791043\,z^{21}$$
$$-117211364660\,z^{20} + 7640170746\,z^{19} + 138621097004\,z^{18} - 123609336747\,z^{17}$$
$$+1181945518\,z^{16} + 18937092538\,z^{15} - 2620479355\,z^{14} - 63367791305\,z^{13}$$
$$+88482019067\,z^{12} - 1576638856\,z^{11} + 68265080910\,z^{10} - 48292301278\,z^{9}$$
$$+707273957\,z^{8} - 3255417425\,z^{7} + 18794493042\,z^{6} - 38464953475\,z^{5}$$
$$+23765746680\,z^{4} + 9532208907\,z^{3}$$

The desired solution to our optimization problem is the largest real root of this polynomial of degree 88. That number equals $z = 2.701610104$. Computing the above polynomial and its real roots took less than 2 seconds by running the following maple code which implements the matrix formula:

```
> f :=    8 + 5*z^3*x-4*z^8*y+3*x^2*y-x*y^2:
> g :=    1-z^9-z^3*x+y+3*z^5*x*y+7*x^2*y+2*x*y^2:
> h :=   -1-5*z-5*z^9*x-5*z^8*y-2*z^9*x*y+x^2*y+4*x*y^2:


> a1 := coeff(coeff(f,x,0),y,0):a2 := coeff(coeff(f,x,1),y,0):
> a3 := coeff(coeff(f,x,0),y,1):a4 := coeff(coeff(f,x,1),y,1):
> a5 := coeff(coeff(f,x,2),y,1):a6 := coeff(coeff(f,x,1),y,2):
> b1 := coeff(coeff(g,x,0),y,0):b2 := coeff(coeff(g,x,1),y,0):
> b3 := coeff(coeff(g,x,0),y,1):b4 := coeff(coeff(g,x,1),y,1):
> b5 := coeff(coeff(g,x,2),y,1):b6 := coeff(coeff(g,x,1),y,2):
> c1 := coeff(coeff(h,x,0),y,0):c2 := coeff(coeff(h,x,1),y,0):
> c3 := coeff(coeff(h,x,0),y,1):c4 := coeff(coeff(h,x,1),y,1):
> c5 := coeff(coeff(h,x,2),y,1):c6 := coeff(coeff(h,x,1),y,2):


> A := array([ [a1,a2,a3,a4,a5,a6],
>              [b1,b2,b3,b4,b5,b6],
>              [c1,c2,c3,c4,c5,c6]]):   with(linalg):


> d := proc(i,j,k) det(submatrix(A,[1,2,3],[i,j,k])) end:


> AmitsFormula := array( [
>[0,-d(1,2,4),0, d(2,3,4),    d(2,3,5),          d(2,3,6),a1,b1,c1],
>[0,-d(1,2,5),0,    0 ,        0 ,               0 ,a2,b2,c2],
>[0,-d(1,2,6),0,-d(1,4,6),-d(1,5,6)-d(3,4,5),-d(3,4,6),a3,b3,c3],
>[0,0,0,d(3,4,5)-d(1,5,6)-d(2,4,6),-d(2,5,6),-d(3,5,6),a4,b4,c4],
>[0,  0,  0,      -d(2,5,6),         0 ,           0 ,a5,b5,c5],
>[0,  0,  0,      -d(3,5,6),    d(4,5,6),          0 ,a6,b6,c6],
>[a1,a2,a3,              a4,          a5,          a6, 0, 0, 0],
>[b1,b2,b3,              b4,          b5,          b6, 0, 0, 0],
>[c1,c2,c3,              c4,          c5,          c6, 0,0,0]]):


> minipoly := sort(det(AmitsFormula),z):
```

```
> fsolve(det(AmitsFormula),z);
   -2.091448184, -.2679041558, 0., 0., 0.,
   .9656692830, 1.102760939, 2.701610104
```

The irreducible minimal polynomial of $z = 2.701610104$ has degree 85 and is gotten by removing the factor z^3 from our polynomial of degree 88. We note that this polynomial was also produced in `maple`, by saying `latex(minipoly);` at the end of the session above.

4.5. The Resultant of Four Trilinear Equations

Polynomials arising in many applications are multihomogeneous. Sometimes we are even luckier and the equations are multilinear, that is, multihomogeneous of degree $(1, 1, \ldots, 1)$. This will happen in Chapter 6. The resultant of a multihomogeneous system is the instance of the sparse resultant where the Newton polytopes are products of simplices. There are lots of nice formulas available for such resultants. For a systematic account see [**SZ94**] and [**DE02**].

In this section we discuss one particular example, namely, the resultant of four trilinear polynomials in three unknowns. This material was prepared by Amit Khetan in response to a question by J. Maurice Rojas. The given equations are

$$f_i = C_{i7}x_1x_2x_3 + C_{i6}x_1x_2 + C_{i5}x_1x_3 + C_{i4}x_1 + C_{i3}x_2x_3 + C_{i2}x_2 + C_{i1}x_3 + C_{i0},$$

where $i = 0, 1, 2, 3$. The four polynomials f_0, f_1, f_2, f_3 in the unknowns x_1, x_2, x_3 share the same Newton polytope, the standard 3-dimensional cube. Hence our system is the unmixed polynomial system supported on the 3-cube.

The resultant $\mathrm{Res}(f_0, f_1, f_2, f_3)$ is the unique (up to sign) irreducible polynomial in the 32 indeterminates C_{ij} which vanishes if $f_0 = f_1 = f_2 = f_3 = 0$ has a common solution (x_1, x_2, x_3) in $\mathbb{C}^3$. If we replace the affine space $\mathbb{C}^3$ by the product of projective lines $\mathbb{P}^1 \times \mathbb{P}^1 \times \mathbb{P}^1$, then the "if" in the previous sentence can be replaced by "if and only if". The resultant is a homogeneous polynomial of degree 24, in fact, it is homogeneous of degree 6 in the coefficients of f_i for each i. In algebraic geometry, we interpret this resultant as the *Chow form* of the Segre variety $\mathbb{P}^1 \times \mathbb{P}^1 \times \mathbb{P}^1 \subset \mathbb{P}^7$.

We first present a Sylvester matrix for Res. Let $S(a, b, c)$ denote the vector space of all polynomials in $\mathbb{Q}[x_1, x_2, x_3]$ of degree less than or equal to a in x_1, less than or equal to b in x_2, and less than or equal to c in x_3. The dimension of $S(a, b, c)$ is $(a+1)(b+1)(c+1)$. Consider the $\mathbb{Q}$-linear map

$$\phi : S(0, 1, 2)^4 \rightarrow S(1, 2, 3), \quad (g_0, g_1, g_2, g_3) \mapsto g_0 f_0 + g_1 f_1 + g_2 f_2 + g_3 f_3.$$

Both the range and the image of the linear map ϕ are vector spaces of dimension 24. We fix the standard monomial bases for both of these vector spaces. Then the linear map ϕ is given by a 24×24 matrix. Each non-zero entry in this matrix is one of the coefficients C_{ij}. In particular, the determinant of ϕ is a polynomial of degree 24 in the 32 unknowns C_{ij}.

PROPOSITION 4.8. *The determinant of the matrix ϕ equals* $\mathrm{Res}(f_0, f_1, f_2, f_3)$.

This formula is a *Sylvester Formula* for the resultant of four trilinear polynomials. The Sylvester formula is easy to generate, but it is not the most efficient representation when it comes to actually evaluating our resultant. A better representation is the following *Bézout formula*.

For $i, j, k, l \in \{0, 1, 2, 3, 4, 5, 6, 7\}$ we define the *bracket variables*

$$[ijkl] \;=\; \det \begin{bmatrix} C_{0i} & C_{0j} & C_{0k} & C_{0l} \\ C_{1i} & C_{1j} & C_{1k} & C_{1l} \\ C_{2i} & C_{2j} & C_{2k} & C_{2l} \\ C_{3i} & C_{3j} & C_{3k} & C_{3l} \end{bmatrix}$$

We shall present a 6×6 matrix B whose entries are linear forms in the bracket variables, such that $\det B = \mathrm{Res}(f_0, f_1, f_2, f_3)$. This construction is described, for arbitrary products of projective spaces, in a recent paper by Dickenstein and Emiris [**DE02**]. First construct the 4×4-matrix M such that

$$M_{0j} = f_j(x_1, x_2, x_3) \quad \text{for } j = 0, 1, 2, 3$$

$$M_{ij} = \frac{f_j(y_1, \ldots, y_i, x_{i+1}, \ldots, x_3) - f_j(y_1, \ldots, y_{i-1}, x_i, \ldots, x_3)}{y_i - x_i}$$

$$\text{for } i = 1, 2, 3 \quad \text{and} \quad j = 0, 1, 2, 3.$$

The first row of the matrix M consists of the given polynomials f_i, while each successive row of M is an *incremental quotient* with each x_i successively replaced by a corresponding y_i. After a bit of simplification, such as subtracting x_1 times the second row from the first, the matrix M gets replaced by a 4×4-matrix of the form

$$\tilde{M} \;=\; \begin{bmatrix} C_{03}x_2x_3 + C_{02}x_2 + C_{01}x_3 + C_{00} & \cdots \\ C_{07}x_2x_3 + C_{06}x_2 + C_{05}x_3 + C_{04} & \cdots \\ C_{07}y_1x_3 + C_{06}y_1 + C_{03}x_3 + C_{02} & \cdots \\ C_{07}y_1y_2 + C_{05}y_1 + C_{03}y_2 + C_{01} & \cdots \end{bmatrix}$$

Let $B(x, y)$ denote the determinant of this matrix. This is a polynomial in two sets of variables. It is called the *(affine) Bézoutian* of the given trilinear forms f_0, f_1, f_2, f_3. It appears from the entries of $\tilde{M}$ that $B(x, y)$ has total degree 8, but this is not the case. In fact, the total degree of this polynomial is only 6. The monomials $x^\alpha y^\beta = x_1^{\alpha_1} x_2^{\alpha_2} x_3^{\alpha_3} y_1^{\beta_1} y_2^{\beta_2} y_3^{\beta_3}$ appearing in $B(x, y)$ satisfy $\alpha_i < i$ and $\beta_i < 3 - i$. This is the content of the lemma below. The coefficient $b_{\alpha\beta}$ of $x^\alpha y^\beta$ in $B(x, y)$ is a linear form in the bracket variables.

LEMMA 4.9. $B(x, y) \in S(0, 1, 2) \otimes S(2, 1, 0)$.

We can interpret the polynomial $B(x, y)$ as as a linear map, also denoted B, from the dual vector space $S(2, 1, 0)^*$ to $S(0, 1, 2)$. Each of these two vector spaces is 6-dimensional and has a canonical monomial basis. The following 6×6-matrix represents the linear map B in the monomial basis:

$[0124]$	$[0234]$	$[0146] - [0245]$	$[0346] - [0247]$	$[0456]$	$[0467]$
$-[0125] - [0134]$	$[1234] + [0235]$	$[0147] + [0156]$ $-[0345] - [1245]$	$-[1247] + [0356]$ $-[0257] + [1346]$	$[1456] + [0457]$	$[1467] + [0567]$
$-[0135]$	$[1235]$	$[0157] - [1345]$	$-[1257] + [1356]$	$[1457]$	$[1567]$
$-[0126]$	$[0236]$	$-[1246] + [0256]$	$[2346] - [0267]$	$[2456]$	$[2467]$
$-[0136] - [0127]$	$[1236] + [0237]$	$-[1247] - [1346]$ $[0257] + [0356]$	$-[0367] - [1267]$ $[2356] + [2347]$	$[3456] + [2457]$	$[2567] + [3467]$
$-[0137]$	$[1237]$	$-[1347] + [0357]$	$-[1367] + [2357]$	$[3457]$	$[3567]$

PROPOSITION 4.10. $\mathrm{Res}(f_0, f_1, f_2, f_3)$ *is the determinant of the above matrix.*

This type of formula is called a *Bézout formula* or sometimes *pure Bézout formula* in the resultant literature. Expanding the determinant gives a polynomial of degree 6 in the brackets with $11,280$ terms. It remains a formidable challenge to further expand this expression into an honest polynomial of degree 24 in the 32 coefficients C_{ij}.

4.6. Exercises

(1) Prove Proposition 4.2.
(2) Compute the resultant $\mathrm{Res}_{1,2,3}$ of three ternary forms ($n = 3$) of degrees one, two and three respectively. This resultant is a polynomial of degree 11 in 19 unknowns. How many monomials appear in its expansion?
(3) Fix your favorite term order on a polynomial ring in 45 unknowns. Determine the leading monomial in the expansion of the resultant $\mathrm{Res}_{4,4,4}$ of three ternary quartics. Hint: Use [**Stu94**].
(4) A cubic curve in $\mathbb{P}^2$ is the zero set of a ternary cubic

$$\begin{aligned} f(x, y, z) \quad = \quad & a_1 x^3 + a_2 x^2 y + a_3 x y^2 + a_4 y^3 + a_5 x^2 z \\ & + a_6 xyz + a_7 y^2 z + a_8 x z^2 + a_9 y z^2 + a_{10} z^3. \end{aligned}$$

Compute the resultant $\mathrm{Res}_{2,2,2}\left(\frac{\partial f}{\partial x}, \frac{\partial f}{\partial y}, \frac{\partial f}{\partial z}\right)$ of the three partial derivatives of f. This is a polynomial of degree 12 in ten unknowns $a_1, \ldots, a_{10}$ which vanishes if and only if the cubic curve has a singularity. How does this polynomial relate to your computations in Exercise (8) in Chapter 2?
(5) What is the *Dixon resultant* and which computer scientists use it? Try to find an answer on the world wide web by searching with Google.
(6) Use the formula for $\mathrm{Res}_{3,3,3}$ at the end of Section 4.2 to solve the equations

$$\begin{aligned} (x + y - z)(x + 2y - 3z)(x + 4y - 9z) \quad &= \quad \alpha, \\ (x - y + z)(x - 2y + 3z)(x - 4y + 9z) \quad &= \quad \beta, \\ (-x + y + z)(-x + 2y + 3z)(-x + 4y + 9z) \quad &= \quad \gamma, \end{aligned}$$

where α, β, γ are parameters. How does x depend on these parameters? Show that there is a unique real solution for $\alpha = 13, \beta = 17, \gamma = 19$.
(7) Give an exact formula for the resultant of three biquadratic equations.
(8) How can resultants help to solve Exercise (1) in Chapter 3?
(9) Give a necessary and sufficient condition for the following system of four equations in three unknowns x, y, z to have a common solution in $(\mathbb{C}^*)^3$:

$$\begin{aligned} a_1 x + a_2 y + a_3 z + a_4 x^{-1} + a_5 y^{-1} + a_6 z^{-1} \quad &= \quad 0, \\ b_1 x + b_2 y + b_3 z + b_4 x^{-1} + b_5 y^{-1} + b_6 z^{-1} \quad &= \quad 0, \\ c_1 x + c_2 y + c_3 z + c_4 x^{-1} + c_5 y^{-1} + c_6 z^{-1} \quad &= \quad 0, \\ d_1 x + d_2 y + d_3 z + d_4 x^{-1} + d_5 y^{-1} + d_6 z^{-1} \quad &= \quad 0. \end{aligned}$$

CHAPTER 5

Primary Decomposition

In this chapter we consider arbitrary systems of polynomial equations in several unknowns. The solution set of these equations may have many different components of different dimensions, and our task is to identify all of these irreducible components. The algebraic technique for doing this is *primary decomposition* [**CLO97**, Section 4.7]. After reviewing the relevant basic results from commutative algebra, we demonstrate how to do such computations in `Singular` and `Macaulay 2`. We then present some particularly interesting examples. Our main objective is to expose non-experts to the joy of decomposing algebraic varieties. Readers wishing to learn more about algorithms for primary decomposition may consult [**DGP99**].

5.1. Prime Ideals, Radical Ideals and Primary Ideals

Let I be an ideal in the polynomial ring $\mathbb{Q}[x] = \mathbb{Q}[x_1, \ldots, x_n]$. Solving the polynomial system I means at least finding the irreducible decomposition

$$\mathcal{V}(I) \quad = \quad \mathcal{V}(P_1) \cup \mathcal{V}(P_2) \cup \cdots \cup \mathcal{V}(P_r) \quad \subset \quad \mathbb{C}^n$$

of the complex variety defined by I. Here each $\mathcal{V}(P_i)$ is an irreducible variety over the field of rational numbers $\mathbb{Q}$. Naturally, if we extend scalars and pass to the complex numbers $\mathbb{C}$, then $\mathcal{V}(P_i)$ may further decompose into more components, but describing those components typically involves numerical computations, for instance, as in [**SVW01**]. The special case where I is zero-dimensional was discussed in Chapter 2. In this chapter we mostly stick to doing arithmetic in $\mathbb{Q}[x]$ only.

Recall that an ideal P in $\mathbb{Q}[x]$ is a *prime ideal* if

$$(5.1) \qquad\qquad (P : f) = P \qquad \text{for all } f \in \mathbb{Q}[x] \backslash P$$

Here $(P : f)$ denotes the set of all polynomials $g \in \mathbb{Q}[x]$ such that $f \cdot g$ lies in P. The zero set of a prime ideal is an *irreducible variety*. Deciding whether a given ideal is prime is not an easy task. See Corollary 5.4 below for a method that works quite well (say, in `Macaulay 2`) on small enough examples.

Fix an ideal I in $\mathbb{Q}[x]$. A prime ideal P is said to be *associated* to I if

$$(5.2) \qquad\qquad \text{there exists } f \in \mathbb{Q}[x] \quad \text{such that } (I : f) = P.$$

A polynomial f which satisfies $(I : f) = P$ is called a *witness* for P in I. We write $\mathrm{Ass}(I)$ for the set of all prime ideals which are associated to I.

PROPOSITION 5.1. *For any ideal $I \subset \mathbb{Q}[x]$, $\mathrm{Ass}(I)$ is non-empty and finite.*

Here are some simple examples of ideals I, primes P and witnesses f.

EXAMPLE 5.2. In each of the following six cases, P is a prime ideal in the polynomial ring in the given unknowns, and the identity $(I : f) = P$ holds.

(a) $I = \langle x_1^4 - x_1^2 \rangle$, $f = x_1^3 - x_1$, $P = \langle x_1 \rangle$.

(a') $I = \langle x_1^4 - x_1^2 \rangle$, $f = x_1^{17} - x_1^{16}$, $P = \langle x_1 + 1 \rangle$.

(b) $I = \langle x_1x_4 + x_2x_3, x_1x_3, x_2x_4 \rangle$, $f = x_4^2$, $P = \langle x_1, x_2 \rangle$.

(b') $I = \langle x_1x_4 + x_2x_3, x_1x_3, x_2x_4 \rangle$, $f = x_1x_4$, $P = \langle x_1, x_2, x_3, x_4 \rangle$.

(c) $I = \langle x_1x_2 + x_3x_4, x_1x_3 + x_2x_4, x_1x_4 + x_2x_3 \rangle$, $f = (x_3^2 - x_4^2)x_4$, $P = \langle x_1, x_2, x_3 \rangle$.

(c') $I = \langle x_1x_2 + x_3x_4, x_1x_3 + x_2x_4, x_1x_4 + x_2x_3 \rangle$, $f = x_1x_4^2 + x_2x_4^2 - x_3x_4^2 + x_3^2x_4$,
$P = \langle x_1 - x_4, x_2 - x_4, x_3 + x_4 \rangle$.

The *radical* of an ideal I equals the intersection of all its associated primes:

(5.3)
$$\mathrm{Rad}(I) \;=\; \bigcap \{\, P \,:\, P \in \mathrm{Ass}(I) \,\}.$$

The computation of the radical and the set of associated primes are built-in commands in `Macaulay 2`. The following session checks whether the ideals in (b) and (c) of Example 5.2 are radical, and it illustrates the identity (5.3).

```
i1 : R = QQ[x1,x2,x3,x4];

i2 : I = ideal( x1*x4+x2*x3, x1*x3, x2*x4 );

i3 : ass(I)
o3 = {ideal (x4, x3), ideal (x2, x1), ideal (x4, x3, x2, x1)}

i4 : radical(I) == I
o4 = false

i5 : radical(I)
o5 = ideal (x2*x4, x1*x4, x2*x3, x1*x3)

i6 : intersect(ass(I))
o6 = ideal (x2*x4, x1*x4, x2*x3, x1*x3)

i7 : ass(radical(I))
o7 = {ideal (x4, x3), ideal (x2, x1)}

i8 : J = ideal( x1*x2+x3*x4,  x1*x3+x2*x4,  x1*x4+x2*x3 );

i9 : ass(J)
o9 = {ideal (x3 + x4, x2 - x4, x1 - x4), ideal (x4, x2, x1),
       ideal (x3 + x4, x2 + x4, x1 + x4), ideal (x4, x3, x1),
       ideal (x3 - x4, x2 + x4, x1 - x4), ideal (x4, x3, x2),
       ideal (x3 - x4, x2 - x4, x1 + x4), ideal (x3, x2, x1)}

i10 : radical(J) == J
o10 = true
```

The following result is a useful method for showing that an ideal is radical.

PROPOSITION 5.3. *Let I be an ideal in $\mathbb{Q}[x]$ and $\prec$ any term order. If the initial monomial ideal $\mathrm{in}_\prec(I)$ is square-free then I is a radical ideal.*

An ideal I in $\mathbb{Q}[x]$ is called *primary* if the set $\mathrm{Ass}(I)$ is a singleton. In that case, its radical $\mathrm{Rad}(I)$ is a prime ideal and $\mathrm{Ass}(I) = \{\mathrm{Rad}(I)\}$.

COROLLARY 5.4. *The following three conditions are equivalent for an ideal I:*

(1) I *is a prime ideal;*
(2) I *is radical and primary;*
(3) $\mathrm{Ass}(I) = \{I\}$.

We can use the condition (3) to test whether a given ideal is prime. Here is an interesting example. Let $X = (x_{ij})$ and $Y = (y_{ij})$ be two $n{\times}n$-matrices both having indeterminate entries. Each entry in their commutator $XY - YX$ is a quadratic polynomial in the polynomial ring $\mathbb{Q}[X, Y]$ generated by the $2n^2$ unknowns x_{ij}, y_{ij}. We let I denote the ideal generated by these n^2 quadratic polynomials. It is known that the *commuting variety* $\mathcal{V}(I)$ is an irreducible variety in $\mathbb{C}^{2n^2}$ but it is unknown whether I is always a prime ideal. The following `Macaulay 2` session proves that I is a prime ideal for $n = 2$.

```
i1 : R = QQ[ x11,x12,x21,x22, y11,y12,y21,y22 ];
i2 : X = matrix({ {x11,x12} , {x21,x22} });
i3 : Y = matrix({ {y11,y12} , {y21,y22} });

i4 : I = ideal flatten ( X*Y - Y*X )

o4 = ideal (- x21*y12 + x12*y21, x21*y12 - x12*y21,
             x21*y11 - x11*y21 + x22*y21 - x21*y22,
           - x12*y11 + x11*y12 - x22*y12 + x12*y22)

i5 : ass(I) == {I}
o5 = true
```

5.2. How to Decompose a Polynomial System

The following is the main result about primary decompositions in $\mathbb{Q}[x]$.

THEOREM 5.5. *Every ideal I in $\mathbb{Q}[x]$ is an intersection of primary ideals,*

$$(5.4) \qquad I \;=\; Q_1 \cap Q_2 \cap \cdots \cap Q_r,$$

where the primes $P_i = \mathrm{Rad}(Q_i)$ are distinct and associated to I.

It is a consequence of (5.3) that the following inclusion holds:

$$\mathrm{Ass}\big(\mathrm{Rad}(I)\big) \quad \subseteq \quad \mathrm{Ass}(I).$$

In the situation of Theorem 5.5, the associated prime P_i is a *minimal prime* of I if it also lies in $\mathrm{Ass}\big(\mathrm{Rad}(I)\big)$. In that case, the corresponding *primary component* Q_i of I is unique. If P_i is a minimal prime of I, and I has no embedded prime containing P_i, then Q_i can be recovered by the formula

$$(5.5) \qquad Q_i \;=\; \big(I : (I : P_i^\infty)\big).$$

The same formula looks like this in the `Macaulay 2` language:

```
Qi   =   ( I : saturate( I, Pi ) )
```

On the other hand, if P_i lies in $\mathrm{Ass}(I) \setminus \mathrm{Ass}\big(\mathrm{Rad}(I)\big)$ then P_i is an *embedded prime* of I and the primary component Q_i in Theorem 5.5 is not unique.

A full implementation of a primary decomposition algorithm is available also in `Singular`. We use the following example to demonstrate how it works.

$$I \;=\; \langle xy, x^3 - x^2, x^2y - xy \rangle \;=\; \langle x \rangle \cap \langle x - 1, y \rangle \cap \langle x^2, y \rangle.$$

The first two components are minimal primes while the third component is an embedded primary component. Geometrically, $\mathcal{V}(I)$ consists of the y-axis, a point on the x-axis, and an embedded point at the origin. Here is `Singular`:

```
> ring R = 0, (x,y), dp;
> ideal I = x*y, x^3 - x^2, x^2*y - x*y;
> LIB "primdec.lib";
> primdecGTZ(I);
 [1]:
    [1]:
       _[1]=x
    [2]:
       _[1]=x
 [2]:
    [1]:
       _[1]=y
       _[2]=x-1
    [2]:
       _[1]=y
       _[2]=x-1
 [3]:
    [1]:
       _[1]=y
       _[2]=x2
    [2]:
       _[1]=x
       _[2]=y
```

The output consists of three pairs denoted [1], [2], [3]. Each pair consists of a primary ideal Q_i in _[1] and the prime ideal $P = \mathrm{Rad}(Q_i)$ in _[2].

We state two more results about primary decomposition which are quite useful in practice. Recall that a *binomial* is a polynomial of the form

$$\alpha \cdot x_1^{i_1} x_2^{i_2} \cdots x_n^{i_n} \; - \; \beta \cdot x_1^{j_1} x_2^{j_2} \cdots x_n^{j_n},$$

where α and β are scalars, possibly zero. An ideal I is a *binomial ideal* if it is generated by a set of binomials. All examples of ideals seen in this chapter so far are binomial ideals. Note that every monomial ideal is a binomial ideal.

The following theorem, due to Eisenbud and Sturmfels [**ES96**], states that primary decomposition is a binomial-friendly operation. Here we must pass to an algebraically closed field such as $\mathbb{C}$. Otherwise the statement is not true as the following primary decomposition in one variable over $\mathbb{Q}$ shows:

$$\langle x^{11} - 1 \rangle \quad = \quad \langle x - 1 \rangle \; \cap \; \langle x^{10} + x^9 + x^8 + x^7 + x^6 + x^5 + x^4 + x^3 + x^2 + x + 1 \rangle.$$

THEOREM 5.6. *If I is a binomial ideal in $\mathbb{C}[x]$ then the radical of I is binomial, every associated prime of I is binomial, and I has a primary decomposition where each primary component is a binomial ideal.*

Of course, these statements are well-known (and easy to prove) when "binomial" is replaced by "monomial". For details on monomial primary decomposition see the chapter by Hoşten and Smith [**HS01**] in the `Macaulay 2` book.

Another class of ideals which behave nicely with regard to primary decomposition are the *Cohen-Macaulay ideals*. The archetype of a Cohen-Macaulay ideal is a *complete intersection*, that is, an ideal I of codimension c which is generated by c polynomials. The case $c = n$ of zero-dimensional complete intersections was discussed at length in earlier chapters, but also higher-dimensional complete intersections come up frequently in practice.

THEOREM 5.7. **(Macaulay's Unmixedness Theorem)** *If I is a complete intersection of codimension c in $\mathbb{Q}[x]$ then I has no embedded primes and every minimal prime of I has codimension c as well.*

When computing a non-trivial primary decomposition, it is advisable to keep track of the degrees of the pieces. The degree of an ideal I is additive in the sense that degree(I) is the sum of degree(Q_i) where Q_i runs over all primary components of maximal dimension in (5.4). Theorem 5.7 implies

COROLLARY 5.8. *If I is a homogeneous complete intersection, then*

$$\text{degree}(I) \quad = \quad \sum_{i=1}^{r} \text{degree}(Q_i).$$

In the following sections we shall illustrate these results for some systems of polynomial equations derived from matrices.

5.3. Adjacent Minors

Questions arising from linear algebra surprisingly often lead to interesting polynomial systems and algebraic varieties. An important example is the variety of all $m \times n$-matrices of rank $\leq k - 1$. This variety is irreducible, and its prime ideal is generated by the set of $k \times k$-subdeterminants of a matrix of indeterminates. Sometimes one cannot guarantee that all such subdeterminants vanish but only a subset of them. In this way, one often gets a larger variety which has the matrices of rank $\leq k - 1$ as a component. The techniques of primary decomposition can be helpful in identifying the other components.

In this section we consider the following specific question: *What does it mean for an $m \times n$-matrix to have all adjacent $k \times k$-subdeterminants vanish?*

To make this question more precise, fix an $m \times n$-matrix of indeterminates $X = (x_{i,j})$ and let $\mathbb{Q}[X]$ denote the polynomial ring in these $m \times n$ unknowns. For any two integers $i \in \{1, \ldots, m - k + 1\}$ and $j \in \{1, \ldots, n - k + 1\}$ we consider the following $k \times k$-minor

$$(5.6) \qquad \det \begin{pmatrix} x_{i,j} & x_{i,j+1} & \cdots & x_{i,j+k-1} \\ x_{i+1,j} & x_{i+1,j+1} & \cdots & x_{i+1,j+k-1} \\ \vdots & \vdots & \ddots & \vdots \\ x_{i+k-1,j} & x_{i+k-1,j+1} & \cdots & x_{i+k-1,j+k-1} \end{pmatrix}$$

Let $A_{k,m,n}$ denote the ideal in $\mathbb{Q}[X]$ generated by these adjacent minors. Thus $A_{k,m,n}$ is an ideal generated by $(n - k + 1)(m - k + 1)$ homogeneous polynomials of degree k in mn unknowns. The variety $\mathcal{V}(A_{m,n,k})$ consists of all complex $m \times n$-matrices whose adjacent $k \times k$-minors vanish. Our problem is to describe all the irreducible components of this variety. Ideally, we would like to know an explicit primary decomposition of the ideal $A_{k,m,n}$.

In the special case $k = m = 2$, our problem has the following beautiful solution. Let us rename the unknowns and consider the $2 \times n$-matrix

$$X \;\; = \;\; \begin{pmatrix} x_1 & x_2 & \cdots & x_n \\ y_1 & y_2 & \cdots & y_n \end{pmatrix}.$$

Our ideal $A_{2,2,n}$ is generated by the $n - 1$ binomials

$$\underline{x_{i-1} \cdot y_i} \;\; - \;\; x_i \cdot y_{i-1} \qquad (i = 2, 3, \ldots, n).$$

These binomials form a Gröbner basis because the underlined leading monomials are relatively prime. This shows that $A_{2,2,n}$ is a complete intersection of codimension $n - 1$. Hence Theorem 5.7 applies here. Moreover, since the leading monomials are square-free, Proposition 5.3 tells us that $A_{2,2,n}$ is a radical ideal. Hence we know already, without having done any computations, that $A_{2,2,n}$ is an intersection of prime ideals each having codimension n. The first case which exhibits the full structure is $n = 5$, here in Macaulay 2:

```
i1: R = QQ[x1,x2,x3,x4,x5,y1,y2,y3,y4,y5];
i2: A225 = ideal( x1*y2 - x2*y1, x2*y3 - x3*y2,
                  x3*y4 - x4*y3, x4*y5 - x5*y4);

i3: ass(A225)
o3 = { ideal(y4, y2, x4, x2),
        ideal(y3, x3, x5*y4 - x4*y5, x2*y1 - x1*y2),
      ideal(y4, x4, x3*y2 - x2*y3, x3*y1 - x1*y3, x2*y1 - x1*y2),
      ideal(y2, x2, x5*y4 - x4*y5, x5*y3 - x3*y5, x4*y3 - x3*y4),
      ideal (x5*y4 - x4*y5, x5*y3 - x3*y5, x4*y3 - x3*y4,
             x5*y2 - x2*y5, x4*y2 - x2*y4, x3*y2 - x2*y3,
             x5*y1-x1*y5, x4*y1-x1*y4, x3*y1-x1*y3, x2*y1-x1*y2)}

i4: A225 == intersect(ass(A225))
o4 = true
```

After a few more experiments one conjectures the following general result:

THEOREM 5.9. *The number of associated primes of $A_{2,2,n}$ is the Fibonacci number $f(n)$, defined by $f(n) = f(n-1) + f(n-2)$ and $f(1) = f(2) = 1$.*

PROOF. Let $\mathcal{F}(n)$ denote the set of all subsets of $\{2, 3, \ldots, n - 1\}$ which do not contain two consecutive integers. The cardinality of $\mathcal{F}(n)$ equals the Fibonacci number $f(n)$. For instance, $\mathcal{F}(5) = \{\emptyset, \{2\}, \{3\}, \{4\}, \{2,4\}\}$. For each element S of $\mathcal{F}(n)$ we define a binomial ideal P_S in $\mathbb{Q}[X]$. The generators of P_S are the variables x_i and y_i for all $i \in S$, and the binomials $x_j y_k - x_k y_j$ for all $j, k \notin S$ such that no element of S lies between j and k. It is easy to see that P_S is a prime ideal of codimension $n - 1$. Moreover, P_S contains $A_{2,2,n}$, and therefore P_S is a minimal prime of $A_{2,2,n}$. We claim that

$$A_{2,2,n} \;\; = \;\; \bigcap_{S \in \mathcal{F}(n)} P_S.$$

In view of Theorem 5.7 and Corollary 5.8, it suffices to prove the identity

$$\sum_{S \in \mathcal{F}(n)} \mathrm{degree}(P_S) \;\; = \;\; 2^{n-1}.$$

First note that $P_\emptyset$ is the determinantal ideal $\langle x_i y_j - x_i x_j : 1 \le i < j \le n \rangle$. The degree of $P_\emptyset$ equals n. Using the same fact for matrices of smaller size, we find that, for S non-empty, the degree of the prime P_S equals the product

$$(i_1 - 1)(i_2 - i_1 - 1)(i_3 - i_2 - 1) \cdots (i_r - i_{r-1} - 1)(n - i_r)$$

$$\text{where } S = \{i_1 < i_2 < \cdots < i_r\}.$$

Consider the surjection $\phi : 2^{\{2,\dots,n\}} \to \mathcal{F}(n)$ defined by

$$\phi(\{j_1 < j_2 < \cdots < j_r\}) = \{j_{r-1}, j_{r-3}, j_{r-5}, \dots\}.$$

The product displayed above is the cardinality of the inverse image $\phi^{-1}(S)$. This proves $\sum_{S \in \mathcal{F}(n)} \#(\phi^{-1}(S)) = 2^{n-1}$, which implies our assertion. □

Our result can be phrased in plain English as follows: *if all adjacent 2×2-minors of a $2 \times n$-matrix vanish then the matrix is a concatenation of $2 \times n_i$-matrices of rank 1 separated by zero columns.* Unfortunately, things are less nice for larger matrices. First of all, the ideal $A_{k,m,n}$ is neither radical nor a complete intersection. For instance, $A_{2,3,3}$ has four associated primes, one of which is embedded. Here is the Singular code for the ideal $A_{2,3,3}$:

```
ring R = 0,(x11,x12,x13,x21,x22,x23,x31,x32,x33),dp;
ideal A233 =   x11*x22-x12*x21, x12*x23-x13*x22,
               x21*x32-x22*x31, x22*x33-x23*x32;
LIB "primdec.lib";
primdecGTZ(A233);
```

The three minimal primes of $A_{2,3,3}$ translate into English as follows: *if all adjacent 2×2-minors of a 3×3-matrix vanish then either the middle column vanishes, or the middle row vanishes, or the matrix has rank at most 1.*

The binomial ideals $A_{2,m,n}$ were studied in [**DES98**] and in [**HS00**]. The motivation was an application to statistics to be described in Section 8.3. We describe the primary decomposition for the case $m = n = 4$. The ideal of adjacent 2×2-minors of a 4×4-matrix is

$$\begin{aligned} A_{2,4,4} = \langle &x_{12}x_{21} - x_{11}x_{22}, \, x_{13}x_{22} - x_{12}x_{23}, \, x_{14}x_{23} - x_{13}x_{24}, \\ &x_{22}x_{31} - x_{21}x_{32}, \, x_{23}x_{32} - x_{22}x_{33}, \, x_{24}x_{33} - x_{23}x_{34}, \\ &x_{32}x_{41} - x_{31}x_{42}, \, x_{33}x_{42} - x_{32}x_{43}, \, x_{34}x_{43} - x_{33}x_{44} \rangle. \end{aligned}$$

Let P denote the prime ideal generated by all thirty-six 2×2-minors of our 4×4-matrix (x_{ij}) of indeterminates. We also introduce the prime ideals

$$C_1 := \langle x_{12}, x_{22}, x_{23}, x_{24}, x_{31}, x_{32}, x_{33}, x_{43} \rangle$$
$$C_2 := \langle x_{13}, x_{21}, x_{22}, x_{23}, x_{32}, x_{33}, x_{34}, x_{42} \rangle.$$

and the prime ideals

$$\begin{aligned} A := \; &\langle x_{12}x_{21} - x_{11}x_{22}, x_{13}, x_{23}, x_{31}, x_{32}, x_{33}, x_{43} \rangle \\ B := \; &\langle x_{11}x_{22} - x_{12}x_{21}, x_{11}x_{23} - x_{13}x_{21}, x_{11}x_{24} - x_{14}x_{21}, x_{31}, x_{32}, \\ &x_{12}x_{23} - x_{13}x_{22}, x_{12}x_{24} - x_{14}x_{22}, x_{13}x_{24} - x_{14}x_{23}, x_{33}, x_{34} \rangle. \end{aligned}$$

Rotating and reflecting the matrix (x_{ij}), we find eight ideals $A_1, A_2, \dots, A_8$ equivalent to A and four ideals B_1, B_2, B_3, B_4 equivalent to B. Note that A_i has codimension 7 and degree 2, B_j has codimension 7 and degree 4, and C_k has codimension 8 and degree 1, while P has codimension 9 and degree 20. The following lemma describes the variety $\mathcal{V}(A_{2,4,4}) \subset \mathbb{C}^{4 \times 4}$ set-theoretically.

LEMMA 5.10. *The minimal primes of $A_{2,4,4}$ are the 15 primes A_i, B_j, C_j and P. Each of these is equal to its primary component in $A_{2,4,4}$. From*

$$\text{Rad}(A_{2,4,4}) \quad = \quad A_1 \cap A_2 \cap \cdots \cap A_8 \cap B_1 \cap B_2 \cap B_3 \cap B_4 \cap C_1 \cap C_2 \cap P.$$

we find that both $A_{2,4,4}$ and $\text{Rad}(A_{2,4,4})$ have codimension 7 and degree 32.

We next present the list of all the embedded components of $I = A_{2,4,4}$. Each of the following five ideals D, E, F, F' and G was shown to be primary by using Algorithm 9.4 in [**ES96**]. Our first primary ideal is

$$D \quad := \quad \langle x_{13}, x_{23}, x_{33}, x_{43} \rangle^2 \; + \; \langle x_{31}, x_{32}, x_{33}, x_{34} \rangle^2 \; +$$
$$\langle \, x_{ik}x_{jl} - x_{il}x_{jk} \; : \; \min\{j,l\} \le 2 \text{ or } (3,3) \in \{(i,k),(j,l),(i,l),(j,k)\}\rangle.$$

The radical of D is a prime of codimension 10 and degree 5. (Commutative algebra experts will notice that $\text{Rad}(D)$ is a *ladder determinantal ideal*.) Up to symmetry, there are four such ideals D_1, D_2, D_3, D_4.

Our second type of embedded primary ideal is

$$E \quad := \quad \big(\, [I + \langle x_{12}^2, x_{21}^2, x_{22}^2, x_{23}^2, x_{24}^2, x_{32}^2, \quad x_{33}^2, x_{34}^2, x_{42}^2, x_{43}^2 \rangle]$$
$$: \; (x_{11}x_{13}x_{14}x_{31}x_{41}x_{44})^2 \,).$$

Its radical $\text{Rad}(E)$ is a monomial prime of codimension 10. Up to symmetry, there are four such primary ideals E_1, E_2, E_3, E_4.

Our third type of primary ideal has codimension 10 as well. It equals

$$F \quad := \quad \big(\, [I + \langle x_{12}^3, x_{13}^3, x_{22}^3, x_{23}^3, x_{31}^3, x_{32}^3, x_{33}^3, x_{34}^3, x_{42}^3, x_{43}^3 \rangle]$$
$$: \; (x_{11}x_{14}x_{21}x_{24}x_{41}x_{44})^2(x_{11}x_{24} - x_{21}x_{14}) \,).$$

Its radical $\text{Rad}(F)$ is a monomial prime. Up to symmetry, there are four such primary ideals F_1, F_2, F_3, F_4. Note how $Rad(F)$ differs from $Rad(E)$.

Our fourth type of primary component is the following ideal of codimension 11:

$$F' \quad := \quad \big(\, [I + \langle x_{12}^3, x_{13}^3, x_{22}^3, x_{23}^3, x_{31}^3, x_{32}^3, x_{33}^3, x_{34}^3, x_{42}^3, x_{43}^3 \rangle]$$
$$: \; (x_{11}x_{14}x_{21}x_{24}x_{41}x_{44})(x_{21}x_{44} - x_{41}x_{24}) \,)$$

Up to symmetry, there are four such primary ideals F_1', F_2', F_3', F_4'. Note that $Rad(F') = Rad(F) + \langle x_{14}x_{21} - x_{11}x_{24} \rangle$. In particular, the ideals F and F' lie in the same *cellular component* of I; see ([**ES96**], Section 6). Our last primary ideal has codimension 12. It is unique up to symmetry.

$$G \quad := \quad \big(\, [I + \langle x_{12}^5, x_{13}^5, x_{21}^5, x_{22}^5, x_{23}^5, x_{24}^5, x_{31}^5, x_{32}^5, x_{33}^5, x_{34}^5, x_{42}^5, x_{43}^5 \rangle]$$
$$: \; (x_{11}x_{14}x_{41}x_{44})^5(x_{11}x_{44} - x_{14}x_{41}) \,).$$

In summary, we have the following theorem.

THEOREM 5.11. *The ideal of adjacent 2×2-minors of a generic 4×4-matrix has 32 associated primes, 15 minimal and 17 embedded. Using the prime decomposition in Lemma 5.10, we get the minimal primary decomposition*

$$A_{2,4,4} \;=\; \text{Rad}(I) \cap D_1 \cap \cdots \cap D_4 \cap E_1 \cap \cdots \cap E_4 \cap F_1 \cap \cdots \cap F_4 \cap F_1' \cap \cdots \cap F_4' \cap G.$$

The correctness of the above intersection can be checked by **Singular** or **Macaulay 2**. It remains an open problem to find a primary decomposition for the ideal of adjacent 2×2-minors for larger sizes. The minimal primes for the $3 \times n$ case are determined in [**HS00**].

Very recently, Serkan Hoşten and Seth Sullivant found a beautiful combinatorial description for the minimal primes of the ideal $A_{2,m,n}$ of adjacent 2×2-minors and also of the ideal $A_{m,m,n}$ of adjacent maximal minors (where $m \leq n$). In the latter case, the ideal is radical, and the number of components is given by a natural generalization of the Fibonacci numbers. In the former case, the embedded primes remain elusive. However, there are reasons to be optimistic that some of their results will extend to multidimensional matrices, which would open up new applications to statistics as described in Chapter 8.

5.4. Permanental Ideals

The *permanent* of an $n \times n$-matrix is the sum over all its $n!$ diagonal products. The permanent looks just like the determinant, except that every minus sign in the expansion is replaced by a plus sign. For instance, the permanent of a 3×3-matrix equals

$$(5.7) \qquad \mathrm{per} \begin{pmatrix} a & b & c \\ d & e & f \\ g & h & i \end{pmatrix} = aei + afh + bfg + bdi + cdh + ceg.$$

In this section we discuss the following problem: *What does it mean for an $m \times n$-matrix to have all its $k \times k$-subpermanents vanish?* As before, we fix an $m \times n$-matrix of indeterminates $X = (x_{i,j})$ and let $\mathbb{Q}[X]$ denote the polynomial ring in these $m \times n$ unknowns. Let $\mathrm{Per}_{k,m,n}$ denote the ideal in $\mathbb{Q}[x]$ generated by all $k \times k$-subpermanents of X. Thus $\mathrm{Per}_{k,m,n}$ represents a system of $\binom{m}{k} \cdot \binom{n}{k}$ polynomial equations of degree k in $m \cdot n$ unknowns.

As our first example consider the three 2×2-permanents in a 2×3-matrix:

$$\mathrm{Per}_{2,2,3} = \langle \underline{x_{11}x_{22}} + x_{12}x_{21}, \ \underline{x_{11}x_{23}} + x_{13}x_{21}, \ \underline{x_{12}x_{23}} + x_{13}x_{22} \rangle.$$

The generators are not a Gröbner basis for any term order. If we pick a term order which selects the underlined leading monomials then the Gröbner basis consists of the three generators together with two square-free monomials:

$$x_{13}x_{21}x_{22} \quad \text{and} \quad x_{12}x_{13}x_{21}.$$

Proposition 5.3 tells us that $\mathrm{Per}_{2,2,3}$ is radical. It is also a complete intersection and hence the intersection of prime ideals of codimension three. We find

$$\mathrm{Per}_{2,2,3} = \langle x_{11}, x_{12}, x_{13} \rangle \cap \langle x_{21}, x_{22}, x_{23} \rangle \cap \langle x_{11}x_{22} + x_{12}x_{21}, x_{13}, x_{23} \rangle$$
$$\cap \langle x_{11}x_{23} + x_{13}x_{21}, x_{12}, x_{22} \rangle \cap \langle x_{12}x_{23} + x_{13}x_{22}, x_{11}, x_{21} \rangle.$$

However, if $m, n \geq 3$ then $P_{2,m,n}$ is not a radical ideal. Let us examine the 3×3-case in Macaulay 2 with variable names as in the 3×3-matrix (5.7).

```
i1 : R = QQ[a,b,c,d,e,f,g,h,i];
i2 : Per233 = ideal( a*e+b*d, a*f+c*d, b*f+c*e,
            a*h+b*g, a*i+c*g, b*i+c*h,
            d*h+e*g, d*i+f*g, e*i+f*h);
i3 : gb Per233

o3 = | fh+ei ch+bi fg+di eg+dh cg+ai bg+ah ce+bf cd+af bd+ae
dhi ahi bfi bei dei afi aeh adi adh abi aef abf aei2 ae2i a2ei|
```

This Gröbner basis shows us that $\mathrm{Per}_{2,3,3}$ is not a radical ideal. We compute the radical using the built-in command:

```
i4 : time radical Per233
        -- used 53.18 seconds

o4 = ideal (f*h + e*i, c*h + b*i, f*g + d*i, e*g + d*h,
  c*g + a*i,  b*g + a*h, c*e + b*f, c*d + a*f, b*d + a*e, a*e*i)
```

The radical has a minimal generator of degree three, while the original ideal was generated by quadrics. We next compute the associated primes. There are 16 such primes, the first 15 are minimal and the last one is embedded:

```
i5 : time ass Per233
        -- used 11.65 seconds

o5 = { ideal (g, f, e, d, a, c*h + b*i),
        ideal (i, h, g, d, a, c*e + b*f),
        ideal (i, h, g, e, b, c*d + a*f),
        ideal (h, f, e, d, b, c*g + a*i),
        ideal (i, f, e, d, c, b*g + a*h),
        ideal (i, h, g, f, c, b*d + a*e),
        ideal (i, f, c, b, a, e*g + d*h),
        ideal (h, e, c, b, a, f*g + d*i),
        ideal (g, d, c, b, a, f*h + e*i),
    ideal (h, g, e, d, b, a), ideal (i, h, g, f, e, d),
    ideal (i, g, f, d, c, a), ideal (f, e, d, c, b, a),
    ideal (i, h, g, c, b, a), ideal (i, h, f, e, c, b),
        ideal (i, h, g, f, e, d, c, b, a) }

i6 : time intersect ass Per233
        -- used 0.24 seconds

o6 = ideal (f*h + e*i, c*h + b*i, f*g + d*i, e*g + d*h,
  c*g + a*i,  b*g + a*h, c*e + b*f, c*d + a*f, b*d + a*e, a*e*i)
```

Note that the lines o4 and o6 have the same output by equation (5.3). However, for this example the obvious command **radical** is slower than the non-obvious command **intersect ass**. The lesson to be learned is that *many roads lead to Rome* and one should always be prepared to apply one's full range of mathematical know-how when trying to crack a polynomial system.

The ideals of 2×2-subpermanents of matrices of any size were studied in full detail by Laubenbacher and Swanson [**LS00**] who gave explicit descriptions of associated primes, and a primary decomposition of $P_{2,m,n}$. The previous **Macaulay 2** session offers a glimpse of their results.

Recently, George Kirkup has taken up the project of extending this work to 3×3-subpermanents. A special role in his theory is played by the prime ideal

$$(5.8) \qquad\qquad J \quad = \quad \left(\mathrm{Per}_{3,3,4} : \left(\prod_{i,j} x_{ij} \right)^{\infty} \right).$$

Here is a brief summary of Kirkup's results. A prime ideal in $\mathbb{Q}[X]$ is of *type 1* if it is generated by all the indeterminates of X except those either in two rows, two columns, or one row and one column. A prime is of *type 2* if it is generated by some 2×2-subpermanent and all the indeterminates of X except in one row or one column (which does not intersect that 2×2 block). Similarly, a prime is of *type 3* if it is generated by a 3×3 permanent and all other indeterminates in X. A prime is of *type 3A* if it contains all the indeterminates in X outside a 3×4 or 4×3 block and in that block is a copy of the special prime ideal J. Finally a prime is of *type 3B* if it is generated by all the indeterminates in X except two 2×2 blocks (which have no common rows or columns) and the two 2×2 subpermanents corresponding to those two blocks. Kirkup's theorem states that the minimal primes of $\mathrm{Per}_{3,m,n}$ are of one of these types. Moreover, if $m, n \geq 4$ then these are all minimal.

We present one more open problem about permanental ideals. Consider the $n \times 2n$-matrix $[X\,X]$ which is gotten by concatenating our matrix of unknowns with itself. We write $\mathrm{Per}_n[X\,X]$ for the ideal of $n \times n$-subpermanents of this $n \times 2n$-matrix. A conjecture on graph polynomials posed by Alon, Jaeger and Tarsi in 1981 suggests that every matrix in the variety of $\mathrm{Per}_n[X\,X]$ should be singular. A discussion of this conjecture can be found in [**Yu99**] and in [**DOS02**]. We offer the following refinement of the Alon-Jaeger-Tarsi conjecture.

CONJECTURE 5.12. *The nth power of the determinant of X lies in $\mathrm{Per}_n[X\,X]$.*

For $n = 2$ this conjecture is easy to check. Indeed, the ideal

$$\mathrm{Per}_2 \begin{pmatrix} x_{11} & x_{12} & x_{11} & x_{12} \\ x_{21} & x_{22} & x_{21} & x_{22} \end{pmatrix} = \langle\, x_{11}x_{22} + x_{12}x_{21},\ x_{11}x_{21},\ x_{12}x_{22} \,\rangle$$

contains $(x_{11}x_{22} - x_{12}x_{21})^2$ but not $x_{11}x_{22} - x_{12}x_{21}$. But already the next two cases $n = 3$ and $n = 4$ pose a nice challenge for primary decomposition. The state of the art regarding the Alon-Jaeger-Tarsi conjecture appears in the work of De Loera, Onn and Sebö [**DOS02**]. These authors discuss the connections to graph theory, and they provide a computer proof of this conjecture up to $n \leq 5$.

5.5. Exercises

(1) Explain how one can find a witness f for a given associated prime P of an ideal I.

(2) Let P be a prime ideal and m a positive integer. Show that P is a minimal prime of P^m. Give an example where P^m is not primary.

(3) For an ideal I of codimension c we define $\mathrm{top}(I)$ as the intersection of all primary components Q_i of codimension c. Explain how one computes $\mathrm{top}(I)$ from I in Macaulay 2 or Singular? Compute $\mathrm{top}(I)$ for
  (a) $I = \langle\, x_1 x_2 x_3,\ x_4 x_5 x_6,\ x_1^2 x_2^3,\ x_3^5 x_4^7,\ x_5^{11} x_6^{13} \,\rangle$,
  (b) $I = \langle\, x_1 x_2 + x_3 x_4 + x_5 x_6, x_1 x_3 + x_4 x_5 + x_6 x_2, x_1 x_4 + x_5 x_6 + x_2 x_3,$
      $x_1 x_5 + x_6 x_2 + x_3 x_4, x_1 x_6 + x_2 x_3 + x_4 x_5 \,\rangle$,
  (c) $I = \langle\, x_1^2 + x_2 x_3 - 1, x_2^2 + x_3 x_4 - 1, x_3^2 + x_4 x_5 - 1, x_4^2 + x_5 x_6 - 1, x_5^2 + x_6 x_1 - 1, x_6^2 + x_1 x_2 - 1 \,\rangle$.

(4) What happens if you apply the formula (5.5) to an embedded prime P_i?

(5) Prove that P is associated to I if and only if $\big(I : (I : P)\big) = P$.

(6) Decompose the two adjacent-minor ideals $A_{2,3,4}$ and $A_{3,3,5}$.

(7) Decompose the permanental ideals $\mathrm{Per}_{2,4,4}$, $\mathrm{Per}_{3,3,5}$ and $\mathrm{Per}_{4,4,5}$.

(8) Find a 3×4-integer matrix with all non-zero entries such that all four 3×3-subpermanents are zero. (Hint: Compute the ideal J in (5.8) and find a rational point in $\mathcal{V}(J)$.)

(9) Compute the primary decomposition of $\mathrm{Per}_3[X\,X]$ in Singular.

(10) Prove Conjecture 5.12 for $n = 4$.

(11) For positive integers d and e consider the ideal

$$I \;=\; \langle\, x_1^d x_2 - x_3^d x_4 ,\; x_1 x_2^e - x_4^{e+1} \,\rangle$$

Find a primary decomposition of I and a minimal generating set for the radical of I. What are the degrees of the generators? This example is due to Chardin and D'Cruz [CD02]. It shows that the *Castelnuovo-Mumford regularity* of $\mathrm{Rad}(I)$ can be higher than that of I.

CHAPTER 6

Polynomial Systems in Economics

The computation of equilibria in economics leads to systems of polynomial equations. In this chapter we discuss the equations satisfied by the Nash equilibria of an *n-person game in normal form*. For $n = 2$ these equations are linear but for $n > 2$ they are multilinear. We derive these multilinear equations, we present algebraic techniques for solving them, and we give a sharp bound for the number of totally mixed Nash equilibria. This bound is due to McKelvey and McLennan [**MM97**] who derived it from Bernstein's Theorem. In Section 6.2 we offer a detailed analysis of the Three-Man Poker Game which appeared in the original paper of Nash [**Nas51**] and leads to solving a quadratic equation. In Section 6.5 we discuss a graphical model for game theory [**KLS01**], and we demonstrate how Verschelde's homotopy software `PHCpack` can be used to compute totally mixed Nash equilibria.

6.1. Three-Person Games with Two Pure Strategies

We present the scenario of a non-cooperative game by means of a small example. Our notation is consistent with that used by Nash [**Nas51**]. There are three players whose names are Adam, Bob and Carl. Each player can choose from two *pure strategies*, say "*buy stock #1*" or "*buy stock #2*". He can mix them by allocating a probability (or, fraction of his money) to each pure strategy. We write a_1 for the probability which Adam allocates to strategy 1, a_2 for the probability which Adam allocates to strategy 2, b_1 for the probability which Bob allocates to strategy 1, etc.. The six probabilities $a_1, a_2, b_1, b_2, c_1, c_2$ are our decision variables. The vector (a_1, a_2) is Adam's strategy, (b_1, b_2) is Bob's strategy, and (c_1, c_2) is Carl's strategy. We use the term *strategy* for what is called *mixed strategy* in the literature. The strategies of our three players satisfy

$$(6.1) \quad a_1, a_2, b_1, b_2, c_1, c_2 \geq 0 \quad \text{and} \quad a_1 + a_2 = b_1 + b_2 = c_1 + c_2 = 1.$$

The data representing a particular game are three *payoff matrices* $A = (A_{ijk})$, $B = (B_{ijk})$, and $C = (C_{ijk})$. Here i, j, k run over $\{1, 2\}$ so that each of A, B, and C is a three-dimensional matrix of format $2 \times 2 \times 2$. Thus our game is given by $24 = 3 \times 2 \times 2 \times 2$ rational numbers $A_{ijk}, B_{ijk}, C_{ijk}$. All of these numbers are known to all three players. The game is for Adam, Bob and Carl to select their strategies. They will then receive the following payoff:

$$\text{Adam's payoff} = \sum_{i,j,k=1}^{2} A_{ijk} \cdot a_i \cdot b_j \cdot c_k$$

$$\text{Bob's payoff} = \sum_{i,j,k=1}^{2} B_{ijk} \cdot a_i \cdot b_j \cdot c_k$$

$$\text{Carl's payoff} = \sum_{i,j,k=1}^{2} C_{ijk} \cdot a_i \cdot b_j \cdot c_k$$

A vector $(a_1, a_2, b_1, b_2, c_1, c_2)$ satisfying (6.1) is called a *Nash equilibrium* if no player can increase his payoff by changing his strategy while the other two players keep their strategies fixed. In other words, the following condition holds: *For all pairs* (u_1, u_2) *with* $u_1, u_2 \geq 0$ *and* $u_1 + u_2 = 1$ *we have*

$$\sum_{i,j,k=1}^{2} A_{ijk} \cdot a_i \cdot b_j \cdot c_k \geq \sum_{i,j,k=1}^{2} A_{ijk} \cdot u_i \cdot b_j \cdot c_k,$$

$$\sum_{i,j,k=1}^{2} B_{ijk} \cdot a_i \cdot b_j \cdot c_k \geq \sum_{i,j,k=1}^{2} B_{ijk} \cdot a_i \cdot u_j \cdot c_k,$$

$$\sum_{i,j,k=1}^{2} C_{ijk} \cdot a_i \cdot b_j \cdot c_k \geq \sum_{i,j,k=1}^{2} C_{ijk} \cdot a_i \cdot b_j \cdot u_k.$$

Given fixed strategies chosen by Adam, Bob and Carl, each of the expressions on the right hand side is a linear function in (u_1, u_2). Therefore the universal quantifier above can be replaced by "*For* $(u_1, u_2) \in \{(1, 0), (0, 1)\}$ *we have*". Introducing three new variables α, β, γ for Adam's, Bob's and Carl's payoffs, the conditions for a Nash equilibrium can be written as follows:

$$\alpha = a_1 \cdot \sum_{j,k=1}^{2} A_{1jk} \cdot b_j \cdot c_k + a_2 \cdot \sum_{j,k=1}^{2} A_{2jk} \cdot b_j \cdot c_k,$$

$$\alpha \geq \sum_{j,k=1}^{2} A_{1jk} \cdot b_j \cdot c_k \quad \text{and} \quad \alpha \geq \sum_{j,k=1}^{2} A_{2jk} \cdot b_j \cdot c_k,$$

$$\beta = b_1 \cdot \sum_{i,k=1}^{2} B_{i1k} \cdot a_i \cdot c_k + b_2 \cdot \sum_{i,k=1}^{2} B_{i2k} \cdot a_i \cdot c_k,$$

$$\beta \geq \sum_{i,k=1}^{2} B_{i1k} \cdot a_i \cdot c_k \quad \text{and} \quad \beta \geq \sum_{i,k=1}^{2} B_{i2k} \cdot a_i \cdot c_k,$$

$$\gamma = c_1 \cdot \sum_{i,j=1}^{2} C_{ij1} \cdot a_i \cdot b_j + c_2 \cdot \sum_{i,j=1}^{2} C_{ij2} \cdot a_i \cdot b_j,$$

$$\gamma \geq \sum_{i,j=1}^{2} C_{ij1} \cdot a_i \cdot b_j \quad \text{and} \quad \gamma \geq \sum_{i,j=1}^{2} C_{ij2} \cdot a_i \cdot b_j.$$

Since $a_1 + a_2 = 1$ and $a_1 \geq 0$ and $a_2 \geq 0$, the first two rows imply:

$$(6.2) \quad a_1 \cdot \left(\alpha - \sum_{j,k=1}^{2} A_{1jk} \cdot b_j \cdot c_k \right) = a_2 \cdot \left(\alpha - \sum_{j,k=1}^{2} A_{2jk} \cdot b_j \cdot c_k \right) = 0.$$

Similarly, we derive the following equations:

$$(6.3) \quad b_1 \cdot \left(\beta - \sum_{i,k=1}^{2} B_{i1k} \cdot a_i \cdot c_k \right) = b_2 \cdot \left(\beta - \sum_{i,k=1}^{2} B_{i2k} \cdot a_i \cdot c_k \right) = 0,$$

$$(6.4) \quad c_1 \cdot \left(\gamma - \sum_{i,j=1}^{2} C_{ij1} \cdot a_i \cdot b_j \right) = c_2 \cdot \left(\gamma - \sum_{i,j=1}^{2} C_{ij2} \cdot a_i \cdot b_j \right) = 0.$$

We regard (6.2), (6.3) and (6.4) as a system of polynomial equations in the nine unknowns $a_1, a_2, b_1, b_2, c_1, c_2, \alpha, \beta, \gamma$. Our discussion shows the following:

PROPOSITION 6.1. *The set of Nash equilibria of the game given by the payoff matrices* A, B, C *is the set of solutions* $(a_1, \ldots, c_2, \alpha, \beta, \gamma)$ *to (6.1), (6.2), (6.3) and (6.4) which make the six expressions in the large parentheses nonnegative.*

For practical computations it is convenient to change variables as follows:

$$a_1 = a, \ a_2 = 1 - a, \ b_1 = b, \ b_2 = 1 - b, \ c_1 = c, \ c_2 = 1 - c.$$

COROLLARY 6.2. *The set of Nash equilibria of the game given by the payoff matrices* A, B, C *consists of the common zeros of the following six polynomials* *subject to a, b, c, and all parenthesized expressions being nonnegative:*

$$a \cdot (\alpha - A_{111}bc - A_{112}b(1-c) - A_{121}(1-b)c - A_{122}(1-b)(1-c)),$$
$$(1-a) \cdot (\alpha - A_{211}bc - A_{212}b(1-c) - A_{221}(1-b)c - A_{222}(1-b)(1-c)),$$
$$b \cdot (\beta - B_{111}ac - B_{112}a(1-c) - B_{211}(1-a)c - B_{212}(1-a)(1-c)),$$
$$(1-b) \cdot (\beta - B_{121}ac - B_{122}a(1-c) - B_{221}(1-a)c - B_{222}(1-a)(1-c)),$$
$$c \cdot (\gamma - C_{111}ab - C_{121}a(1-b) - C_{211}(1-a)b - C_{221}(1-a)(1-b)),$$
$$(1-c) \cdot (\gamma - C_{112}ab - C_{122}a(1-b) - C_{212}(1-a)b - C_{222}(1-a)(1-b)).$$

A Nash equilibrium is called *totally mixed* if all six probabilities $a, 1-a, b$, $1-b, c, 1-c$ are strictly positive. If we are only interested in totally mixed equilibria then we can erase the left factors in the six polynomials and eliminate α, β, γ by subtracting the second polynomial from the first, the fourth polynomial from the third, and the last polynomial from the fifth.

COROLLARY 6.3. *The set of totally mixed Nash equilibria of the game (A, B, C) consists of the common zeros $(a, b, c) \in (0,1)^3$ of three bilinear polynomials:*

$$(A_{111} - A_{112} - A_{121} + A_{122} - A_{211} + A_{212} + A_{221} - A_{222}) \cdot bc + A_{122} - A_{222}$$
$$+ (A_{112} - A_{122} - A_{212} + A_{222}) \cdot b + (A_{121} - A_{122} - A_{221} + A_{222}) \cdot c,$$
$$(B_{111} - B_{112} + B_{122} - B_{121} - B_{211} + B_{212} - B_{222} + B_{221}) \cdot ac + B_{212} - B_{222}$$
$$+ (B_{211} - B_{212} - B_{221} + B_{222}) \cdot c + (B_{112} - B_{122} - B_{212} + B_{222}) \cdot a,$$
$$(C_{111} - C_{112} + C_{122} - C_{121} - C_{211} + C_{212} - C_{222} + C_{221}) \cdot ab + C_{221} - C_{222}$$
$$+ (C_{121} - C_{221} - C_{122} + C_{222}) \cdot a + (C_{222} - C_{221} - C_{212} + C_{211}) \cdot b.$$

These three equations have two complex solutions, for general payoff matrices A, B, C. Indeed, the mixed volume of the three Newton squares equals 2. In the next section we give an example where both roots are real and lie in the open cube $(0,1)^3$, meaning there are two totally mixed Nash equilibria. In Exercise (9) the reader is asked to construct a game for Adam, Bob and Carl such that the two Nash equilibria have a prescribed square root among their coordinates.

6.2. Two Numerical Examples Involving Square Roots

Consider the game described in the previous section with the payoff matrices

(6.5)

$$
\begin{array}{c}
\begin{array}{cccccccc} 111 & 112 & 121 & 122 & 211 & 212 & 221 & 222 \end{array} \\
\begin{array}{c} A = \\ B = \\ C = \end{array}
\left(
\begin{array}{cccccccc}
0 & 6 & 11 & 1 & 6 & 4 & 6 & 8 \\
12 & 7 & 6 & 8 & 10 & 12 & 8 & 1 \\
11 & 11 & 3 & 3 & 0 & 14 & 2 & 7
\end{array}
\right)
\end{array}
$$

For instance, $B_{112} = 7$ and $C_{212} = 14$. The equations in Corollary 6.2 are

$$a \cdot (\alpha - 6b(1-c) - 11(1-b)c - (1-b)(1-c)) = 0,$$
$$(1-a) \cdot (\alpha - 6bc - 4b(1-c) - 6(1-b)c - 8(1-b)(1-c)) = 0,$$
$$b \cdot (\beta - 12ac - 7a(1-c) - 6(1-a)c - 8(1-a)(1-c)) = 0,$$
$$(1-b) \cdot (\beta - 10ac - 12a(1-c) - 8(1-a)c - (1-a)(1-c)) = 0,$$
$$c \cdot (\gamma - 11ab - 11a(1-b) - 3(1-a)b - 3(1-a)(1-b)) = 0,$$
$$(1-c) \cdot (\gamma - 14a(1-b) - 2(1-a)b - 7(1-a)(1-b)) = 0.$$

These equations are radical and they have 16 solutions all of which are real. Namely, a vector $(a, b, c, \alpha, \beta, \gamma)$ is a solution if and only if it lies in the set

$$\{ (7/12, 7/9, 0, \, 44/9, 89/12, 28/9), \, (1/2, 5/11, 1, \, 6, 9, 7)^{*},$$
$$(4, 0, 7/12, \, 41/6, 337/12, 35), \, (-1/10, 1, 1/4, \, 9/2, 297/40, 11/5),$$
$$(0, 4/5, 7/9, \, 86/15, 58/9, 3)^{*}, \, (1, 3/14, 5/7, \, 663/98, 74/7, 11)^{*},$$
$$(0, 0, 0, \, 8, 1, 7), \, (0, 0, 1, \, 6, 8, 3), \, (0, 1, 0, \, 4, 8, 2), \, (0, 1, 1, \, 6, 6, 3),$$
$$(1, 0, 0, \, 1, 12, 14), \, (1, 0, 1, \, 11, 10, 11), \, (1, 1, 0, \, 6, 7, 0), \, (1, 1, 1, \, 0, 12, 11),$$
$$(0.8058, 0.2607, 0.6858, \, 6.3008, 9.6909, 9.4465)^{*}$$
$$(0.4234, 0.4059, 0.8623, \, 6.0518, 8.4075, 6.3869)^{*} \}$$

However, some of these solution vectors are not Nash equilibria. For instance, the third vector has $a = 4$ which violates the non-negativity of $(1 - a)$. The first vector $(a, b, c, \alpha, \beta, \gamma) = (7/12, 7/9, 0, \, 44/9, 89/12, 28/9)$ violates the non-negativity of $(\gamma - 11ab - 11a(1 - b) - 3(1 - a)b - 3(1 - a)(1 - b))$, etc... This process eliminates 11 of the 16 candidate vectors. The remaining five are marked with a star. We conclude: *The game (6.5) has five isolated Nash equilibria. Of these five, the last two are totally mixed Nash equilibria.*

The two totally mixed Nash equilibria can be represented algebraically by extracting a square root. Namely, we first erase the left factors $a, \dots, (1 - c)$ from the six equations, and thereafter we compute the Gröbner basis:

$$\{ \underline{1011\alpha} + 1426c - 7348, \; \underline{96\beta} + 698c - 1409, \; \underline{3\gamma} + 52c - 64,$$
$$\underline{24a} + 52c - 55, \; \underline{1011b} - 832c + 307, \; \underline{208c^2} - 322c + 123 \}.$$

As with all our Gröbner bases, leading terms are underlined. These six equations are easy to solve. The solutions are the last two vectors above.

Our second example is the Three-Man Poker Game discussed in Nash's 1951 paper [**Nas51**]. This game leads to algebraic equations which can be solved by extracting the square root of 321. The following material was prepared by Ruchira Datta. The game was originally solved by Nash in collaboration with Shapley [**NS50**]. We believe that it is of some historical interest.

This is a greatly simplified version of poker. The cards are of only two kinds, *high* and *low*. The three players A, B, and C ante up two chips each to start. Then each player is dealt one card. We assume that each of the eight possible hands is equally likely. Starting with player A, each player is given a chance to "open", i.e., to place the first bet (two chips are always used to bet). If no one does so, the players retrieve their antes from the pot. Once a player has opened, the other two players are again given a chance to bet, i.e., they may "call". Finally, the cards are revealed and those players with the highest cards among those who placed bets share the pot equally.

Once the game is open, one should call if one has a high card and pass if one has a low card. The former is obvious; the latter follows because it might be the strategy of the player who opened the game, to only open on a high card. In this case one would definitely lose one's bet as well as the ante. So the only question is whether to open the game. Player C should obviously open if he has a high card. It turns out that player A should never open if he has a low card (this requires proof). Thus player A has two pure strategies: when he has a high card, to open or not to open. We denote his probability of opening in this case by a. (His subsequent moves, and his moves in case he has a low card, are determined.) Player C also has two pure strategies: when he has a low card, to open or not to open. We denote his probability of opening in this case by c. Player B has four pure strategies: for each of his possible cards, to open or not to open. We denote his probability of opening when he has a high card by d, and his probability of opening when he has a low card by e. It turns out that the equilibrium strategy is totally mixed in these four parameters.

The payoff matrix (where by payoff we mean the *expected value* of the payoff) contains $48 = 3 \times 2 \times 4 \times 2$ rational entries. As in the examples above, this can be written as a 3×16 matrix. Here is the left ($a = 0$) block:

(6.6)

$$
\begin{array}{c}
 \\
A = \\
B = \\
C =
\end{array}
\begin{array}{cccccccc}
0000 & 0001 & 0010 & 0011 & 0100 & 0101 & 0110 & 0111 \\
\frac{-1}{4} & \frac{-1}{4} & \frac{-1}{4} & 0 & \frac{-1}{4} & 0 & \frac{-1}{4} & \frac{1}{4} \\
\frac{1}{4} & \frac{1}{4} & \frac{-1}{4} & 0 & \frac{1}{2} & \frac{-1}{4} & 0 & \frac{-1}{2} \\
0 & 0 & \frac{1}{2} & 0 & \frac{-1}{4} & \frac{1}{4} & \frac{1}{4} & \frac{1}{4}
\end{array}
$$

and here is the right ($a = 1$) block:

(6.7)

$$
\begin{array}{c}
 \\
A = \\
B = \\
C =
\end{array}
\begin{array}{cccccccc}
1000 & 1001 & 1010 & 1011 & 1100 & 1101 & 1110 & 1111 \\
\frac{1}{8} & \frac{1}{8} & 0 & \frac{-1}{2} & \frac{1}{4} & \frac{1}{4} & \frac{1}{8} & \frac{-3}{8} \\
\frac{-1}{4} & \frac{-1}{4} & \frac{-1}{4} & \frac{1}{4} & \frac{1}{8} & \frac{-7}{8} & \frac{1}{8} & \frac{-3}{8} \\
\frac{1}{8} & \frac{1}{8} & \frac{1}{4} & \frac{1}{4} & \frac{-3}{8} & \frac{5}{8} & \frac{-1}{4} & \frac{3}{4}
\end{array}
$$

(We split the matrix into blocks to fit the page.) Here the indices across the top indicate the pure strategies chosen by the players. If we write $a_0 = a$, $a_1 = 1 - a$, $d_0 = d$, $d_1 = 1 - d$, $e_0 = e$, $e_1 = 1 - e$, $c_0 = c$, and $c_1 = 1 - c$, then for instance B_{1010} is B's payoff when player A does *not* open on a high card (so $a_1 = 1$), player B *does* open on a high card (so $d_0 = 1$) and does not open on a low card (so $e_1 = 1$), and player C does open on a low card (so $c_0 = 1$). In general, X_{ijkl} is player X's payoff when $a_i = 1$, $d_j = 1$, $e_k = 1$, and $c_l = 1$. The equation for the expected payoff β of player B is

$$
\beta = d \cdot e \cdot \sum_{i,k=0}^{1} B_{i00k} \cdot a_i \cdot c_k \;+\; d \cdot (1 - e) \cdot \sum_{i,k=0}^{1} B_{i01k} \cdot a_i \cdot c_k
$$
$$
+ (1 - d) \cdot e \cdot \sum_{i,k=0}^{1} B_{i10k} \cdot a_i \cdot c_k \;+\; (1-d)(1-e) \cdot \sum_{i,k=0}^{1} B_{i11k} \cdot a_i \cdot c_k.
$$

We have a modified version of Corollary 6.2 with eight polynomials instead of six. The first polynomial becomes:

$$
\begin{aligned}
a \cdot \big(\alpha &- A_{0000}dec - A_{0001}de(1 - c) \\
&- A_{0010}d(1 - e)c - A_{0011}d(1 - e)(1 - c) \\
&- A_{0100}(1 - d)ec - A_{0101}(1 - d)e(1 - c) \\
&- A_{0110}(1 - d)(1 - e)c - A_{0111}(1 - d)(1 - e)(1 - c)\big)
\end{aligned}
$$

The second, fifth, and sixth polynomials are modified analogously. The third and fourth polynomials are replaced by four polynomials, the first of which is

$$
d \cdot e \cdot \big(\beta - B_{0000}ac - B_{0001}a(1 - c) - B_{1000}(1 - a)c - B_{1001}(1 - a)(1 - c)\big)
$$

Again, we can cancel the left factors of all the polynomials since the equilibrium is totally mixed. Eliminating α and γ as before gives us the following two trilinear polynomials:

$$
\begin{aligned}
(A_{0000} &- A_{0001} - A_{0010} + A_{0011} - A_{0100} + A_{0101} + A_{0110} - A_{0111} \\
&- A_{1000} + A_{1001} + A_{1010} - A_{1011} + A_{1100} - A_{1101} - A_{1110} + A_{1111}) \cdot cde \\
+ (A_{0010} &- A_{0011} - A_{0110} + A_{0111} - A_{1010} + A_{1011} + A_{1110} - A_{1111}) \cdot cd \\
+ (A_{0100} &- A_{0101} - A_{0110} + A_{0111} - A_{1100} + A_{1101} + A_{1110} - A_{1111}) \cdot ce \\
+ (A_{0001} &- A_{0011} - A_{0101} + A_{0111} - A_{1001} + A_{1011} + A_{1101} - A_{1111}) \cdot de \\
+ (A_{0110} &- A_{0111} - A_{1110} + A_{1111}) \cdot c + (A_{0011} - A_{0111} - A_{1011} + A_{1111}) \cdot d \\
+ (A_{0101} &- A_{0111} - A_{1101} + A_{1111}) \cdot e + (A_{0111} - A_{1111})
\end{aligned}
$$

and

$$
\begin{aligned}
(C_{0000} &- C_{0001} - C_{0010} + C_{0011} - C_{0100} + C_{0101} + C_{0110} - C_{0111} \\
&- C_{1000} + C_{1001} + C_{1010} - C_{1011} + C_{1100} - C_{1101} - C_{1110} + C_{1111}) \cdot ade \\
+ (C_{0010} &- C_{0011} - C_{0110} + C_{0111} - C_{1010} + C_{1011} + C_{1110} - C_{1111}) \cdot ad \\
+ (C_{0100} &- C_{0101} - C_{0110} + C_{0111} - C_{1100} + C_{1101} + C_{1110} - C_{1111}) \cdot ae \\
+ (C_{1000} &- C_{1001} - C_{1010} + C_{1011} - C_{1100} + C_{1101} + C_{1110} - C_{1111}) \cdot de \\
+ (C_{0110} &- C_{0111} - C_{1110} + C_{1111}) \cdot a + (C_{1010} - C_{1011} - C_{1110} + C_{1111}) \cdot d \\
+ (C_{1100} &- C_{1101} - C_{1110} + C_{1111}) \cdot e + (C_{1110} - C_{1111}).
\end{aligned}
$$

(For each term, take the bitstring that indexes its coefficient and mask off the bits corresponding to variables that don't occur in its monomial, which will always be one; then the parity of the resulting bitstring gives the sign of the term.) There are four polynomials in β; subtracting each of the others from the first gives the following three bilinear polynomials:

$$
\begin{aligned}
(B_{0000} &- B_{0001} - B_{0010} + B_{0011} - B_{1000} + B_{1001} + B_{1010} - B_{1011})ac + B_{1001} - B_{1011} \\
&+ (B_{0001} - B_{0011} - B_{1001} + B_{1011}) \cdot a + (B_{1000} - B_{1001} - B_{1010} + B_{1011}) \cdot c, \\
(B_{0000} &- B_{0001} - B_{0100} + B_{0101} - B_{1000} + B_{1001} + B_{1100} - B_{1101})ac + B_{1001} - B_{1101} \\
&+ (B_{0001} - B_{0101} - B_{1001} + B_{1101}) \cdot a + (B_{1000} - B_{1001} - B_{1100} + B_{1101}) \cdot c, \\
(B_{0000} &- B_{0001} - B_{0110} + B_{0111} - B_{1000} + B_{1001} + B_{1110} - B_{1111})ac + B_{1001} - B_{1111} \\
&+ (B_{0001} - B_{0111} - B_{1001} + B_{1111}) \cdot a + (B_{1000} - B_{1001} - B_{1110} + B_{1111}) \cdot c.
\end{aligned}
$$

So the set of totally mixed Nash equilibria consists of the common zeros $(a, d, e, c) \in (0, 1)^4$ of these five polynomials. Substituting our payoff matrix into the last polynomial gives

$$
\frac{1}{8} + \frac{5}{8}a - \frac{1}{2}c = 0.
$$

Solving for c gives

$$
c = \frac{5a + 1}{4}
$$

and substituting into the previous two polynomials yields

$$
-\frac{3}{8} + \frac{21}{16}a - \frac{5}{16}a^2 = 0
$$

and

$$\frac{3}{8} - \frac{21}{16}a + \frac{5}{16}a^2 = 0.$$

Solving for a in the range $0 < a < 1$ gives

$$a = \frac{21 - \sqrt{321}}{10}.$$

Substituting into the two trilinear polynomials yields two linear equations for d and e; solving these yields

$$d = \frac{5 - 2a}{5 + a}, \quad e = \frac{4a - 1}{a + 5},$$

which agrees with the result in Nash's 1951 paper [**Nas51**].

6.3. Equations Defining Nash Equilibria

We consider a finite n-person game in normal form. The players are labeled $1, 2, \ldots, n$. The ith player can select from d_i pure strategies which we call $1, 2, \ldots, d_i$. The game is defined by n payoff matrices $X^{(1)}, X^{(2)}, \ldots, X^{(n)}$, one for each player. Each matrix $X^{(i)}$ is an n-dimensional matrix of format $d_1 \times d_2 \times \cdots \times d_n$ whose entries are rational numbers. The entry $X^{(i)}_{j_1 j_2 \cdots j_n}$ represents the payoff for player i if player 1 selects the pure strategy j_1, player 2 selects the pure strategy j_2, etc. Each player is to select a (mixed) strategy, which is a probability distribution on his set of pure strategies. We write $p^{(i)}_j$ for the probability which player i allocates to the strategy j. The vector $p^{(i)} = (p^{(i)}_1, p^{(i)}_2, \ldots, p^{(i)}_{d_i})$ is called the *strategy* of player i. The *payoff* π_i for player i is the value of the multilinear form given by his matrix $X^{(i)}$:

$$\pi_i = \sum_{j_1=1}^{d_1} \sum_{j_2=1}^{d_2} \cdots \sum_{j_n=1}^{d_n} X^{(i)}_{j_1 j_2 \cdots j_n} \cdot p^{(1)}_{j_1} p^{(2)}_{j_2} \cdots p^{(n)}_{j_n}.$$

Summarizing, the data for our problem are the payoff matrices $X^{(i)}$, so the problem is specified by $nd_1 d_2 \cdots d_n$ rational numbers. We must solve for the $d_1 + d_2 + \cdots + d_n$ unknowns $p^{(i)}_j$. Since the unknowns are probabilities,

$$(6.8) \qquad \forall\, i, j\ :\ p^{(i)}_j \geq 0 \quad \text{and} \quad \forall\, i\ :\ p^{(i)}_1 + p^{(i)}_2 + \cdots + p^{(i)}_{d_i} = 1.$$

These conditions specify that $p = (p^{(i)}_j)$ is a point in the product of simplices

$$(6.9) \qquad \Delta = \Delta_{d_1-1} \times \Delta_{d_2-1} \times \cdots \times \Delta_{d_n-1}.$$

A point $p \in \Delta$ is a *Nash equilibrium* if none of the n players can increase his payoff by changing his strategy while the other $n - 1$ players keep their strategies fixed. We shall write this as a system of polynomial constraints in the unknown vectors $p \in \Delta$ and $\pi = (\pi_1, \ldots, \pi_n) \in \mathbb{R}^n$. For each of the unknown probabilities $p^{(i)}_k$ we consider the following multilinear polynomial:

$$(6.10)$$

$$p^{(i)}_k \cdot \left(\pi_i - \sum_{j_1=1}^{d_1} \cdots \sum_{j_{i-1}=1}^{d_{i-1}} \sum_{j_{i+1}=1}^{d_{i+1}} \cdots \sum_{j_n=1}^{d_n} X^{(i)}_{j_1 \ldots j_{i-1} k j_{i+1} j_n} \cdot p^{(1)}_{j_1} \cdots p^{(i-1)}_{j_{i-1}} p^{(i+1)}_{j_{i+1}} \cdots p^{(n)}_{j_n} \right)$$

Hence (6.10) together with (6.8) represents a system of $n + d_1 + \cdots + d_n$ polynomial equations in $n + d_1 + \cdots + d_n$ unknowns, where each polynomial is the product of a linear polynomial and a multilinear polynomial of degree $n - 1$.

THEOREM 6.4. *A vector $(p, \pi) \in \Delta \times \mathbb{R}^n$ represents a Nash equilibrium for the game with payoff matrices $X^{(1)}, \ldots, X^{(n)}$ if and only if (p, π) is a zero of the polynomials (6.10) and each parenthesized expression in (6.10) is nonnegative.*

Nash [**Nas51**] proved that every game has at least one equilibrium point (p, π). His proof and many subsequent refinements made use of fixed point theorems from topology. Numerical algorithms based on combinatorial refinements of these fixed point theorems have been developed, notably in the work of Scarf [**Sca73**]. The algorithms converge to one Nash equilibrium but they do not give any additional information about the number of Nash equilibria or, if that number is infinite, about the dimension and component structure of the semi-algebraic set of Nash equilibria. For that purpose one needs the more refined algebraic techniques discussed here.

There is an obvious combinatorial subproblem arising from the equations, namely, in order for the product (6.10) to be zero, one of the two factors must be zero and the other factor must be non-negative. Thus our problem is that of a non-linear *complementarity problem*. The case $n = 2$ is the linear complementarity problem. In this case we must solve a disjunction of systems of linear equations, which implies that each Nash equilibrium has rational coordinates and can be computed using exact arithmetic. A classical simplex-like algorithm due to Lemke and Howson [**LH64**] finds one Nash equilibrium in this manner. However, it is unknown whether this task can be accomplished in polynomial time. For a survey on complexity questions regarding Nash equilibria of bimatrix games see [**vSt02**].

It is even more challenging to enumerate all Nash equilibria for a bimatrix game. The problem is similar to enumerating all vertices of a convex polyhedron given by linear inequalities. In the latter case, the *Upper Bound Theorem* gives a sharp estimate for the maximal number of vertices, but the analogous problem for concerning the maximum number of Nash equilibria of a bimatrix game is open in general. For the state of the art see [**vSt99**]. We illustrate the issue of combinatorial complexity with a simple example.

EXAMPLE 6.5. (A two-person game with exponentially many Nash equilibria) Take $n = 2$, $d_1 = d_2 =: d$ and both $X^{(1)}$ and $X^{(2)}$ to be the $d \times d$-unit matrix. In this game, the two players both have payoff 1 if their choices agree and otherwise they have payoff 0. Here the equilibrium equations (6.10) take the form

$$(6.11) \quad p_k^{(1)} \cdot \left(\pi_1 - p_k^{(2)} \right) \quad = \quad p_k^{(2)} \cdot \left(\pi_2 - p_k^{(1)} \right) \quad = \quad 0 \quad \text{for} \ k = 1, 2, \ldots, d.$$

The Nash equilibria are solutions of (6.11) such that all $p_k^{(i)}$ are between 0 and π_i and $p_1^{(1)} + \cdots + p_d^{(1)} = p_1^{(2)} + \cdots + p_d^{(2)} = 1$. Their number equals $2^d - 1$.

For instance, for $d = 2$ the equilibrium equations (6.11) have five solutions, which we compute using the program Macaulay 2 as follows:

```
i1 : R = QQ[p,q,Pi1,Pi2];
i2 : I = ideal( p * (Pi1 - q), (1 - p) * (Pi1 - 1 + q),
               q * (Pi2 - p), (1 - q) * (Pi2 - 1 + p) );

i3 : decompose(I)
o3 = { ideal (Pi2 - 1, Pi1 - 1, p, q),
```

```
    ideal (Pi2 - 1, Pi1 - 1, p - 1, q - 1),
    ideal (2Pi2 - 1, 2Pi1 - 1, 2p - 1, 2q - 1),
    ideal (Pi2, Pi1, p, q - 1),
    ideal (Pi2, Pi1, p - 1, q) }
```

Only the first three of these five components correspond to Nash equilibria. For $d = 2$, the $2^d - 1 = 3$ Nash equilibria are $(p, q) = (0, 0)$, $(\frac{1}{2}, \frac{1}{2})$, $(1, 1)$.

In what follows we shall disregard the issues of combinatorial complexity discussed above. Instead we focus on the algebraic complexity of our problem. To this end, we consider only *totally mixed Nash equilibria*, that is, we add the requirement that all probabilities $p_j^{(i)}$ be strictly positive. In our algebraic view, this is no restriction in generality because the vanishing of some of our unknowns yields smaller system of polynomial equations with fewer unknowns but of the same multilinear structure. From now on, the $p_j^{(i)}$ will stand for real variables whose values are strictly between 0 and 1. This allows us to remove the left factors $p^{(i)}$ in (6.10) and work with the parenthesized $(n-1)$-linear polynomials instead. Eliminating the unknowns π_i, we get the following polynomials for $i = 1, \ldots, n$, and $k = 2, 3, \ldots, d_i$:

$$\sum_{j_1=1}^{d_1} \cdots \sum_{j_{i-1}=1}^{d_{i-1}} \sum_{j_{i+1}=1}^{d_{i+1}} \cdots \sum_{j_n=1}^{d_n} (X^{(i)}_{j_1 \ldots j_{i-1} k j_{i+1} j_n} - X^{(i)}_{j_1 \ldots j_{i-1} 1 j_{i+1} j_n}) p_{j_1}^{(1)} \cdots p_{j_{i-1}}^{(i-1)} p_{j_{i+1}}^{(i+1)} \cdots p_{j_n}^{(n)}$$

This is a system of $d_1 + \cdots + d_n - n$ equations in $d_1 + \cdots + d_n$ unknowns, which satisfy the n linear equations in (6.8). Corollary 6.3 generalizes as follows.

THEOREM 6.6. *The totally mixed Nash equilibria of the n-person game with payoff matrices $X^{(1)}, \ldots, X^{(n)}$ are the common zeros in the interior of the polytope Δ of the $d_1 + \cdots + d_n - n$ multilinear polynomials above.*

In what follows, we always eliminate n of the variables by setting

$$p_{d_i}^{(i)} = 1 - \sum_{j=1}^{d_i-1} p_j^{(i)} \qquad \text{for } i = 1, 2, \ldots, n.$$

What remains is a system of δ multilinear polynomials in δ unknowns, where $\delta := d_1 + \cdots + d_n - n$. We shall study these equations in the next section.

6.4. The Mixed Volume of a Product of Simplices

Consider the $d_i - 1$ polynomials which appear in Theorem 6.6 for a fixed upper index i. They share the same Newton polytope, namely, the product of simplices

$$(6.12) \qquad \Delta^{(i)} = \Delta_{d_1-1} \times \cdots \times \Delta_{d_{i-1}-1} \times \{0\} \times \Delta_{d_{i+1}-1} \times \cdots \times \Delta_{d_n-1}.$$

Here Δ_{d_i-1} is the convex hull of the unit vectors and the origin in $\mathbb{R}^{d_i-1}$. Hence the Newton polytope $\Delta^{(i)}$ is a polytope of dimension $\delta - d_i + 1$ in $\mathbb{R}^\delta$. Combining all Newton polytopes, we get the following δ-tuple of polytopes

$$\Delta[d_1, \ldots, d_n] := \left(\Delta^{(1)}, \ldots, \Delta^{(1)}, \Delta^{(2)}, \ldots, \Delta^{(2)}, \ldots, \Delta^{(n)}, \ldots, \Delta^{(n)} \right),$$

where $\Delta^{(i)}$ appears $d_i - 1$ times.

COROLLARY 6.7. *The totally mixed Nash equilibria of an n-person game where player i has d_i pure strategies are the zeros of a sparse polynomial system with support $\Delta[d_1, \ldots, d_n]$, and every such system arises from some game.*

We are now in the situation of Bernstein's Theorem, which tells us that the expected number of complex zeros in $(\mathbb{C}^*)^\delta$ of a sparse system of δ polynomials in δ unknowns equals the mixed volume of the Newton polytopes. The following result of McKelvey & McLennan [**MM97**] gives a combinatorial description for the mixed volume of the tuple of polytopes $\Delta[d_1, \ldots, d_n]$.

THEOREM 6.8. *The maximum number of isolated totally mixed Nash equilibria for any n-person game where the ith player has d_i pure strategies equals the mixed volume of $\Delta[d_1, \ldots, d_n]$. This mixed volume coincides with the number of partitions of the δ-element set of unknowns $\{ p_k^{(i)} : i = 1, \ldots, n,\ k = 2, \ldots, d_i \}$ into n disjoint subsets $B_1, B_2, \ldots, B_n$ such that*

- *the cardinality of the ith block B_i is equal to $d_i - 1$, and*
- *the ith block B_i is disjoint from $\{ p_1^{(i)}, p_2^{(i)}, \ldots, p_{d_i}^{(i)} \}$, i.e., no variable with upper index i is allowed to be in B_i.*

This theorem says, in particular, that the maximum number of complex zeros of a sparse system with Newton polytopes $\Delta[d_1, \ldots, d_n]$ can be attained by counting real zeros only. Moreover, it can be attained by counting only real zeros which have all their coordinates strictly between 0 and 1. The key idea in proving Theorem 6.8 is to replace each of the given multilinear equations by a product of linear forms. This technique was discussed at the end of Section 3.4. In terms of Newton polytopes, this means that $\Delta^{(i)}$ is expressed as the Minkowski sum of the $n-1$ simplices

$$(6.13) \qquad \{\mathbf{0}\} \times \cdots \times \{\mathbf{0}\} \times \Delta_{d_j-1} \times \{\mathbf{0}\} \times \cdots \times \{\mathbf{0}\}.$$

We shall illustrate Theorem 6.8 and this factoring construction for the case $n = 3$, $d_1 = d_2 = d_3 = 3$. Our familiar players Adam, Bob and Carl reenter the scene in this case. A new stock #3 has come on the market, and our friends can now each choose from three pure strategies. The probabilities which Adam allocates to stocks #1, #2 and #3 are a_1, a_2, and $1 - a_1 - a_2$. There are now six equilibrium equations in the six unknowns $a_1, a_2, b_1, b_2, c_1, c_2$. The number of set partitions of $\{a_1, a_2, b_1, b_2, c_1, c_2\}$ described in Theorem 6.8 is **ten**. The ten allowed partitions are

$$
\begin{array}{ll}
\{b_1, b_2\} \cup \{c_1, c_2\} \cup \{a_1, a_2\} & \{c_1, c_2\} \cup \{a_1, a_2\} \cup \{b_1, b_2\} \\
\{b_1, c_1\} \cup \{a_1, c_2\} \cup \{a_2, b_2\} & \{b_1, c_1\} \cup \{a_2, c_2\} \cup \{a_1, b_2\} \\
\{b_1, c_2\} \cup \{a_1, c_1\} \cup \{a_2, b_2\} & \{b_1, c_2\} \cup \{a_2, c_1\} \cup \{a_1, b_2\} \\
\{b_2, c_1\} \cup \{a_1, c_2\} \cup \{a_2, b_1\} & \{b_2, c_1\} \cup \{a_2, c_2\} \cup \{a_1, b_1\} \\
\{b_2, c_2\} \cup \{a_1, c_1\} \cup \{a_2, b_1\} & \{b_2, c_2\} \cup \{a_2, c_1\} \cup \{a_1, b_1\}.
\end{array}
$$

This number **ten** is the mixed volume of six 4-dimensional polytopes, each a product of two triangles, regarded as a face of the product of three triangles:

$$
\begin{aligned}
\Delta[2, 2, 2] \quad = \quad (\quad &\bullet \times \Delta_2 \times \Delta_2, \ \bullet \times \Delta_2 \times \Delta_2, \ \Delta_2 \times \bullet \times \Delta_2, \\
&\Delta_2 \times \bullet \times \Delta_2, \ \Delta_2 \times \Delta_2 \times \bullet, \ \Delta_2 \times \Delta_2 \times \bullet \ )
\end{aligned}
$$

Theorem 6.8 tells us that Adam, Bob and Carl can be made happy in ten possible ways, i.e, their game can have as many as ten totally mixed Nash equilibria. We shall construct payoff matrices which attain this number.

Consider the following six bilinear equations in factored form:

$$(200b_1 + 100b_2 - 100)(200c_1 + 100c_2 - 100) = 0$$
$$(190b_1 + 110b_2 - 101)(190c_1 + 110c_2 - 101) = 0$$
$$(200a_1 + 100a_2 - 100)(180c_1 + 120c_2 - 103) = 0$$
$$(190a_1 + 110a_2 - 101)(170c_1 + 130c_2 - 106) = 0$$
$$(180a_1 + 120a_2 - 103)(180b_1 + 120b_2 - 103) = 0$$
$$(170a_1 + 130a_2 - 106)(170b_1 + 130b_2 - 106) = 0.$$

These equations have the Newton polytopes $\Delta[2,2,2]$, and the coefficients are chosen so that all ten solutions have their coordinates between 0 and 1. We now need to find $3 \times 3 \times 3$-payoff matrices (A_{ijk}), (B_{ijk}), and (C_{ijk}) which give rise to these equations. Clearly, the payoff matrices are not unique. To make them unique we require the normalizing condition that each player's payoff is zero when he picks stock #1. In symbols, $A_{1jk} = B_{i1k} = C_{ij1} = 0$ for all $i, j, k \in \{1, 2, 3\}$. The remaining 54 parameters are now uniquely determined. To find them, we expand our six polynomials in a different basis, like the one used in Corollary 6.2. The rewritten equations are

$$10000b_1c_1 - 10000b_1(1 - c_1 - c_2) - 10000(1 - b_1 - b_2)c_1$$
$$+10000(1 - b_1 - b_2)(1 - c_1 - c_2) = 0,$$
$$7921b_1c_1 + 801b_1c_2 - 8989b_1(1 - c_1 - c_2) + 801b_2c_1 + 81b_2c_2$$
$$-909b_2(1 - c_1 - c_2) - 8989(1 - b_1 - b_2)c_1 - 909(1 - b_1 - b_2)c_2$$
$$+10201(1 - b_1 - b_2)(1 - c_1 - c_2) = 0,$$
$$7700a_1c_1 + 1700a_1c_2 - 10300a_1(1 - c_1 - c_2) - 7700(1 - a_1 - a_2)c_1$$
$$-1700(1 - a_1 - a_2)c_2 + 10300(1 - a_1 - a_2)(1 - c_1 - c_2) = 0,$$
$$5696a_1c_1 + 2136a_1c_2 - 9434a_1(1 - c_1 - c_2) + 576a_2c_1 + 216a_2c_2$$
$$-954a_2(1 - c_1 - c_2) - 6464(1 - a_1 - a_2)c_1 - 2424(1 - a_1 - a_2)c_2$$
$$+10706(1 - a_1 - a_2)(1 - c_1 - c_2) = 0,$$
$$5929a_1b_1 + 1309a_1b_2 - 7931a_1(1 - b_1 - b_2) + 1309a_2b_1 + 289a_2b_2$$
$$-1751a_2(1 - b_1 - b_2) - 7931(1 - a_1 - a_2)b_1 - 1751(1 - a_1 - a_2)b_2$$
$$+10609(1 - a_1 - a_2)(1 - b_1 - b_2) = 0,$$
$$4096a_1b_1 + 1536a_1b_2 - 6784a_1(1 - b_1 - b_2) + 1536a_2b_1 + 576a_2b_2$$
$$-2544a_2(1 - b_1 - b_2) - 6784(1 - a_1 - a_2)b_1 - 2544(1 - a_1 - a_2)b_2$$
$$+11236(1 - a_1 - a_2)(1 - b_1 - b_2) = 0.$$

The 18 coefficients appearing in the first two equations are the entries in Adam's payoff matrix:

$$A_{211} = 10000, A_{212} = 0, \ldots, a_{233} = 10000; \ A_{311} = 7921, \ldots, A_{333} = 10201.$$

Similarly, we get Bob's payoff matrix from the middle two equations, and we get Carl's payoff matrix from the last two equations. In this manner, we have constructed an explicit three-person game with three pure strategies per player which has ten totally mixed Nash equilibria.

Multilinear equations are particularly well-suited for the use of *numerical homotopy methods*. For the starting system of such a homotopy one can take products of linear forms as outlined above. We present another concrete example in the next section. We believe that considerable progress can still be made in the numerical computation of totally mixed Nash equilibria.

One special case of Theorem 6.8 deserves special attention: $d_1 = d_2 = \cdots = d_n = 2$. This concerns an n-person game where each player has two pure strategies. The corresponding polytope tuple $\Delta[1, 1, \ldots, 1]$ consists of the n distinct facets of the n-dimensional cube. Here parallel pairs of facets of the n-cube are identified, which is why our n-cube has only n facets instead of $2n$. In this special case, the partitions described in Theorem 6.8 correspond to the *derangements* of the set $\{1, 2, \ldots, n\}$, that is, permutations of $\{1, 2, \ldots, n\}$ without fixed points.

COROLLARY 6.9. *The following three numbers coincide, for every* $n \in \mathbb{N}$:

- *The maximum number of isolated totally mixed Nash equilibria for an n-person game where each player has two pure strategies,*
- *the mixed volume of the n distinct facets of the n-cube,*
- *the number of derangements of an n-element set.*

Counting derangements is a classical problem is combinatorics. Their number grows as follows: $1, 2, 9, 44, 265, 1854, 14833, 133496, \ldots$. For instance, the number of derangements of $\{1, 2, 3, 4, 5\}$ is 44. A 5-person game with two mixed strategies can have as many as 44 totally mixed Nash equilibria.

6.5. Computing Nash Equilibria with PHCpack

In this section we demonstrate a practical application of numerical homotopy methods. We will use Jan Verschelde's software package PHCpack to solve a certain game with eight players. This program is freely available and easy to download from http://www.math.uic.edu/~jan/. Numerical homotopy methods are well suited for solving multilinear equations. They are the author's method of choice for computing all totally mixed Nash equilibria of a game.

The particular game to be chosen was inspired by recent work of Kearns, Littman and Singh [**KLS01**] on *Graphical Models for Game Theory*. We briefly summarize the setting of that paper. We are given a simple graph G with n nodes, and our n players are thought to be located at these nodes. Each player's payoff is local in the sense that the payoff π_i of player i depends only on the choices made by those players which are neighbors of i in G. The strategy selected by any player j such that $\{i, j\}$ is not an edge of G has no influence on π_i. More formally, our payoff matrices are assumed to satisfy the following hypothesis relative to the graph G:

$$X^{(i)}_{j_1 j_2 \cdots j_n} = X^{(i)}_{k_1 k_2 \cdots k_n} \quad \text{whenever}$$
$$\forall \nu \in \{1, 2, \ldots, n\} : \ j_\nu = k_\nu \text{ or } \{i, \nu\} \text{ is not an edge of } G.$$

Kearns, Littman and Singh [**KLS01**] assume that each of the n players has only a binary choice. In other words, there are only two pure strategies available:

$$d_1 = d_2 = \cdots = d_n = 2.$$

The totally mixed Nash equilibria of this game are given by a system of multilinear equations in n unknowns $p^{(1)}, p^{(2)}, \ldots p^{(n)}$, where $p^{(i)}$ denotes the probability allocated by player i to his first choice. In the situation of Corollary 6.9, the ith equation does not involve the unknown $p^{(i)}$. In the presence of the graph G the following holds: *the ith equation is a multilinear form in the unknowns $p^{(j)}$ where* *j runs over all neighbors of i.* Thus we are faced with solving a system of n multilinear equations in n unknowns where the unknowns in the ith equation involve only neighbors of i in G. Corollary 6.9 generalizes to the graphical case as follows:

THEOREM 6.10. *For a graph G on $\{1, 2, \ldots, n\}$ the following numbers coincide:*

- *the maximum number of isolated totally mixed Nash equilibria of the game with graph G, assuming binary choices for each of the n players,*
- *the number of all permutations π of $\{1, 2, \ldots, n\}$ such that $\{i, \pi(i)\}$ is an edge of G for all $i \in \{1, 2, \ldots, n\}$,*
- *the permanent of the $n \times n$-adjacency matrix of G.*

Our example is a game where G is the edge graph of the 3-dimensional cube. The eight players are associated to the vertices of the cube as follows:

Adam	Bob	Carl	Dick	Frank	Gary	Hugh	Jim
000	001	010	011	100	101	110	111
a	b	c	d	f	g	h	j

Thus Adam's neighbors are Bob, Carl and Frank. The choices made by Dick, Gary, Hugh and Jim are irrelevant for Adam's payoff. The unknown b is the probability allocated by Bob to the first choice. Thus Adam's equation is a trilinear form in the three unknowns b, c, and f. We shall consider the specific game on the 3-cube whose eight equations are as follows:

```
8
(3*b-1)*(3*c-1)*(3*f-1)-0.1;
(3*a-1)*(3*d-1)*(3*g-1)-0.1;
(5*a-1)*(5*d-1)*(3*h-1)-0.1;
(5*b-1)*(5*c-1)*(3*j-1)-0.1;
(7*a-1)*(5*g-1)*(5*h-1)-0.1;
(7*b-1)*(5*f-1)*(5*j-1)-0.1;
(7*c-1)*(7*f-1)*(7*j-1)-0.1;
(7*d-1)*(7*g-1)*(7*h-1)-0.1;
```

These nine lines are in a format readable to PHCpack. Let us type exactly these nine lines into file called cubegame. If we delete the trailing term $-0.1 = 1/10$ from each of the eight equations, then our system fully factors and there are 81 distinct rational solutions. Each of these 81 solutions represents a Nash equilibrium as it has all of its coordinates between 0 and 1. Indeed, this count is consistent with Theorem 6.10: *there are precisely 81 permutations mapping each vertex of the 3-cube to a neighboring vertex.*

We now solve the given system with the trailing terms -0.1 by typing

phc −b cubegame cubegameout

The marker −b tells PHCpack to use "black box mode", which is the way to go for beginners. The program runs for about two minutes and then prints output both on the old file cubegame and on the new file cubegameout. The latter file contains a detailed version of the results. It starts like this:

```
8
27*b*c*f-9*b*c-9*b*f-9*c*f+ 3*b+ 3*c+ 3*f-1.10000000E+00;
27*a*d*g-9*a*d-9*a*g-9*d*g+ 3*a+ 3*d+ 3*g-1.10000000E+00;
75*a*d*h-25*a*d-15*a*h-15*d*h+ 5*a+ 5*d+ 3*h-1.10000000E+00;
75*b*c*j-25*b*c-15*b*j-15*c*j+ 5*b+ 5*c+ 3*j-1.10000000E+00;
```

```
175*a*g*h-35*a*g-35*a*h-25*g*h+ 7*a+ 5*g+ 5*h-1.1000000E+00;
175*b*f*j-35*b*f-35*b*j-25*f*j+ 7*b+ 5*f+ 5*j-1.1000000E+00;
343*c*f*j-49*c*f-49*c*j-49*f*j+ 7*c+ 7*f+ 7*j-1.10000000E+00;
343*d*g*h-49*d*g-49*d*h-49*g*h+ 7*d+ 7*g+ 7*h-1.10000000E+00;
```

These are just the input polynomials in expanded form. First the program computes the mixed volume using the methods explained at the end of Section 3.4.

```
ROOT COUNTS :
total degree : 6561
7-homogeneous Bezout number : 81
  with partition : {b }{c }{f }{a j }{d }{g }{h }
general linear-product Bezout number : 81
  based on the set structure :
      {b }{c }{f }
      {a }{d }{g }
      {a }{d }{h }
      {b }{c }{j }
      {a }{g }{h }
      {b }{f }{j }
      {c }{f }{j }
      {d }{g }{h }
mixed volume : 81


TIMING INFORMATION for Root Counting
The elapsed time in seconds was       88.0500 =  0h 1m28s 50ms
User time in seconds was              88.0500 =  0h 1m28s 50ms
System CPU time in seconds was         0.0000 =  0h 0m 0s  0ms
....
```

At the bottom of the file cubegameout we find the following crucial information:

```
A list of 81 solutions has been refined :
Number of regular solutions   : 81.
Number of singular solutions  : 0.
Number of real solutions      : 49.
Number of complex solutions   : 32.
Number of clustered solutions : 0.
Number of failures            : 0.
...
The elapsed time in seconds was     158.060 =  0h 2m38s 60ms
...
```

Hence our system has 81 distinct complex solutions of which 49 are real. But not all real solutions are Nash equilibria. There are 33 real solutions which have at least one negative coordinate. Here is one example of a real solution which is not a Nash equilibrium, in the format found on the file cubegameout.

```
solution 8: start residual: 7.459E-17 #iterations: 1 success
...
  a :  1.55970479507211E-01    9.62195295633190E-49
  b :  1.25274260526218E-01    1.28292706084425E-48
  c :  2.95132526635802E-01    3.42113882891801E-49
  d :  3.57332205266636E-01    2.99349647530326E-48
```

```
f :   7.99323811855881E-01   -1.09476442525376E-46
g : -5.36793856105409E-01    1.12213353588511E-46
h :   1.40857082427868E-01   -1.12256117823872E-49
j :   1.45773653038247E-01    3.74187059412907E-49
== err :   5.143E-15 =   ....  1.709E-16 = real regular ==
```

This complex solution vector (a, b, c, d, f, g, h, j) is numerically recognized as being real. The imaginary part of each coordinate is on the order of 10^{-48}. It is not a Nash equilibrium because the coordinate $g = -0.5368$ is negative.

At this point we wish to comment on our choice of variable names. We did not use the letters e and i as these are reserved in PHCpack. The symbols i and I stand for $\sqrt{-1}$, and the symbols e and E denote floating point numbers in scientific notation, e.g., 9.62E-49 = 9.62e-49. Avoiding the use of these two letters is one of the basic principles of polynomial system solving.

Our system has exactly 16 real solutions whose coordinates lie between 0 and 1. We list these points with each coordinate rounded to three decimals. Here is the final conclusion for this example. *Our game has precisely* 16 *totally mixed isolated Nash equilibria. They are given by the rows of the table*

Adam	Bob	Carl	Dick	Frank	Gary	Hugh	Jim
a	b	c	d	f	g	h	j
0.022	0.147	0.144	0.398	0.439	0.150	0.295	0.785
0.668	0.668	0.175	0.175	0.263	0.263	0.217	0.217
0.125	0.022	0.398	0.295	0.150	0.799	0.146	0.295
0.668	0.125	0.295	0.175	0.799	0.263	0.217	0.146
0.022	0.125	0.295	0.398	0.799	0.150	0.295	0.146
0.147	0.147	0.144	0.144	0.439	0.439	0.785	0.785
0.147	0.125	0.295	0.144	0.799	0.439	0.785	0.146
0.022	0.022	0.398	0.398	0.150	0.150	0.295	0.295
0.125	0.147	0.144	0.295	0.439	0.799	0.146	0.785
0.668	0.147	0.144	0.175	0.439	0.263	0.217	0.785
0.147	0.022	0.398	0.144	0.150	0.439	0.785	0.295
0.125	0.125	0.295	0.295	0.799	0.799	0.146	0.146
0.668	0.022	0.398	0.175	0.150	0.263	0.217	0.295
0.125	0.668	0.175	0.295	0.263	0.799	0.146	0.217
0.022	0.668	0.175	0.398	0.263	0.150	0.295	0.217
0.147	0.668	0.175	0.144	0.263	0.439	0.785	0.217

6.6. Exercises

(1) Consider three equations in unknowns a, b, c as in Corollary 6.3:
$$\lambda_0 bc + \lambda_1 b + \lambda_2 c + \lambda_3 = \mu_0 ac + \mu_1 a + \mu_2 c + \mu_3$$
$$= \nu_0 ab + \nu_1 a + \nu_2 b + \nu_3 = 0.$$

Find necessary and sufficient conditions, in terms of the nine parameters λ_i, μ_j, ν_k for this system to have two real roots (a, b, c) both of which satisfy $0 < a, b, c < 1$. (In other words, characterize those 3-person games with 2 pure strategies which have 2 totally mixed Nash equilibria.)

(2) Find all irreducible components of the variety defined by the equations (6.11). How many components do not correspond to Nash equilibria?

(3) Determine the exact maximum number of isolated totally mixed Nash equilibria of any 5-person game where each player has 5 pure strategies.

(4) Pick your favorite integer N between 0 and 44. Construct an explicit five-person game with two mixed strategies per player which has exactly N totally mixed Nash equilibria.

(5) Write eight explicit payoff matrices of format $2 \times 2 \times \cdots \times 2$, one for each of the eight players Adam, Bob, Carl, Dick, Frank, Gary, Hugh and Jim. In other words, describe the 8-person game which gives rise to the algebraic equations in Section 6.5.

(7) Suppose that the Adam-Bob-Carl-Dick-Frank-Gary-Hugh-Jim interaction model changes as follows: the edge graph of the 3-cube is enlarged by adding one diagonal for each of the six facets of the cube. For the new graph with 18 edges, what is the expected number of totally mixed Nash equilibria? Does this number depend on your choice of diagonals?

(8) Use $\texttt{Singular}$ to solve the equations in the previous three exercises.

(9) Prove that there is nothing special about the number 321 appearing in Nash's poker game. More precisely, for every positive integer p which is not a perfect square, there exists a 3-person game of format $2 \times 2 \times 2$ which has two totally mixed Nash equilibria whose coordinates are irrational and lie in the field $\mathbb{Q}(\sqrt{p})$. (In the weeks after the CBMS conference, Ruchira Datta proved a much more general result, to the effect that every real algebraic variety can be realized as the set of totally mixed Nash equilibria of a 3-person game, and also of a multi-person game of format $2 \times 2 \times \cdots \times 2$.)

CHAPTER 7

Sums of Squares

This chapter concerns polynomial problems over the real numbers $\mathbb{R}$. This means that the input consists of polynomials in $\mathbb{R}[x_1, \ldots, x_n]$ where each coefficient is given either as a rational number or a floating point number. A trivial but crucial observation about real numbers is that *sums of squares are non-negative*. Sums of squares lead us to *Semidefinite Programming*, an exciting subject of current interest in numerical optimization and its engineering applications [**VB96**]. We will give an introduction to semidefinite programming with a view towards solving polynomial equations and inequalities over $\mathbb{R}$. A crucial role is played by the *Real Nullstellensatz* (Theorem 7.5) which tells us that either a polynomial problem has a solution or there exists a certificate that no solution exists. Pablo Parrilo showed in his dissertation [**Par00**] that semidefinite programming provides a numerical method for computing such certificates, and he implemented this in SOStools.

7.1. Positive Semidefinite Matrices

We begin by reviewing some basic material from linear algebra. Let $V \simeq \mathbb{R}^m$ be an m-dimensional real vector space which has a known basis. Every quadratic form on V is represented uniquely by a symmetric $m \times m$-matrix A. Namely, the quadratic form associated with a real symmetric matrix A is

$$(7.1) \qquad \phi : V \to \mathbb{R}, \quad u \mapsto u^T \cdot A \cdot u.$$

The matrix A has only real eigenvalues. It can be diagonalized over the real numbers by an orthogonal matrix Λ, whose columns are eigenvectors of A:

$$(7.2) \qquad \Lambda^T \cdot A \cdot \Lambda \;=\; \mathrm{diag}(\lambda_1, \lambda_2, \ldots, \lambda_m).$$

Computing this identity is a task in numerical linear algebra, a task that matlab performs well. Given (7.2) our quadratic form can be written as

$$(7.3) \qquad \phi(u) \;=\; \sum_{j=1}^{m} \lambda_j \cdot \Big(\sum_{i=1}^{m} \Lambda_{ij} u_i \Big)^2.$$

This expression is an alternating sum of squares of linear forms on V.

PROPOSITION 7.1. *For a symmetric $m \times m$-matrix A with entries in $\mathbb{R}$, the following five conditions are equivalent:*

   (a) *$u^T \cdot A \cdot u \geq 0$ for all $u \in \mathbb{R}^m$,*
   (b) *all eigenvalues of A are nonnegative real numbers,*
   (c) *all diagonal subdeterminants of A are nonnegative,*
   (d) *there exists a real $m \times m$-matrix B such that $A = B \cdot B^T$,*
   (e) *the quadratic form $u^T \cdot A \cdot u$ is a sum of squares of linear forms on $\mathbb{R}^m$.*

A matrix A which satisfies the conditions (a) – (e) is called *positive semidefinite*. By a *diagonal subdeterminant* of A we mean an $i \times i$-subdeterminant with the same row and column indices, for any $i \in \{1, 2, \ldots, m\}$. Thus condition (c) amounts to checking $2^m - 1$ polynomial inequalities in the entries of A. If we wish to check whether A is *positive definite*, which is the situation when all eigenvalues are strictly positive, then it suffices to take the m principal minors, which are gotten by taking the first i rows and first i columns only.

We call the identity $A = B \cdot B^T$ in (d) a *Cholesky decomposition* of A. In numerical analysis texts this term is often reserved for such a decomposition where B is lower triangular. We allow B to be any real matrix. Note that the factor matrix B is easily expressed in terms of the (floating point) data computed in (7.2) and vice versa. Namely, we take

$$B \quad = \quad \Lambda \cdot \mathrm{diag}(\sqrt{\lambda_1}, \sqrt{\lambda_2}, \ldots, \sqrt{\lambda_m}).$$

In view of (7.3), this proves the equivalence of (d) and (e): knowledge of the matrix B is equivalent to writing the quadratic form ϕ as a sum of squares.

Let $\mathrm{Sym}_2(V)$ denote the real vector space consisting of all symmetric $m \times m$-matrices. The *positive semidefinite cone* or *PSD cone* is

$$PSD(V) \quad = \quad \{\, A \in \mathrm{Sym}_2(V) \ : \ A \text{ is positive semidefinite}\,\}.$$

This is a full-dimensional closed semi-algebraic convex cone in the vector space $\mathrm{Sym}_2(V) \simeq \mathbb{R}^{\binom{m+1}{2}}$. The set $PSD(V)$ is closed and convex because it is the solution set of an infinite system of linear inequalities in (a), one for each $u \in \mathbb{R}^m$. It is semi-algebraic because it can be defined by $2^m - 1$ polynomial inequalities as in (c). It is full-dimensional because every matrix A with strictly positive eigenvalues λ_i has an open neighborhood in $PSD(V)$. The extreme rays of the cone $PSD(V)$ are the squares of linear forms, such as $\phi(u) = (c_1 u_1 + c_2 u_2 + \cdots + c_m u_m)^2$.

In what follows we use the symbol ℓ to denote a linear function (plus a constant) on the vector space $\mathrm{Sym}_2(V)$. Explicitly, for an indeterminate symmetric matrix $A = (a_{ij})$, a linear function ℓ can be written as follows:

$$\ell(A) \quad = \quad u_{00} + \sum_{1 \leq j < k \leq m}^{m} u_{jk} \cdot a_{jk}$$

where the u_{jk} are constants. An *affine subspace* is the solution set to a system of linear equations $\ell_1(A) = \cdots = \ell_r(A) = 0$. Semidefinite programming concerns the intersection of an affine subspace with the positive semidefinite cone [**VB96**]. There are highly efficient algorithms for solving the following problems.

Semidefinite Programming: Decision Problem
Given linear functions $\ell_1, \ldots, \ell_r$, does there exist a positive semidefinite matrix $A \in \mathrm{PSD}(V)$ which satisfies the equations $\ell_1(A) = \cdots = \ell_r(A) = 0$?

Semidefinite Programming: Optimization Problem
Given linear functions $\ell_0, \ell_1, \ldots, \ell_r$, minimize $\ell_0(A)$ subject to $A \in \mathrm{PSD}(V)$ and $\ell_1(A) = \cdots = \ell_r(A) = 0$.

It is instructive to examine these two problems for the special case when A is assumed to be a diagonal matrix, say, $A = \mathrm{diag}(\lambda_1, \ldots, \lambda_m)$. Then $A \in \mathrm{PSD}(V)$ is equivalent to $\lambda_1, \ldots, \lambda_m \geq 0$, and our first problem is to solve a linear system of equations in the non-negative reals. This is the Decision Problem of *Linear*

Programming. The second problem amounts to minimizing a linear function over a convex polyhedron, which is the Optimization Problem of Linear Programming. Thus Linear Programming is the restriction of Semidefinite Programming to diagonal matrices.

Consider the following simple semidefinite programming decision problem for $m = 3$. Suppose we wish to find a positive semidefinite matrix

$$A \;=\; \begin{pmatrix} a_{11} & a_{12} & a_{13} \\ a_{12} & a_{22} & a_{23} \\ a_{13} & a_{23} & a_{33} \end{pmatrix} \in \mathrm{PSD}(\mathbb{R}^3) \qquad \text{which satisfies}$$

(7.4) $a_{11} = 1,\ a_{12} = 0,\ a_{23} = -1,\ a_{33} = 2$ and $2a_{13} + a_{22} = -1$.

It turns out that this particular problem has a unique solution:

(7.5) $A \;=\; \begin{pmatrix} 1 & 0 & -1 \\ 0 & 1 & -1 \\ -1 & -1 & 2 \end{pmatrix} \;=\; \begin{pmatrix} 1 & 0 & 0 \\ 0 & 1 & 0 \\ -1 & -1 & 0 \end{pmatrix} \cdot \begin{pmatrix} 1 & 0 & 0 \\ 0 & 1 & 0 \\ -1 & -1 & 0 \end{pmatrix}^T$

We will use this example to sketch the connection to sums of squares. Consider the following fourth degree polynomial in one unknown:

$$f(x) \;=\; x^4 - x^2 - 2x + 2.$$

We wish to know whether $f(x)$ is non-negative on $\mathbb{R}$. Since $f(x)$ is a polynomial in one variable only, this is equivalent to asking whether $f(x)$ can be written as a sum of squares of quadratic polynomials.

Consider the possible representations of our polynomial as a matrix product:

(7.6) $f(x) \;=\; \begin{pmatrix} x^2 & x & 1 \end{pmatrix} \cdot \begin{pmatrix} a_{11} & a_{12} & a_{13} \\ a_{12} & a_{22} & a_{23} \\ a_{13} & a_{23} & a_{33} \end{pmatrix} \cdot \begin{pmatrix} x^2 \\ x \\ 1 \end{pmatrix}$

This identity holds if and only if the linear equations (7.4) are satisfied. By condition (e) in Proposition 7.1, the polynomial in (7.6) is a sum of squares if and only if the matrix $A = (a_{ij})$ is positive semidefinite. Thus the semidefinite programming decision problem specified by (7.4) is equivalent to the question whether $f(x)$ is a sum of squares. The answer is affirmative and given in (7.5). From the Cholesky decomposition of $A = (a_{ij})$ in (7.5) we get

$$f(x) \;=\; \begin{pmatrix} x^2 - 1 & x - 1 & 0 \end{pmatrix} \cdot \begin{pmatrix} x^2 - 1 \\ x - 1 \\ 0 \end{pmatrix} \;=\; (x^2 - 1)^2 + (x - 1)^2.$$

7.2. Zero-dimensional Ideals and SOStools

Let I be a zero-dimensional ideal in $S = \mathbb{R}[x_1, \dots, x_n]$ which is given to us by an explicit Gröbner basis $\mathcal{G}$ with respect to some term order $\prec$. Thus we are in the situation of Chapter 2. The set $\mathcal{B} = \mathcal{B}_\prec(I)$ of standard monomials is an effective basis for the $\mathbb{R}$-vector space $V = S/I$. Suppose that $\#(\mathcal{B}) = m$, so that $S/I \simeq \mathbb{R}^m$. Every quadratic form on V is represented by an $m \times m$-matrix A whose rows and columns are indexed by $\mathcal{B}$. Let X denote the column vector of length m whose entries are the monomials in $\mathcal{B}$. Then $X^T \cdot A \cdot X$ is a polynomial in $S = \mathbb{R}[x_1, \dots, x_n]$. It can be regarded as an element of $S/I = \mathbb{R}\mathcal{B}$ by taking its normal form modulo the Gröbner basis $\mathcal{G}$. In this section we apply semidefinite programming to the quadratic forms $X^T \cdot A \cdot X$ on V. The point of departure is the following theorem.

THEOREM 7.2. *The following three statements are equivalent:*
(a) *The ideal I has no real zeros.*
(b) *The constant -1 is a sum of squares in $V = S/I$.*
(c) *There exists a positive semidefinite $m \times m$-matrix A such that*

$$(7.7) \qquad\qquad X^T \cdot A \cdot X + 1 \quad \text{lies in the ideal } I.$$

The equivalence of (b) and (c) follows from Proposition 7.1. The implication from (b) to (a) is obvious. The implication from (a) to (b) is proved by reduction to the case $n = 1$. For one variable, it follows from the familiar fact that a polynomial in $\mathbb{R}[x]$ with no real roots can be factored into a product of irreducible quadratic polynomials. See Corollary 7.7 for a generalization. The condition (7.7) can be written as

$$(7.8) \qquad X^T \cdot A \cdot X + 1 \quad \text{reduces to zero modulo the Gröbner basis } \mathcal{G}.$$

This is a linear system of equations in the unknown entries of the symmetric matrix A. We wish to decide whether A lies in cone $\mathrm{PSD}(V)$. Thus the question whether the given ideal I has a real zero or not has been reformulated as a decision problem of semidefinite programming. A positive solution A to the semidefinite programming problem provides a certificate for the non-existence of real roots.

The following ideal (for $n = 3$) appeared as an example in Chapter 2:

$$I \;=\; \langle\, \underline{z^2} + \tfrac{1}{5}x - \tfrac{1}{5}y + \tfrac{2}{25},\; \underline{y^2} - \tfrac{1}{5}x + \tfrac{1}{5}z + \tfrac{2}{25},$$
$$\underline{x^2} + \tfrac{1}{5}y - \tfrac{1}{5}z + \tfrac{2}{25},\; \underline{xy} + xz + yz + \tfrac{1}{25} \,\rangle$$

The four given generators are a Gröbner basis. We have $\mathbb{R}[x, y, z]/I \simeq \mathbb{R}^6$. The column vector of standard monomials is $X = \big(\, 1,\, x,\, y,\, z,\, xz,\, yz \,\big)^T$. We wish to show that I has no real zeros, by finding a representation (7.7). We use the software SOStools which was developed by Pablo Parrilo and his collaborators at Caltech. It is available at http://www.cds.caltech.edu/sostools/.

The following SOStools sessions were prepared by Ruchira Datta. We write g1, g2, g3, g4 for the given generators of the ideal I. Our decision variables are p1, a sum of squares, and p2, p3, p4, p5, arbitrary polynomials. They are supposed to satisfy

$$\mathrm{p1} + 1 + \mathrm{p2} \cdot \mathrm{g1} + \mathrm{p3} \cdot \mathrm{g2} + \mathrm{p4} \cdot \mathrm{g3} + \mathrm{p5} \cdot \mathrm{g4} \;=\; 0.$$

Here is how to say this in SOStools:

```
>> clear; maple clear; echo on
>> syms x y z;
>> vartable = [x; y; z];
>> prog = sosprogram(vartable);
>> Z = [ 1; x; y; z; x*z; y*z ];
>> [prog,p{1}] = sossosvar(prog,Z);
>> for i = 1:4
       [prog,p{1+i}] = sospolyvar(prog,Z);
   end;
>> g{1} = z^2 + x/5 - y/5 + 2/25;
>> g{2} = y^2 - x/5 + z/5 + 2/25;
>> g{3} = x^2 + y/5 - z/5 + 2/25;
```

```
>> g{4} = x*y + x*z + y*z + 1/25;
>> expr = p{1} + 1;
>> for i = 1:4
       expr = expr + p{1+i}*g{i};
    end;
>> prog = soseq(prog,expr);
>> prog = sossolve(prog);
```

The program prepares the semidefinite programming problem (SDP) and then it calls on another program SeDuMi for solving the SDP by interior point methods. The numerical output produced by SeDuMi looks like this:

```
SeDuMi 1.05 by Jos F. Sturm, 1998, 2001.
Alg = 2: xz-corrector,
Step-Differentiation, theta = 0.250, beta = 0.500
eqs m = 35, order n = 87, dim = 117, blocks = 2
nnz(A) = 341 + 0, nnz(ADA) = 563, nnz(L) = 336
it :  b*y         gap    delta  rate   t/tP*  t/tD*  feas cg cg
 0 :          2.82E-01 0.000
 1 : 3.23E+00 6.35E-03 0.000 0.0225 0.9905 0.9900  -0.07  1  1
 2 : 2.14E-04 3.33E-06 0.000 0.0005 0.9999 0.9999   0.97  1  1
 3 : 2.15E-11 3.34E-13 0.000 0.0000 1.0000 1.0000   1.00  1  1
iter seconds digits       c*x                b*y
 3      0.8   Inf  0.0000000000e+00   2.1543738837e-11
|Ax-b| = 2.1e-12, [Ay-c]_+ = 6.2E-12,|x|= 7.5e+01,|y|= 2.3e-11
Max-norms: ||b||=1, ||c|| = 0,
Cholesky |add|=0, |skip| = 0, ||L.L|| = 2.79883.


Residual norm: 2.1405e-12
       cpusec: 0.8200
         iter: 3
    feasratio: 1.0000
         pinf: 0
         dinf: 0
       numerr: 0
```

The bottom two entries pinf: 0 and dinf: 0 indicate that the SDP was feasible and a solution p1, ... , p5 has been found. At this point we may already conclude that I has no real zeros. We can now ask SOStools to display the sum of squares p1 it has found. This is done by typing

```
>> SOLp1 = sosgetsol(prog,p{1})
```

Rather than looking at the messy output, let us now return to our general discussion. Suppose that I is a zero-dimensional ideal which has real roots, perhaps many of them. Then we might be interested in selecting the *best* real root, in the sense that it minimizes some polynomial function.

Real Root Optimization Problem
Given a polynomial $f \in S$, minimize $f(u)$ subject to $u \in \mathcal{V}(I) \cap \mathbb{R}^n$.

This problem is equivalent to finding the largest real number λ such that $f(x) - \lambda$ is non-negative on $\mathcal{V}(I) \cap \mathbb{R}^n$. In the context of semidefinite programming, it makes sense to consider the following optimization problem:

Sum of Squares in an Artinian Ring

Given a polynomial $f \in S$, maximize $\lambda \in \mathbb{R}$ subject to

$$X^T \cdot A \cdot X - f(x) + \lambda \in I \quad \text{and} \quad A \text{ positive semidefinite.}$$

The latter problem can be easily solved using semidefinite programming, and it always leads to a lower bound λ for the true minimum. Recent unpublished work of Parrilo shows that this lower bound is always tight. We illustrate the basic idea with a trivial example in one variable. Consider the optimization problem

$$\text{Minimize } x \text{ subject to } x^2 - 5x + 6 = 0.$$

Its reformulation as a Sum of Squares problem is as follows:

Maximize λ such that $x - \lambda$ is a sum of squares modulo $\langle x^2 - 5x + 6 \rangle$.

The solution to this semidefinite program is $\lambda = 2$, the desired answer, since

$$(x - 2) \quad = \quad (x - 2)^2 - (x^2 - 5x + 6).$$

I learned the following result from Pablo Parrilo, while both of us enjoyed a few frosty days at the University of Saskatchewan in Saskatoon in March 2002.

THEOREM 7.3. **(Parrilo)** *Let I be a zero-dimensional radical ideal in $S = \mathbb{R}[x_1, \dots, x_n]$, and let $g \in S$ be a polynomial which is nonnegative on $\mathcal{V}(I) \cap \mathbb{R}^n$. Then g is a sum of squares in S/I.*

PROOF. For each real root u of I, pick a polynomial $p_u(x)$ which vanishes on $\mathcal{V}(I) \setminus \{u\}$ but $p_u(u) = 1$. For each pair of imaginary roots $U = \{u, \overline{u}\}$, we pick a polynomial $q_U(x)$ with real coefficients which vanishes on $\mathcal{V}(I) \setminus U$ but $q_U(u) = q_U(\overline{u}) = 1$, and we construct a sum of squares $s_U(x)$ in $S = \mathbb{R}[x_1, \dots, x_n]$ such that g is congruent to s_U modulo $\langle x - u \rangle \cap \langle x - \overline{u} \rangle$. The following polynomial has real coefficients and is obviously a sum of squares:

$$G(x) \quad = \sum_{u \in \mathcal{V}(I) \cap \mathbb{R}^n} g(u) \cdot p_u(x)^2 + \sum_{U \in \mathcal{V}(I) \setminus \mathbb{R}^n} s_U(x) \cdot q_U(x)^2.$$

By construction, the difference $g(x) - G(x)$ vanishes on the complex variety of I. Since I is a radical ideal, the Nullstellensatz implies that $g(x) - G(x)$ lies in I. This proves that the image of $g(x)$ in S/I is a sum of squares. □

COROLLARY 7.4. *If I is radical then the* Real Root Optimization Problem *is solved exactly by its relaxation* Sum of Squares in an Artinian Ring.

7.3. Global Optimization

In this section we discuss the problem of finding the global minimum of a polynomial function on $\mathbb{R}^n$, along the lines presented in more detail in [**PaS01**]. Let f be a polynomial in $\mathbb{R}[x_1, \dots, x_n]$ which attains a minimum value $f^* = f(u)$ as u ranges over all points in $\mathbb{R}^n$. Our goal is to find the real number f^*. Naturally, we also wish to find a point u at which this value is attained, but let us concentrate on finding f^* first.

For example, the following class of polynomials is obviously bounded below and provides a natural test family:

$$(7.9) \qquad f(x_1, \dots, x_n) \quad = \quad x_1^{2d} + x_2^{2d} + \cdots + x_n^{2d} + g(x_1, \dots, x_n)$$

where g is an arbitrary polynomial of degree at most $2d - 1$. In fact, it is possible to deform any instance of our problem to one that lies in this family.

An optimal point $u \in \mathbb{R}^n$ of our minimization problem is a zero of the critical ideal

$$I = \langle \frac{\partial f}{\partial x_1}, \frac{\partial f}{\partial x_2}, \dots, \frac{\partial f}{\partial x_n} \rangle \subseteq S.$$

Hence one possible approach would be to locate the real roots of I and then to minimize f over that set. For instance, in the situation of (7.9), the n partial derivatives of f are already a Gröbner basis of I with respect to the total degree term order, so it should be quite easy to apply any of the methods we already discussed for finding real roots. The trouble is that the Bézout number of the critical ideal I equals $(2d - 1)^n$. This number grows exponentially in n for fixed d. A typical case we might wish to solve in practice is minimizing a quartic in eleven variables. For $2d = 4$ and $n = 11$ we get $(2d - 1)^n = 3^{11} = 177,147$. What we are faced with is doing linear algebra with square matrices of size $177,147$, an impossible task.

Consider instead the following relaxation of our problem. This relaxation was first proposed and studied by N. Shor [**Sho98**].

Global Minimization: SOS Relaxation
Find the largest $\lambda \in \mathbb{R}$ such that $f(x_1, \dots, x_n) - \lambda$ is a sum of squares.

The optimal value λ^* for this problem clearly satisfies $\lambda^* \leq f^*$. It is well-known from the solution to Hilbert's 17th problem that there exist positive polynomials which are not sums of squares. Such polynomials f have the property $\lambda^* < f^*$. For instance, consider Motzkin's polynomial

$$(7.10) \qquad f(x, y) = x^4 y^2 + x^2 y^4 - 3x^2 y^2.$$

For this polynomial we even have $\lambda^* = -\infty$ and $f^* = -1$. However, the experiments in [**PaS01**] suggest that the equality $f^* = \lambda^*$ almost always holds in random instances. Moreover, the semidefinite algorithm for computing λ^* allows us to certify $f^* = \lambda^*$ and to find a matching $u \in \mathbb{R}^n$ in these cases.

The SOS Relaxation can be translated into a semidefinite programming problem where the underlying vector space is the space of polynomials of degree at most d,

$$V = \mathbb{R}[x_1, \dots, x_n]_{\leq d} \simeq \mathbb{R}^{\binom{n+d}{d}}.$$

Note that the dimension $\binom{n+d}{d}$ of this space grows polynomially in n when d is fixed. For a concrete example consider again the problem of minimizing a quartic in eleven variables. Here $d = 2$ and $n = 11$, so we are dealing with symmetric matrices of order $\binom{n+d}{d} = \binom{13}{2} = 78$. This number is considerably smaller than $177,147$. Linear algebra for square matrices of order 78 is quite tractable, and a standard semidefinite programming implementation finds the exact minimum of a random instance of (7.9) in about ten minutes. Here is an explicit example in SOStools, with its SeDuMi output suppressed:

```
>> clear; maple clear; echo on
>> syms x1 x2 x3 x4 x5 x6 x7 x8 x9 x10 x11 lambda;
>> vartable = [x1; x2; x3; x4; x5; x6; x7; x8; x9; x10; x11];
>> prog=sosprogram(vartable,[lambda]);
>> f =   x1^4 + x2^4 + x3^4 + x4^4 + x5^4 + x6^4 + x7^4 + x8^4
        + x9^4 + x10^4 + x11^4 - 59*x9 + 45*x2*x4  - 8*x3*x11
```

```
        - 93*x1^2*x3 + 92*x1*x2*x7 + 43*x1*x4*x7 - 62*x2*x4*x11
        + 77*x4*x5*x8 + 66*x4*x5*x10 + 54*x4*x10^2 - 5*x7*x9*x11;
>> prog=sosineq(prog,f+lambda);
>> prog=sossetobj(prog,lambda);
>> prog=sossolve(prog);
>> SOLlambda=sosgetsol(prog,lambda)


SOLlambda =


.12832e8
```

With a few more lines of SOStools and matlab code, we can now verify that $\lambda^* = 0.12832e8 = f^*$ holds and we can find a point $u \in \mathbb{R}^{11}$ such that $f(u) = f^*$.

7.4. The Real Nullstellensatz

In this section we consider an arbitrary system of polynomial equations and inequalities in n real variables $x = (x_1, \ldots, x_n)$. The Real Nullstellensatz states that such a system either has a solution $u \in \mathbb{R}^n$ or there exists a certain *certificate* that no solution exists. This result can be regarded as a common generalization of Hilbert's Nullstellensatz (for polynomial equations over $\mathbb{C}$) and of Linear Programming Duality (for linear inequalities over $\mathbb{R}$). The former states that a set of polynomials $f_1, \ldots, f_r$ either has a common complex zero or there exists a certificate of nonsolvability of the form $\sum_{i=1}^r p_i f_i = 1$, where the p_i are polynomial multipliers. One of the many equivalent formulations of Linear Programming duality states the following: A system of strict linear inequalities $h_1(x) > 0, \ldots, h_t(x) > 0$ either has a solution, or there exists nonnegative real numbers α_i, not all zero, such that

$$\sum_{i=1}^t \alpha_i \cdot h_i(x) = 0.$$

Such an identity is an obvious certificate of non-solvability.

The Real Nullstellensatz states the existence of certificates for all polynomial systems. The following version of this result is due to Stengle [**Ste74**].

THEOREM 7.5. **(Real Nullstellensatz)** *The system of polynomial equations and inequalities*

$$f_1(x) = 0, \ f_2(x) = 0, \ \ldots, \ f_r(x) = 0,$$
$$g_1(x) \geq 0, \ g_2(x) \geq 0, \ \ldots, \ g_s(x) \geq 0,$$
$$h_1(x) > 0, \ h_2(x) > 0, \ \ldots, \ h_t(x) > 0,$$

either has a solution in $\mathbb{R}^n$, or there exists a polynomial identity

$$\sum_{i=1}^r \alpha_i f_i + \sum_{\nu \in \{0,1\}^s} (\sum_j b_{j\nu}^2) \cdot g_1^{\nu_1} \cdots g_s^{\nu_s}$$
$$+ \sum_{\nu \in \{0,1\}^t} (\sum_j c_{j\nu}^2) \cdot h_1^{\nu_1} \cdots h_t^{\nu_t} + \sum_k d_k^2 + \prod_{l=1}^t h_l^{u_l} = 0,$$

where $u_j \in \mathbb{N}$ and $a_i, b_{j\nu}, c_{j\nu}, d_k$ are polynomials.

It is instructive to consider some special cases of this theorem. For instance, consider the case $r = s = 0$ and $t = 1$. In that case we must decide the solvability of a single strict inequality $h(x) > 0$. This inequality has no solution, i.e., $-h(x)$

is a nonnegative polynomial on $\mathbb{R}^n$, if and only if there exists an identity of the following form

$$(\sum_j c_j)^2 \cdot h + \sum_k d_k^2 + h^u = 0.$$

Here u is either 0 or 1. In either case, we can solve for $-h$ and conclude that $-h$ is a ratio of two sum of squares of polynomials. This expression can obviously be rewritten as a sum of squares of rational functions. This proves:

COROLLARY 7.6. **(Artin's Theorem)** *Every polynomial which is nonnegative on $\mathbb{R}^n$ is a sum of squares of rational functions.*

Another case deserves special attention, namely, the case $s = t = 0$. There are no inequalities, but we are to solve r polynomial equations

(7.11) $$f_1(x) = f_2(x) = \cdots = f_r(x) = 0.$$

For this polynomial system, the expression $\prod_{l=1}^{t} h_l^{u_l}$ in the Real Nullstellensatz certificate is the empty product, which evaluates to 1. Hence if (7.11) has no real solutions, then there exists an identity

$$\sum_{i=1}^{r} \alpha_i f_i + \sum_k d_k^2 + 1 = 0.$$

This implies that Theorem 7.2 holds not just in the zero-dimensional case.

COROLLARY 7.7. *Let I be any ideal in $S = \mathbb{R}[x_1, \ldots, x_n]$ whose real variety $\mathcal{V}(I) \cap \mathbb{R}^n$ is empty. Then -1 is a sum of squares of polynomials modulo I.*

Here is our punchline, first stated in the dissertation of Pablo Parrilo [**Par00**]: *A Real Nullstellensatz certificate of bounded degree can be computed efficiently by semidefinite programming. Here we can also optimize parameters which appear linearly in the coefficients.*

This suggests the following algorithm for deciding a system of polynomial equations and inequalities: decide whether there exists a witness for infeasibility of degree $\leq D$, for some $D \gg 0$. If our system is feasible, then we might like to minimize a polynomial $f(x)$ over the solution set. The *Dth SDP relaxation* would be to ask for the largest real number λ such that the given system together with the inequality $f(x) - \lambda < 0$ has an infeasibility witness of degree D. This generalizes what was proposed in the previous section.

It is possible, at least in principle, to use an a priori bound for the degree D in the Real Nullstellensatz. However, the currently known bounds are still very large. Lombardi and Roy [**Roy01**] recently announced a bound which is triply-exponential in the number n of variables. We hope that such bounds can be further improved, at least for some natural families of polynomial problems arising in optimization.

Here is a very simple example in the plane to illustrate the method:

(7.12) $$f := x - y^2 + 3 \geq 0, \qquad g := y + x^2 + 2 = 0.$$

By the Real Nullstellensatz, the system $\{f \geq 0, g = 0\}$ has no solution (x, y) in the real plane $\mathbb{R}^2$ if and only if there exist polynomials $s_1, s_2, s_3 \in \mathbb{R}[x, y]$ that satisfy the following:

(7.13) $$s_1 + s_2 \cdot f + 1 + s_3 \cdot g \equiv 0, \quad \text{where } s_1 \text{ and } s_2 \text{ are sums of squares.}$$

The Dth SDP relaxation of the polynomial problem $\{f \geq 0, g = 0\}$ asks whether there exists a solution (s_1, s_2, s_3) to (7.13) where the polynomial s_1 has degree $\leq D$ and the polynomials s_2, s_3 have degree $\leq D - 2$. For each fixed integer $D > 0$ this can be tested by semidefinite programming. Specifically, we can use the program SOStools. For $D = 2$ we find the solution

$$s_1 = \tfrac{1}{3} + 2\left(y + \tfrac{3}{2}\right)^2 + 6\left(x - \tfrac{1}{6}\right)^2, \qquad s_2 = 2, \qquad s_3 = -6.$$

The resulting identity (7.13) proves that the polynomial system $\{f \geq 0, g = 0\}$ is inconsistent.

7.5. Symmetric Matrices with Double Eigenvalues

The material in this section is independent from the previous sections. It is inspired by a lecture of Peter Lax in the Berkeley Mathematics Colloquium in February 2001 and by discussions with Beresford Parlett and David Eisenbud.

Given three real symmetric $n \times n$-matrices A_0, A_1 and A_2, how many real matrices of the form $A_0 + xA_1 + yA_2$ have a double eigenvalue? Peter Lax [**Lax98**] proved that there is always at least one such matrix if $n \equiv 2 \,(\mathrm{mod}\,4)$. We shall extend the result of Lax as follows:

THEOREM 7.8. *Given three general symmetric $n \times n$-matrices A_0, A_1, A_2, there are exactly $\binom{n+1}{3}$ pairs of complex numbers (x, y) for which $A_0 + xA_1 + yA_2$ has a critical double eigenvalue.*

A *critical* double eigenvalue is one at which the complex discriminantal hypersurface $\Delta = 0$ (described below) is singular. This theorem implies the result of Lax because all real double eigenvalues are critical, and

$$\binom{n+1}{3} = \tfrac{1}{6} \cdot (n-1) \cdot n \cdot (n+1) \quad \text{is odd if and only if} \quad n \equiv 2 \,(\mathrm{mod}\,4).$$

In the language of algebraic geometry, Theorem 7.8 states that the complexification of the set of all real $n \times n$-symmetric matrices which have a double eigenvalue is a projective variety of degree $\binom{n+1}{3}$. Surprisingly, this variety is not a hypersurface but has codimension 2. We also propose the following refinement of Theorem 7.8 in terms of real algebraic geometry:

CONJECTURE 7.9. *There exist three real symmetric $n \times n$-matrices A_0, A_1 and A_2 such that all $\binom{n+1}{3}$ complex solutions (x, y) to the problem in Theorem 7.8 have real coordinates.*

Consider the case $n = 3$. The *discriminant* Δ of the symmetric matrix

$$(7.14) \qquad\qquad X = \begin{pmatrix} a & b & c \\ b & d & e \\ c & e & f \end{pmatrix}$$

is the discriminant of its characteristic polynomial. This is an irreducible homogeneous polynomial with 123 terms of degree 6 in the indeterminates a, b, c, d, e, f. It can be written as a sum of squares of ten cubic polynomials:

$$
\begin{aligned}
\Delta \;=\; & 2(-acd + acf + b^2c - bde + bef - c^3 + cd^2 - cdf)^2 \\
& + 2(-abd + abf + b^3 - bc^2 + bdf - bf^2 - cde + cef)^2 \\
& + 2(abd - abf + ace - b^3 - bdf + be^2 + bf^2 - cef)^2 \\
& + 2(abe - acd + acf - bde - c^3 + cd^2 - cdf + ce^2)^2 \\
& + 2(-a^2e + abc + ade + aef - bcd - c^2e - def + e^3)^2 \\
& + 2(-a^2e + abc + ade + aef - b^2e - bcf - def + e^3)^2 \\
& + 14(b^2e - bcd + bcf - c^2e)^2 \;+\; 14(ace - bc^2 + be^2 - cde)^2 \\
& + 14(abe - b^2c - bef + ce^2)^2 \;+\; (a^2d - a^2f - ab^2 + ac^2 \\
& \quad - ad^2 + af^2 + b^2d - c^2f + d^2f - de^2 - df^2 + e^2f)^2
\end{aligned}
$$

This polynomial defines a hypersurface in complex projective 5-space $\mathbb{P}^5$. What we are interested in is the complexification of the set of **real** points of this hypersurfaces. (These real points are precisely the real symmetric 3×3-matrices which have a double eigenvalue.) This is the subvariety of $\mathbb{P}^5$ defined by the ten cubic polynomials appearing in the above representation of Δ. These cubics arise from the following determinantal presentation of our variety due to Ilyushechkin [**Ily92**]. Consider the following two 3×6-matrices of linear forms:

$$
F^T \;=\; \begin{pmatrix} -b & b & 0 & a-d & -e & c \\ -c & 0 & c & -e & a-f & b \\ 0 & -e & e & -c & b & d-f \end{pmatrix}
$$

$$
G = \begin{pmatrix} 1 & 1 & 1 & 0 & 0 & 0 \\ a & d & f & b & c & e \\ a^2+b^2+c^2 & b^2+d^2+e^2 & c^2+e^2+f^2 & ab+bd+ce & ac+be+cf & bc+de+ef \end{pmatrix}
$$

The kernel of either matrix equals the row span of the other matrix,

$$
G \cdot F \;=\; \begin{pmatrix} 0 & 0 & 0 \\ 0 & 0 & 0 \\ 0 & 0 & 0 \end{pmatrix}
$$

and this holds even when we take the kernel or row span as modules over the polynomial ring $S = \mathbb{R}[a,b,c,d,e,f]$. In other words, we have an exact sequence of free S-modules:

$$
0 \;\longrightarrow\; S^3 \;\xrightarrow{F}\; S^6 \;\xrightarrow{G}\; S^3.
$$

The set of ten cubics defining our variety coincides with the set of non-zero maximal minors of F and also with the set of non-zero maximal minors of G. For instance, the 12-term cubic in the last summand of our formula for Δ equals the determinant of the last three columns of F or of the first three columns of F. In fact, we have the following identity

$$
\Delta \;=\; \det\!\left(F^T \cdot \mathrm{diag}(2,2,2,1,1,1) \cdot F\right) \;=\; \det\!\left(G \cdot \mathrm{diag}(1,1,1,2,2,2) \cdot G^T\right).
$$

The following two facts are easily checked with `maple`:

1. The subvariety of $\mathbb{P}^5$ defined by the 3×3-minors of either F or G is irreducible of codimension 2 and degree 4.
2. There exists a real 2-plane in $\mathbb{P}^5$ whose intersection with that subvariety consists of four distinct points whose coordinates are real.

These two points are exactly what is claimed for $n = 3$ in our conjecture.

The exact sequence and the above formula for Δ exist for all values of n. This beautiful construction is due to Ilyushechkin [**Ily92**]. We shall describe it in commutative algebra language. We write $\mathrm{Sym}_2(\mathbb{R}^n)$ for the space of symmetric $n \times n$-matrices, and we write $\wedge_2(\mathbb{R}^n)$ for the space of antisymmetric $n \times n$-matrices. These are real vector spaces of dimension $\binom{n+1}{2}$ and $\binom{n}{2}$ respectively. Let $X = (x_{ij})$ be a symmetric $n \times n$-matrix with indeterminate entries. Let $S = \mathbb{R}[X]$ denote the polynomial ring over the real numbers generated by the $\binom{n+1}{2}$ variables x_{ij} and consider the free S-modules

$$\wedge_2(S^n) = \wedge_2(\mathbb{R}^n) \otimes S \quad \text{and} \quad \mathrm{Sym}_2(S^n) = \mathrm{Sym}_2(\mathbb{R}^n) \otimes S.$$

LEMMA 7.10. *The following is an exact sequence of free S-modules:*

$$(7.15) \qquad 0 \longrightarrow \wedge_2(S^n) \xrightarrow{F} \mathrm{Sym}_2(S^n) \xrightarrow{G} S^n \longrightarrow 0,$$

where the maps are defined as

$$F(A) = AX - XA \quad \text{and} \quad G(B) = \big(\mathrm{trace}(BX^i)\big)_{i=0,\dots,n-1}.$$

PROOF. It is easily seen that the sequence is a complex and is generically exact. The fact that it is exact follows from the Buchsbaum-Eisenbud criterion [**Eis95**, Theorem 20.9], or, more specifically, by applying [**Eis95**, Exercise 20.4] to the localizations of S at maximal minors of F. □

The following sum of squares representation is due to Ilyushechkin [**Ily92**].

THEOREM 7.11. *The discriminant of a symmetric $n \times n$-matrix X equals*

$$(7.16) \qquad \Delta \;=\; \det\big(\mathbf{F}^T \cdot \mathbf{F}\big) \;=\; \det\big(\mathbf{G} \cdot \mathbf{G}^T\big),$$

where $\mathbf{F}$ and $\mathbf{G}$ are matrices representing the maps F and G in suitable bases.

We now come to the proof of Theorem 7.8.

PROOF. The dual sequence to (7.15) is also exact and it provides a minimal free resolution of the module $\mathrm{coker}(F^T)$. This module is Cohen-Macaulay of codimension 2 and the resolution can be written with degree shifts as follows:

$$0 \longrightarrow \oplus_{i=1}^n S(-i) \xrightarrow{G^T} S(-1)^{\binom{n+1}{2}} \xrightarrow{F^T} S^{\binom{n}{2}}.$$

The Hilbert series of the shifted polynomial ring S is $x^i \cdot (1-x)^{-\binom{n+1}{2}}$. The Hilbert series of the module $S(-1)^{\binom{n+1}{2}}$ is $\binom{n+1}{2} \cdot x \cdot (1-x)^{-\binom{n+1}{2}}$. The Hilbert series of the module $\mathrm{coker}(F^T)$ is the alternating sum of the Hilbert series of the modules in (7.16), and it equals

$$\left\{ \binom{n}{2} - \binom{n+1}{2} \cdot x + \sum_{i=1}^n x^i \right\} \cdot (1-x)^{-\binom{n+1}{2}}.$$

Removing a factor of $(1-x)^2$ from the parenthesized sum, we can rewrite this expression for the Hilbert series of $\mathrm{coker}(F^T)$ as follows:

$$\left\{ \sum_{i=2}^n \binom{i}{2} x^{n-i} \right\} \cdot (1-x)^{-\binom{n+1}{2}+2}.$$

We know already that $\operatorname{coker}(F^T)$ is a Cohen-Macaulay module of codimension 2. Therefore we can conclude the following formula for its degree:

$$(7.17) \qquad \text{degree}\left(\operatorname{coker}(F^T)\right) \;=\; \sum_{i=2}^{n} \binom{i}{2} \;=\; \binom{n+1}{3}.$$

Finally, let X be the support of the module $\operatorname{coker}(F^T)$. Thus X is precisely our codimension 2 variety which is cut out by the vanishing of the maximal minors of the matrix F. The generic fiber of the vector bundle on X represented by $\operatorname{coker}(F^T)$ is a one-dimensional space, since the rank drop of the matrix F is only one if the underlying symmetric matrix has only one double eigenvalue and $n-2$ distinct eigenvalues. We conclude that the degree of X equals the degree of the module $\operatorname{coker}(F^T)$. The identity in (7.17) now completes the proof of Theorem 7.8. $\qquad\square$

7.6. Exercises

(1) Solve the following one-variable problem using SOStools: Minimize x subject to $x^{11} - 6x^7 + x^2 + 1 = 0$.

(2) Take $g(x_1, x_2, \ldots, x_{10})$ to be your favorite inhomogeneous polynomial of degree three in ten variables. Make sure it looks random enough. Use SOStools to find the global minimum in $\mathbb{R}^{10}$ of the quartic polynomial

$$x_1^4 + x_2^4 + \cdots + x_{10}^4 \;+\; g(x_1, x_2, \ldots, x_{10}).$$

(3) Suppose that two polynomial inequalities $f(x, y, z) \geq 0$ and $g(x, y, z) \geq 0$ have no common solution in $\mathbb{R}^3$. What does the real Nullstellensatz say about this situation? How would you compute a witness?

(4) Nina and Pascal stand in the playground 10 meters apart and they each hold a ball of radius 10 cm. Suddenly they throw their balls at each other in a straight line at the same constant speed, say, 1 meter per second. At what time (measured in seconds) will their balls first hit? Formulate this using polynomial equations (and inequalities?) and explain how semidefinite programming can be used to solve it. Nina next suggests to Pascal that they replace their balls by more interesting semialgebraic objects, for instance, those defined by $x^{a_i} + y^{a_2} + z^{a_3} \leq 1$ for arbitrary integers a_1, a_2, a_3. Update your model and your SDP.

(5) Find the smallest positive real number a such that the following three equations have a common solution in $\mathbb{R}^3$:

$$x^6 + 1 + ay^2 + az \;=\; y^6 + 1 + az^2 + ax$$
$$=\; z^6 + 1 + ax^2 + ay \;=\; 0.$$

(6) What does the Duality Theorem of Semidefinite Programming say? What is the dual solution to the SDP problem which asks for a sum of squares representation of $f(x) - \lambda$? Can you explain the cryptic sentence "With a few more lines..." at the end of the third section?

(7) Write the discriminant Δ of the symmetric 3×3-matrix (7.14) as a sum of squares, where the number of squares is as small as possible.

(8) Consider the following configuration of eight points and eight lines in the projective plane, where each line contains three points and each point lies on three lines. The collinear triples of points are

$$124 \quad 235 \quad 346 \quad 457 \quad 568 \quad 671 \quad 782 \quad 813.$$

No other triple is collinear. Prove that such a configuration exists over the complex numbers $\mathbb{C}$ but does not exist over the real numbers $\mathbb{R}$. Provide a Real Nullstellensatz certificate for the non-existence over $\mathbb{R}$.

(9) Compute the discriminant of the generic real symmetric 4×4-matrix. Prove Conjecture 7.9 for $n = 4$.

CHAPTER 8

Polynomial Systems in Statistics

In this chapter we encounter three classes of polynomial systems arising in statistics and probability. The first one concerns the algebraic conditions characterizing conditional independence statements for discrete random variables. Computational algebra provides useful tools for analyzing such statements and for making inferences about conditional independence. A particular emphasis is placed on *graphical models* in the sense of Lauritzen's book [**Lau96**]. The second class consists of binomial equations which represent certain moves for Markov chains. We discuss joint work with Diaconis and Eisenbud [**DES98**] on the use of primary decomposition for quantifying the connectivity of Markov chains. The third class consists of the polynomial equations satisfied by the maximum likelihood equations in a log-linear model. We present a classical numerical algorithm, called *iterative proportional scaling*, for solving the maximum likelihood equations. For additional background regarding the use of Gröbner bases in statistics we refer to the book *Algebraic Statistics* by Pistone, Riccomagno and Wynn [**PRW01**].

8.1. Conditional Independence

The set of probability distributions that satisfy a conditional independence statement is the zero set of certain polynomials and can hence be studied using methods from algebraic geometry. We call such a set an *independence variety*. In what follows we describe the polynomials defining independence varieties and we present some fundamental algebraic problems about them.

Let $X_1, \ldots, X_n$ denote discrete random variables, where X_i takes values in the set $[d_i] = \{1, 2, \ldots, d_i\}$. We write $D = [d_1] \times [d_2] \times \cdots \times [d_n]$ so that $\mathbb{R}^D$ denotes the real vector space of n-dimensional tables of format $d_1 \times d_2 \times \cdots \times d_n$. We introduce an indeterminate $p_{u_1 u_2 \ldots u_n}$ which represents the probability of the event $X_1 = u_1, X_2 = u_2, \ldots, X_n = u_n$. These indeterminates generate the ring $\mathbb{R}[D]$ of polynomial functions on the space of tables $\mathbb{R}^D$.

A conditional independence statement about $X_1, X_2, \ldots, X_n$ has the form

(8.1)   *A is independent of B given C*   (in symbols: $A \perp B \,|\, C$)

where A, B and C are pairwise disjoint subsets of $\{X_1, \ldots, X_n\}$. If C is the empty set then (8.1) just reads *A is independent of B*.

PROPOSITION 8.1. *The independence statement (8.1) translates into a set of quadratic polynomials in $\mathbb{R}[D]$ indexed by*

(8.2)
$$\binom{\prod_{X_i \in A}[d_i]}{2} \times \binom{\prod_{X_j \in B}[d_j]}{2} \times \prod_{X_k \in C}[d_k].$$

PROOF. Picking any element of the set (8.2) means choosing two distinct elements a and a' in $\prod_{X_i \in A}[d_i]$, two distinct elements b and b' in $\prod_{X_j \in B}[d_j]$, and an element c in $\prod_{X_k \in C}[d_k]$. This determines an expression involving probabilities:

$$\text{Prob}(A = a, B = b, C = c) \cdot \text{Prob}(A = a', B = b', C = c)$$
$$- \quad \text{Prob}(A = a', B = b, C = c) \cdot \text{Prob}(A = a, B = b', C = c).$$

The vanishing of this expression, for all a, a', b, b', c, is equivalent to the validity of the independence statement $A \perp B \,|\, C$.

To get our quadrics indexed by (8.2), we translate each of the probabilities $\text{Prob}(\,\cdots\cdots\,)$ into a linear polynomial in $\mathbb{R}[D]$. Namely, $\text{Prob}(A = a, B = b, C = c)$ equals the sum of all indeterminates $p_{u_1 u_2 \cdots u_n}$ which satisfy:

- for all $X_i \in A$, the X_i-coordinate of a equals u_i,
- for all $X_j \in B$, the X_j-coordinate of b equals u_j, and
- for all $X_k \in C$, the X_k-coordinate of c equals u_k.

We define $I_{A \perp B | C}$ to be the ideal in the polynomial ring $\mathbb{R}[D]$ which is generated by the quadratic polynomials indexed by (8.2) and described above. $\qquad\square$

We illustrate the definition of the ideal $I_{A \perp B | C}$ with some simple examples. Take $n = 3$ and $d_1 = d_2 = d_3 = 2$, so that $\mathbb{R}^D$ is the 8-dimensional space of $2 \times 2 \times 2$-tables, and

$$\mathbb{R}[D] \quad = \quad \mathbb{R}[p_{111}, p_{112}, p_{121}, p_{122}, p_{211}, p_{212}, p_{221}, p_{222}].$$

The statement $\{X_2\}$ *is independent of* $\{X_3\}$ *given* $\{X_1\}$ describes the ideal

$$(8.3) \qquad I_{X_2 \perp X_3 | X_1} \quad = \quad \langle p_{111}p_{122} - p_{112}p_{121}, p_{211}p_{222} - p_{212}p_{221} \rangle.$$

The statement $\{X_2\}$ *is independent of* $\{X_3\}$ determines the principal ideal

$$(8.4) \quad I_{X_2 \perp X_3} \quad = \quad \langle\, (p_{111} + p_{211})(p_{122} + p_{222}) - (p_{112} + p_{212})(p_{121} + p_{221}) \,\rangle.$$

The ideal $I_{X_1 \perp \{X_2, X_3\}}$ representing the statement $\{X_1\}$ *is independent of* $\{X_2, X_3\}$ is generated by the six 2×2-subdeterminants of the 2×4-matrix

$$(8.5) \qquad\qquad \begin{pmatrix} p_{111} & p_{112} & p_{121} & p_{122} \\ p_{211} & p_{212} & p_{221} & p_{222} \end{pmatrix}$$

The *variety* $V_{A \perp B | C}$ is defined as the set of common zeros in $\mathbb{C}^D$ of the polynomials in $I_{A \perp B | C}$. Thus $V_{A \perp B | C}$ is a set of complex $d_1 \times \cdots \times d_n$-tables, but in statistics applications we only care about the subset $V_{A \perp B | C}^{\geq 0}$ of tables whose entries are non-negative reals. These correspond to probability distributions that satisfy the independence fact $A \perp B | C$. We also consider the subsets $V_{A \perp B | C}^{\mathbb{R}}$ of real tables and $V_{A \perp B | C}^{>0}$ of strictly positive tables. The variety $V_{A \perp B | C}$ is irreducible because the ideal $I_{A \perp B | C}$ is a prime ideal.

LEMMA 8.2. *For any independence statement (8.1), the ideal $I_{A \perp B | C}$ prime.*

PROOF. This is derived from the well-known fact that the ideal generated by all 2×2-subdeterminants of a matrix of indeterminates is a prime ideal. Indeed, for fixed $c \in \prod_{X_k \in C}[d_k]$, we can form the matrix with entries

$$\text{Prob}(A = a, B = b, C = c).$$

The rows of this matrix are indexed by $\prod_{X_i \in A}[d_i]$ and the columns are indexed by $\prod_{X_j \in B}[d_j]$. The entries in this matrix are linear forms in $\mathbb{R}[D]$. These linear forms are sums of pairwise disjoint sets of indeterminates. Hence the ideal of 2×2-minors is a prime ideal in $\mathbb{R}[D]$. Our ideal $I_{A \perp B | C}$ is the sum of these prime ideals, as c ranges over $\prod_{X_k \in C}[d_k]$. Again, the sets of indeterminates appearing among the generators of each summand are pairwise disjoint, and hence the resulting ideal $I_{A \perp B | C}$ is prime as well. $\qquad \square$

Many statistical models for categorical data can be described by a finite set of independence statements (8.1). An *independence model* is such a set:

$$\mathcal{M} = \left\{ A^{(1)} \perp B^{(1)} | C^{(1)}, A^{(2)} \perp B^{(2)} | C^{(2)}, \ldots, A^{(m)} \perp B^{(m)} | C^{(m)} \right\}.$$

This class of models includes all directed and undirected graphical models, to be discussed below. The ideal of the model $\mathcal{M}$ is defined as the sum

$$I_{\mathcal{M}} = I_{A^{(1)} \perp B^{(1)} | C^{(1)}} + I_{A^{(2)} \perp B^{(2)} | C^{(2)}} + \cdots + I_{A^{(m)} \perp B^{(m)} | C^{(m)}}.$$

The *independence variety* is the set of tables which satisfy these polynomials:

$$V_{\mathcal{M}} = V_{A^{(1)} \perp B^{(1)} | C^{(1)}} \cap V_{A^{(2)} \perp B^{(2)} | C^{(2)}} \cap \cdots \cap V_{A^{(m)} \perp B^{(m)} | C^{(m)}}.$$

PROBLEM 8.3. *For which models $\mathcal{M}$ is the independence ideal $I_{\mathcal{M}}$ a prime ideal, and for which models $\mathcal{M}$ is the independence variety $V_{\mathcal{M}}$ irreducible?*

As an example consider the following model for binary random variables:

$$\text{MyModel} = \left\{ X_2 \perp X_3, X_1 \perp \{X_2, X_3\} \right\}$$

The ideal of this model is neither prime nor radical. It decomposes as

$$(8.6) \quad I_{\text{MyModel}} = I_{X_2 \perp X_3} + I_{X_1 \perp \{X_2, X_3\}} = I_{\text{Segre}} \cap \left(P^2 + I_{X_1 \perp \{X_2, X_3\}} \right)$$

where the first component is the independence ideal for the model

$$\text{Segre} = \left\{ X_1 \perp \{X_2, X_3\}, X_2 \perp \{X_1, X_3\}, X_3 \perp \{X_1, X_2\} \right\}$$

Thus I_{Segre} is the prime ideal of the Segre embedding of $\mathbb{P}^1 \times \mathbb{P}^1 \times \mathbb{P}^1$ into $\mathbb{P}^7$. The second component in (8.6) is a primary ideal with radical

$$P = \langle p_{111} + p_{211}, p_{112} + p_{212}, p_{121} + p_{221}, p_{122} + p_{222} \rangle.$$

Since this ideal has no non-trivial zeros in the positive orthant, we conclude that MyModel is equivalent to the complete independence model Segre.

$$V^{\geq 0}_{\text{MyModel}} = V^{\geq 0}_{\text{Segre}}.$$

Thus the equation (8.6) proves the following rule for binary random variables:

$$(8.7) \qquad X_2 \perp X_3 \text{ and } X_1 \perp \{X_2, X_3\} \text{ implies } X_2 \perp \{X_1, X_3\}$$

It would be a nice project to determine the primary decompositions for all models on few random variables, say $n \leq 5$. The combinatorial techniques introduced by Hoşten and Shapiro [**HS00**] should be particularly helpful for this. A catalogue of all resulting rules is likely to be useful for applications in artificial intelligence.

Clearly, some of the rules will be subject to the hypothesis that all probabilities involved be strictly positive. A good example is Proposition 3.1 in [**Lau96**, page 29], which states that, for strictly positive densities,

$$X_1 \perp X_2 | X_3 \text{ and } X_1 \perp X_3 | X_2 \text{ implies } X_1 \perp \{X_2, X_3\}.$$

It corresponds to the primary decomposition

$$I_{X_1 \perp X_2 \mid X_3} + I_{X_1 \perp X_3 \mid X_2}$$
$$= I_{X_1 \perp \{X_2, X_3\}} \cap \langle p_{111}, p_{122}, p_{211}, p_{222} \rangle \cap \langle p_{112}, p_{121}, p_{212}, p_{221} \rangle.$$

The conditional independence statement (8.1) is called *saturated* if

$$A \cup B \cup C = \{X_1, X_2, \dots, X_n\}.$$

In that case $I_{A \perp B \mid C}$ is a generated by differences of monomials. Such an ideal is called a *binomial ideal*. Recall from Chapter 5 that every binomial ideal has a primary decomposition into binomial ideals.

PROPOSITION 8.4. *The ideal $I_\mathcal{M}$ is a binomial ideal if and only if the model $\mathcal{M}$ consists of saturated independence statements.*

8.2. Graphical Models

The property that the ideal $I_\mathcal{M}$ is binomial holds for the important class of *undirected graphical models*. Let G be an undirected graph with vertices $X_1, X_2, \dots, X_n$. From the graph G one derives three natural sets of saturated independence conditions:

$$(8.8) \qquad \text{pairwise}(G) \subseteq \text{local}(G) \subseteq \text{global}(G).$$

See ([**Lau96**], page 32) for details and definitions. For instance, pairwise(G) consists of all independence statements

$$X_i \perp X_j \mid \{X_1, \dots, X_n\} \backslash \{X_i, X_j\}$$

where X_i and X_j are **not** connected by an edge in G. It is known that the ideal $I_{global(G)}$ is prime if and only if G is a decomposable graph. This situation was studied by Takken [**Tak99**], Dobra and Sullivant [**DS02**] and Geiger, Meek and Sturmfels [**GMS02**]. These authors showed that the quadratic generators of $I_{\text{global}(G)}$ form a Gröbner basis.

PROBLEM 8.5. *For decomposable graphical models G, including chains, study the primary decomposition of the binomial ideals $I_{\text{pairwise}(G)}$ and $I_{\text{local}(G)}$.*

For a general undirected graph G, the following problem makes sense:

PROBLEM 8.6. *Study the primary decomposition of the ideal $I_{\text{global}(G)}$.*

The most important component in this decomposition is the prime ideal

$$(8.9) \qquad T_G := (I_{\text{pairwise}(G)} : p^\infty) = (I_{\text{global}(G)} : p^\infty).$$

This equation follows from the Hammersley-Clifford Theorem [**Lau96**, Theorem 3.9]. Here p denotes the product of all the indeterminates $p_{u_1 u_2 \dots u_n}$. The ideal T_G is called the *toric ideal* of the graphical model G. The most basic invariants of any projective variety are its dimension and its degree. There is an easy formula for the dimension of the variety of T_G, but its degree remains mysterious:

PROBLEM 8.7. *What is the degree of the toric ideal T_G of a graphical model?*

EXAMPLE 8.8. We illustrate these definitions and problems for the graph G which is the 4-chain $X_1 - X_2 - X_3 - X_4$. Here each X_i is a binary random variable. The ideal coding the pairwise Markov property equals $I_{\text{pairwise}(G)} =$

$$\langle p_{1121}p_{2111} - p_{1111}p_{2121}, p_{1112}p_{2111} - p_{1111}p_{2112}, p_{1112}p_{1211} - p_{1111}p_{1212},$$
$$p_{1122}p_{2112} - p_{1112}p_{2122}, p_{1122}p_{2121} - p_{1121}p_{2122}, p_{1122}p_{1221} - p_{1121}p_{1222},$$
$$p_{1221}p_{2211} - p_{1211}p_{2221}, p_{1212}p_{2211} - p_{1211}p_{2212}, p_{2112}p_{2211} - p_{2111}p_{2212},$$
$$p_{1222}p_{2212} - p_{1212}p_{2222}, p_{1222}p_{2221} - p_{1221}p_{2222}, p_{2122}p_{2221} - p_{2121}p_{2222} \rangle$$

Solving these twelve binomial equations is not so easy. First, $I_{\text{pairwise}(G)}$ is not a radical ideal, which means that there exists a polynomial f with $f^2 \in I_{\text{pairwise}(G)}$ but $f \notin I_{\text{pairwise}(G)}$. Using the division algorithm modulo $I_{\text{pairwise}(G)}$, one checks that the following binomial enjoys this property

$$f = p_{1111}p_{1212}p_{1222}p_{2121} - p_{1111}p_{1212}p_{1221}p_{2122}.$$

An ideal basis of the radical of $I_{\text{pairwise}(G)}$ consists of the 12 quadrics and eight quartics such as f. The variety defined by $I_{\text{pairwise}(G)}$ has 25 irreducible components. One these components is defined by the toric ideal

$$T_G = I_{\text{pairwise}(G)} + \langle p_{1122}p_{2221} - p_{1121}p_{2222}, p_{1221}p_{2212} - p_{1212}p_{2221},$$
$$p_{1222}p_{2211} - p_{1211}p_{2222}, p_{1112}p_{2211} - p_{1111}p_{2112}, p_{1222}p_{2121} - p_{1221}p_{2122},$$
$$p_{1121}p_{2112} - p_{1112}p_{2121}, p_{1212}p_{2111} - p_{1211}p_{2112}, p_{1122}p_{2111} - p_{1111}p_{2122} \rangle.$$

The twenty binomial generators of the toric ideal T_G form a Gröbner basis. The corresponding toric variety in $\mathbb{P}^{15}$ has dimension 7 and degree 34. Each of the other 24 minimal primes of $I_{\text{pairwise}(G)}$ is generated by a subset of the indeterminates. More precisely, among the components of our model there are four linear subspaces of dimension eight, such as the variety of

$$\langle p_{1111}, p_{1112}, p_{1121}, p_{1122}, p_{2211}, p_{2212}, p_{2221}, p_{2222} \rangle,$$

there are 16 linear subspaces of dimension six, such as the variety of

$$\langle p_{1111}, p_{1112}, p_{1121}, p_{1122}, p_{1212}, p_{1221}, p_{2112}, p_{2212}, p_{2221}, p_{2222} \rangle,$$

and there are four linear subspaces of dimension four, such as the variety of

$$(8.10) \quad \langle p_{1111}, p_{1112}, p_{1121}, p_{1211}, p_{1221}, p_{1222}, p_{2112}, p_{2121}, p_{2122}, p_{2211}, p_{2212}, p_{2222} \rangle.$$

Each of these irreducible components gives a simplex of probability distributions which satisfies the pairwise Markov property but does not factor in the four-chain model. For instance, the ideal in (8.10) represents the tetrahedron with vertices indexed by the four missing strings 1122, 1212, 2111 and 2221.

In this example, the solution to Problem 8.7 is the number 34. The degree of any projective toric variety equals the normalized volume of the associated convex polytope ([**Ful93**], Section 5.3). In the setting of [**Stu95**], this polytope is the convex hull of the columns of an integer matrix A. The integer matrix A which encodes the toric ideal T_G equals

1111	1112	1121	1122	1211	1212	1221	1222	2111	2112	2121	2122	2211	2212	2221	2222
1	1	1	1	0	0	0	0	0	0	0	0	0	0	0	0
0	0	0	0	1	1	1	1	0	0	0	0	0	0	0	0
0	0	0	0	0	0	0	0	1	1	1	1	0	0	0	0
0	0	0	0	0	0	0	0	0	0	0	0	1	1	1	1
1	1	0	0	0	0	0	0	1	1	0	0	0	0	0	0
0	0	1	1	0	0	0	0	0	0	1	1	0	0	0	0
0	0	0	0	1	1	0	0	0	0	0	0	1	1	0	0
0	0	0	0	0	0	1	1	0	0	0	0	0	0	1	1
1	0	0	0	1	0	0	0	1	0	0	0	1	0	0	0
0	1	0	0	0	1	0	0	0	1	0	0	0	1	0	0
0	0	1	0	0	0	1	0	0	0	1	0	0	0	1	0
0	0	0	1	0	0	0	1	0	0	0	1	0	0	0	1

The convex hull of the 16 columns of this matrix is a 7-dimensional polytope in $\mathbb{R}^{12}$. The normalized volume of this polytope equals 34.

We briefly rephrase some of the algebra in this example in the usual statistical notation for graphical models as in [**Lau96**]. The sufficient statistics of this graphical model are given by the three vectors $\mathbf{n}_{1,2}, \mathbf{n}_{2,3}, \mathbf{n}_{3,4}$, corresponding to the cliques of G. These functions are put in the matrix A with rows indexed by their twelve components $\mathbf{n}_{11\bullet\bullet}, \mathbf{n}_{12\bullet\bullet}, \ldots, \mathbf{n}_{\bullet\bullet22}$. If $A_{(\cdot, ijkl)}$ is the column of A indexed by $ijkl$, the probabilities in the log-linear model could be parametrized by

$$p_{ijkl} \quad = \quad \frac{1}{z_\theta} \cdot \exp\big((\theta_{12}|\theta_{23}|\theta_{34}) \cdot A_{(\cdot, ijkl)}\big),$$

where θ_{12} is a real vector of four components and z_θ is a normalizing constant. This seems at first to have 12 parameters, but the matrix A has rank 8 only, so four constraints can be imposed for parameter identifiability. This corresponds to the dimension 8 of the affine variety defined by the ideal T_G of algebraic relations among the p_{ijkl}. Since the constant vector is in the row space of A, and the probabilities sum to one, there is one further constraint and there are in fact 7 free parameters. The number 7 is the dimension of the projective variety defined by T_G.   □

We can generalize the definition of the toric ideal T_G from graphical models to arbitrary independence models $\mathcal{M}$. For any subset A of $\{X_1, \ldots, X_n\}$ and any element a of $\prod_{X_i \in A}[d_i]$, we consider the linear form $\mathrm{Prob}(A = a)$ which is the sum of all indeterminates $p_{u_1 u_2 \cdots u_n}$ such that the X_i-coordinate of a equals u_i for all $X_i \in A$. Let $\mathbf{p}$ denote the product of all such linear forms $\mathrm{Prob}(A = a)$. We define the following ideal by saturation:

$$T_{\mathcal{M}} \quad = \quad (I_{\mathcal{M}} : \mathbf{p}^\infty).$$

PROBLEM 8.9. *Is $T_{\mathcal{M}}$ the vanishing ideal of the set of those probability distributions which are limits of strictly positive distributions which satisfy $\mathcal{M}$.*

An affirmative answer to this question would imply that $T_{\mathcal{M}}$ is always a radical ideal. Perhaps it is even always prime? A nice example is the model $\mathcal{M} = \{X_1 \perp X_2, X_1 \perp X_3, X_2 \perp X_3\}$ for three binary random variables. Its ideal $I_{\mathcal{M}}$ is the intersection of four prime ideals, the last one of which is $T_{\mathcal{M}}$:

$$
\begin{aligned}
I_{\mathcal{M}} \quad = \quad & \langle\, \mathrm{Prob}(X_1 = 1), \mathrm{Prob}(X_1 = 2), \mathrm{Prob}(X_2 = 1), \mathrm{Prob}(X_2 = 2) \,\rangle \\
\cap \quad & \langle\, \mathrm{Prob}(X_1 = 1), \mathrm{Prob}(X_1 = 2), \mathrm{Prob}(X_3 = 1), \mathrm{Prob}(X_3 = 2) \,\rangle \\
\cap \quad & \langle\, \mathrm{Prob}(X_2 = 1), \mathrm{Prob}(X_2 = 2), \mathrm{Prob}(X_3 = 1), \mathrm{Prob}(X_3 = 2) \,\rangle \\
\cap \quad & \langle\, \underline{p_{112}p_{221}} + p_{112}p_{222} - p_{121}p_{212} - p_{121}p_{222} - p_{122}p_{212} + p_{122}p_{221}, \\
& \quad \underline{p_{121}p_{212}} - p_{111}p_{221} - p_{111}p_{222} + p_{121}p_{211} - p_{211}p_{222} + p_{212}p_{221}, \\
& \quad \underline{p_{111}p_{212}} + p_{111}p_{222} - p_{112}p_{211} - p_{112}p_{221} + p_{211}p_{222} - p_{212}p_{221}, \\
& \quad \underline{p_{111}p_{221}} + p_{111}p_{222} - p_{121}p_{211} + p_{121}p_{212} - p_{122}p_{211} - p_{122}p_{221}, \\
& \quad \underline{p_{111}p_{122}} + p_{111}p_{222} - p_{112}p_{121} - p_{112}p_{221} + p_{121}p_{222} - p_{122}p_{221} \,\rangle.
\end{aligned}
$$

The five generators for $T_{\mathcal{M}}$ are a Gröbner basis with leading terms underlined.

An important class of non-saturated independence models arise from directed graphs as in [**Lau96**, Section 3.2.2]. Let G be an acyclic directed graph with vertices $X_1, X_2, \ldots, X_n$. For any vertex X_i, let $\mathrm{pa}(X_i)$ denote the set of parents of X_i in G and let $\mathrm{nd}(X_i)$ denote the set of non-descendants of X_i in G which are not parents of X_i. The *directed graphical model* of G is described by the following set of independence statements:

$$
\mathrm{local}(G) \quad = \quad \big\{\, X_i \perp \mathrm{nd}(X_i) \,|\, \mathrm{pa}(X_i) \ : \ i = 1, 2, \ldots, n \,\big\}.
$$

Theorem 3.27 in Lauritzen's book [**Lau96**] states that this model is well-behaved, in the sense that every non-negative solution to $I_{\mathrm{local}(G)}$ admits a recursive factorization according to the model G. However, this is no longer true when we allow negative real coordinates. We have the following algebraic result.

PROPOSITION 8.10. *The real variety of the ideal $I_{\mathrm{local}(G)}$ describing the local Markov property of a directed graphical model G is generally not irreducible.*

We prove this proposition by means of an explicit example. Consider the directed graph G on four binary random variables with four edges $X_1 \to X_2, X_1 \to X_3, X_2 \to X_4$ and $X_3 \to X_4$. Here

$$
\mathrm{local}(G) \quad = \quad \big\{\, X_2 \perp X_3 \,|\, X_1, \ X_4 \perp X_1 \,|\, \{X_2, X_3\} \,\big\}.
$$

The ideal associated with this directed graphical model equals

$$
\begin{aligned}
I_{\mathrm{local}(G)} \quad = \quad & \langle\, (p_{1111} + p_{1112})(p_{1221} + p_{1222}) - (p_{1121} + p_{1122})(p_{1211} + p_{1212}), \\
& \quad (p_{2111} + p_{2112})(p_{2221} + p_{2222}) - (p_{2121} + p_{2122})(p_{2211} + p_{2212}), \\
& \quad p_{1111}p_{2112} - p_{1112}p_{2111}, \ p_{1121}p_{2122} - p_{1122}p_{2121}, \\
& \quad p_{1211}p_{2212} - p_{1212}p_{2211}, \ p_{1221}p_{2222} - p_{1222}p_{2221} \,\rangle
\end{aligned}
$$

This ideal is a complete intersection, so its variety has codimension six. The six quadrics form a Gröbner basis with respect to a suitable monomial order. Hence $I_{\mathrm{local}}(G)$ is a radical ideal by Proposition 5.3.

We do not know the answer to the following question in general.

PROBLEM 8.11. *Does the ideal $I_{\mathrm{local}(G)}$ of a directed graphical model G always have a quadratic Gröbner basis? Is it always radical?*

Returning to our example, we now apply the techniques of Chapter 5 to find that here $I_{\mathrm{local}(G)}$ is the irredundant intersection of five prime ideals:

$$
(8.11) \qquad I_{\mathrm{local}(G)} \quad = \quad P_{\bullet 1 \bullet \bullet} \cap P_{\bullet \bullet 1 \bullet} \cap P_{\bullet 2 \bullet \bullet} \cap P_{\bullet \bullet 2 \bullet} \cap T_{\mathrm{local}(G)}.
$$

The first four components are extraneous as far as statistics goes. They are

$$P_{\bullet 1\bullet\bullet} = \langle p_{2121} + p_{2122}, p_{2111} + p_{2112}, p_{1121} + p_{1122}, p_{1111} + p_{1112} \rangle + I_{\text{local}(G)},$$
$$P_{\bullet\bullet 1\bullet} = \langle p_{2211} + p_{2212}, p_{2111} + p_{2112}, p_{1211} + p_{1212}, p_{1111} + p_{1112} \rangle + I_{\text{local}(G)},$$
$$P_{\bullet 2\bullet\bullet} = \langle p_{2221} + p_{2222}, p_{2211} + p_{2212}, p_{1221} + p_{1222}, p_{1211} + p_{1212} \rangle + I_{\text{local}(G)},$$
$$P_{\bullet\bullet 2\bullet} = \langle p_{2221} + p_{2222}, p_{2121} + p_{2122}, p_{1221} + p_{1222}, p_{1121} + p_{1122} \rangle + I_{\text{local}(G)}.$$

The important prime component has codimension 6 and degree 48:

$$(8.12) \qquad\qquad T_{\text{local}(G)} \;=\; \left(I_{\text{local}(G)} : \mathbf{p}^{\infty} \right).$$

As defined above, here $\mathbf{p}$ denotes the product of the 16 unknowns p_{ijkl} and the 8 eight parenthesized expressions. We find that $T_{\text{local}(G)}$ is minimally generated by 9 quartics modulo $I_{\text{local}(G)}$. For the sake of symmetry, we prefer to display the following redundant set of 16 quartic generators: $T_{\text{local}(G)} \;=\;$

$$I_{\text{local}(G)} \;+\; \left\langle\, p_{111i}p_{212j}p_{221k}p_{122l} - p_{211i}p_{112j}p_{121k}p_{222l} \,:\, i,j,k,l \in \{1,2\} \,\right\rangle.$$

The decomposition (8.11) easily gives a proof of Proposition 8.10. Each of the ideals $P_{\bullet 1\bullet\bullet}$, $P_{\bullet\bullet 1\bullet}$, $P_{\bullet 2\bullet\bullet}$ and $P_{\bullet\bullet 2\bullet}$ defines a variety in $\mathbb{R}^{16} = \mathbb{R}^{2\times2\times2\times2}$ which has points not in the variety of $T_{\text{local}(G)}$. For the sake of concreteness, here is a zero of $I_{\text{local}(G)}$ which is not a zero of $T_{\text{local}(G)}$.

$$p_{1111} = -1\,,\; p_{1112} = 1\,,\; p_{1121} = 1\,,\; p_{1122} = -1\,,$$
$$p_{1211} = 1\,,\; p_{1212} = -1\,,\; p_{1221} = 1\,,\; p_{1222} = -1\,,$$
$$p_{2111} = 1\,,\; p_{2112} = -1\,,\; p_{2121} = 1\,,\; p_{2122} = -1\,,$$
$$p_{2211} = 1\,,\; p_{2212} = -1\,,\; p_{2221} = 1\,,\; p_{2222} = -1\,.$$

In other words, this real vector satisfies the independence conditions given in local(G) but it does not have a recursive factorization in the model G.

Experts in log-linear models will note that these 16 quartic generators of $T_{\text{local}(G)}$ express independence in the *hierarchical model* consisting of the triangle $\{2,3,4\}$ and the edges $\{1,2\}$ and $\{1,3\}$. It would be very interesting to determine the minimal generators of $T_{\text{local}(G)}$ for larger directed graphs G. We also do not know the answer to the following question:

PROBLEM 8.12. *Is the ideal $T_{\text{local}(G)}$ in (8.12) prime for every directed graph G?*

The answer is "yes" for our particular example. We will prove this by showing that $T_{\text{local}(G)}$ is the vanishing ideal of an irreducible variety, namely, the variety of all points in $\mathbb{C}^{16} = \mathbb{C}^{2\times2\times2\times2}$ which admit a recursive factorization as described in [**Lau96**, Section 3.2.2]. We write this factorization in algebraic notation as a homomorphism of polynomial rings.

We introduce $9 = 2^0 + 2^1 + 2^1 + 2^2$ new unknowns to represent the probabilities of each node given its parents. Note that in a general directed binary graphical model, each node v contributes $2^{\text{indegree}(v)}$ such unknowns. The quantity $\sum_v 2^{\text{indegree}(v)}$ counts degrees of freedom. It is the dimension of the projective variety of $T_{\text{local}(G)}$. In our example, we associate the letters a, b, c, d with the random variables X_1, X_2, X_3, X_4 in this order. The 9 new unknowns are $a, b_1, b_2, c_1, c_2, d_{11}, d_{12}, d_{21}, d_{22}$. For instance, the unknown d_{21} stands for the probability of the event "$X_4 = 1$ given $X_2 = 2$ and $X_3 = 1$".

We express our directed graphical model G as a homomorphism ϕ from the polynomial ring $\mathbb{R}[p_{1111}, p_{1112}, \dots, p_{2222}]$ in 16 unknowns to the polynomial ring $\mathbb{R}[a, b_1, b_2, c_1, c_2, d_{11}, d_{12}, d_{21}, d_{22}]$ in 9 unknowns. The homomorphism is given by

$$
\begin{aligned}
\phi(p_{1111}) &= a \cdot b_1 \cdot c_1 \cdot d_{11} \\
\phi(p_{1112}) &= a \cdot b_1 \cdot c_1 \cdot (1 - d_{11}) \\
\phi(p_{1121}) &= a \cdot b_1 \cdot (1 - c_1) \cdot d_{12} \\
\phi(p_{1122}) &= a \cdot b_1 \cdot (1 - c_1) \cdot (1 - d_{12}) \\
\phi(p_{1211}) &= a \cdot (1 - b_1) \cdot c_1 \cdot d_{21} \\
\phi(p_{1212}) &= a \cdot (1 - b_1) \cdot c_1 \cdot (1 - d_{21}) \\
\phi(p_{1221}) &= a \cdot (1 - b_1) \cdot (1 - c_1) \cdot d_{22} \\
\phi(p_{1222}) &= a \cdot (1 - b_1) \cdot (1 - c_1) \cdot (1 - d_{22}) \\[6pt]
\phi(p_{2111}) &= (1 - a) \cdot b_2 \cdot c_2 \cdot d_{11} \\
\phi(p_{2112}) &= (1 - a) \cdot b_2 \cdot c_2 \cdot (1 - d_{11}) \\
\phi(p_{2121}) &= (1 - a) \cdot b_2 \cdot (1 - c_2) \cdot d_{12} \\
\phi(p_{2122}) &= (1 - a) \cdot b_2 \cdot (1 - c_2) \cdot (1 - d_{12}) \\
\phi(p_{2211}) &= (1 - a) \cdot (1 - b_2) \cdot c_2 \cdot d_{21} \\
\phi(p_{2212}) &= (1 - a) \cdot (1 - b_2) \cdot c_2 \cdot (1 - d_{21}) \\
\phi(p_{2221}) &= (1 - a) \cdot (1 - b_2) \cdot (1 - c_2) \cdot d_{22} \\
\phi(p_{2222}) &= (1 - a) \cdot (1 - b_2) \cdot (1 - c_2) \cdot (1 - d_{22}).
\end{aligned}
$$

We compute the kernel of the ring homomorphism ϕ in `Macaulay 2` or `Singular`. After about one minute, we obtain the following result:

$$
(8.13) \qquad \text{kernel}(\phi) = T_{\text{local}(G)} + \left\langle 1 - \sum_{i=1}^{2} \sum_{j=1}^{2} \sum_{k=1}^{2} \sum_{l=1}^{2} p_{ijkl} \right\rangle.
$$

Clearly, the sum of the factored probabilities $\phi(p_{ijkl})$ must be equal to 1. This explains the extra generator. Our computation proves that the inhomogeneous ideal on the right hand side of (8.13) is a prime ideal. From this we conclude that the homogeneous ideal $T_{\text{local}(G)}$ is prime as well. This answers the question in Problem 8.12 affirmatively for this particular graph G.

In this section we explored statistical models which are described by conditional independence statements. These furnish a wealth of interesting algebraic varieties which are cut out by quadratic equations. Gaining a better understanding of independence varieties and their equations is likely to have a significant impact for the study of multidimensional tables and its applications to problems in statistics.

8.3. Random Walks on the Integer Lattice

Let $\mathcal{B}$ be a (typically finite) subset of the integer lattice $\mathbb{Z}^n$. The elements of $\mathcal{B}$ are regarded as the *moves* or *steps* in a random walk on the lattice points in the non-negative orthant. More precisely, let $G_{\mathcal{B}}$ be the graph with vertices the set $\mathbb{N}^n$ of non-negative integer vectors, where a pair of vectors u, v is connected by an edge if and only if either $u - v$ or $v - u$ lies in $\mathcal{B}$. The problem to be addressed in this section is to characterize the connected components of the graph $G_{\mathcal{B}}$. Having a good understanding of the connected components and their higher connectivity properties is a necessary precondition for any study of specific Markov chains and their mixing time.

EXAMPLE 8.13. Let $n = 5$ and consider the set of moves

$$\mathcal{B} \quad = \quad \left\{ (1, -1, -1, 1, 0), \, (1, -1, 0, -1, 1), \, (0, 1, -1, -1, 1) \right\}.$$

These three vectors span the kernel of the matrix

$$A \quad = \quad \begin{pmatrix} 1 & 1 & 1 & 1 & 1 \\ 1 & 2 & 3 & 4 & 5 \end{pmatrix}$$

The two rows of the matrix A represent *linear invariants* of the walk given by $\mathcal{B}$. Two vectors $u, v \in \mathbb{N}^5$ lie in the same component of $G_{\mathcal{B}}$ only if they have the same linear invariants. The converse is not quite true: we need additional inequalities. Two non-negative integer vectors u and v lie in the same connected component of $G_{\mathcal{B}}$ if and only if $A \cdot u = A \cdot v$ and

$$u_1 + u_2 + u_3 \geq 1, \, u_1 + u_2 + u_4 \geq 1, \, u_2 + u_4 + u_5 \geq 1, \, u_3 + u_4 + u_5 \geq 1,$$
$$v_1 + v_2 + v_3 \geq 1, \, v_1 + v_2 + v_4 \geq 1, \, v_2 + v_4 + v_5 \geq 1, \text{ and } v_3 + v_4 + v_5 \geq 1.$$

Returning to the general case, let $\mathcal{L}$ denote the sublattice of $\mathbb{Z}^n$ generated by $\mathcal{B}$. Computing the linear invariants amounts to computing the image under the canonical map $\mathbb{Z}^n \to \mathbb{Z}^n/\mathcal{L}$. If $\mathbb{Z}^n/\mathcal{L}$ is torsion-free then this map can be represented by an integer matrix A. A necessary condition for u and v to lie in the same component of $\mathcal{G}_{\mathcal{B}}$ is that they have the same image under the linear map A. Thus we are looking for conditions (e.g. linear inequalities) which, in conjunction with the obvious condition $u - v \in \mathcal{L}$, will ensure that v can be reached from u in a random walk on $\mathbb{N}^n$ using steps from $\mathcal{B}$ only.

We encode every vector u in $\mathcal{B}$ by a difference of two monomials, namely,

$$x^{u+} - x^{u-} \quad = \quad \prod_{i : u_i > 0} x_i^{u_i} \quad - \quad \prod_{j : u_j < 0} x_j^{-u_j}.$$

Let $I_{\mathcal{B}}$ denote the ideal in $S = \mathbb{Q}[x_1, \dots, x_n]$ generated by the binomials $x^{u+} - x^{u-}$ where u runs over $\mathcal{B}$. Thus every binomial ideal encountered in this book can be interpreted as a graph on non-negative lattice vectors.

THEOREM 8.14. *Two vectors $u, v \in \mathbb{N}^n$ lie in the same connected component of $G_{\mathcal{B}}$ if and only if the binomial $x^u - x^v$ lies in the binomial ideal $I_{\mathcal{B}}$.*

Our algebraic approach in studying the connectivity properties of graph $G_{\mathcal{B}}$ is to compute a suitable ideal decomposition:

$$I_{\mathcal{B}} \quad = \quad I_{\mathcal{L}} \cap J_1 \cap J_2 \cap \cdots \cap J_r.$$

This decomposition could be a binomial primary decomposition, or it could be some coarser decomposition where each J_i still has many associated primes. The key requirement is that membership in each component J_i should be describable by some easy combinatorial condition. Sometimes we can only give sufficient conditions for membership of $x^u - x^v$ in each J_i, and this will lead to sufficient conditions for u and v being in the same component of $G_{\mathcal{B}}$. The *lattice ideal* $I_{\mathcal{L}}$ encodes the congruence relation modulo $\mathcal{L} = \mathbb{Z}\mathcal{B}$. Two vectors u and v in $\mathbb{N}^n$ have the same linear invariants if and only if $x^u - x^v$ lies in $I_{\mathcal{L}}$. Note that the lattice ideal $I_{\mathcal{L}}$ is prime if and only if $\mathbb{Z}^n/\mathcal{L}$ is torsion-free. This ideal always appears in the primary decomposition of $I_\mathcal{B}$ because

$$\left(I_\mathcal{B} \,:\, (x_1 x_2 \cdots x_n)^\infty \right) \;=\; I_\mathcal{L}.$$

This identity of ideals has the following interpretation for our application: Two vectors $u, v \in \mathbb{N}^5$ lie in the same component of $G_\mathcal{B}$ only if they have the same linear invariants and their coordinates are positive enough.

Our discussion implies that Gröbner basis software can be used to determine the components of the graph $G_\mathcal{B}$. For instance, the system of inequalities in Example 8.13 is the output o3 of the following Macaulay 2 session:

```
i1 : R = QQ[x1,x2,x3,x4,x5];
i2 : IB = ideal(x1*x4-x2*x3,x1*x5-x2*x4,x2*x5-x3*x4);
i3 : toString ass(IB)
o3 = { ideal(x1,x2,x3), ideal(x1,x2,x4),
       ideal(x2,x4,x5), ideal(x3,x4,x5),
       ideal(x4^2-x3*x5, x3*x4-x2*x5, x2*x4-x1*x5,
          x3^2-x1*x5, x2*x3-x1*x4, x2^2-x1*x3) }
i4 : IB == intersect ass(IB)
o4 = true
```

Two-dimensional contingency tables are ubiquitous in statistics, and it is a classical problem to study random walks on the set of all contingency tables with fixed margins. For instance, consider the set $\mathbb{N}^{4\times 4}$ of non-negative integer 4×4-matrices. The ambient lattice $\mathbb{Z}^{4\times 4}$ is isomorphic to $\mathbb{Z}^{16}$. The linear invariants are given by the row sums and column sums of the matrices. Equivalently, the sublattice $\mathcal{L}$ consists of all matrices in $\mathbb{Z}^{4\times 4}$ whose row sums and column sums are zero. The lattice ideal $I_\mathcal{L}$ is the prime ideal generated by the thirty-six 2×2-minors of a 4×4-matrix (x_{ij}) of indeterminates.

A natural question is to study the connectivity of the graph $G_\mathcal{B}$ defined by some basis $\mathcal{B}$ for the lattice $\mathcal{L}$. For instance, take $\mathcal{B}$ to be the set of nine *adjacent* 2×2-*moves*. The corresponding binomial ideal equals

$$\begin{aligned} I_\mathcal{B} \;=\; \big\langle \;\; & x_{12}x_{21} - x_{11}x_{22},\, x_{13}x_{22} - x_{12}x_{23},\, x_{14}x_{23} - x_{13}x_{24}, \\ & x_{22}x_{31} - x_{21}x_{32},\, x_{23}x_{32} - x_{22}x_{33},\, x_{24}x_{33} - x_{23}x_{34}, \\ & x_{32}x_{41} - x_{31}x_{42},\, x_{33}x_{42} - x_{32}x_{43},\, x_{34}x_{43} - x_{33}x_{44} \big\rangle. \end{aligned}$$

Theorem 8.14 tells us that two non-negative integer 4×4-matrices (a_{ij}) and (b_{ij}) with the same row and column sums can be connected by a sequence of adjacent 2×2-moves if and only if the binomial

$$\prod_{1\leq i,j\leq 4} x_{ij}^{a_{ij}} \;-\; \prod_{1\leq i,j\leq 4} x_{ij}^{b_{ij}} \qquad \text{lies in the ideal } I_\mathcal{B}.$$

The primary decomposition of $I_\mathcal{B}$ was computed in Chapter 5. This primary decomposition implies the following combinatorial result:

PROPOSITION 8.15. *Two non-negative integer 4×4-matrices with the same row and column sums can be connected by a sequence of adjacent 2×2-moves if both of them satisfy the following six inequalities:*

(i) $a_{21} + a_{22} + a_{23} + a_{24} \geq 2$;

(ii) $a_{31} + a_{32} + a_{33} + a_{34} \geq 2$;

(iii) $a_{12} + a_{22} + a_{32} + a_{42} \geq 2$;
(iv) $a_{13} + a_{23} + a_{33} + a_{43} \geq 2$;
(v) $a_{12} + a_{22} + a_{23} + a_{24} + a_{31} + a_{32} + a_{33} + a_{43} \geq 1$;
(vi) $a_{13} + a_{21} + a_{22} + a_{23} + a_{32} + a_{33} + a_{34} + a_{42} \geq 1$.

We remark that these sufficient conditions remain valid if (at most) one of the four inequalities "≥ 2" is replaced by "≥ 1." No further relaxation of the conditions (i)–(vi) is possible, as is shown by the following two pairs of matrices, which cannot be connected by an adjacent 2×2-walk:

$$
\begin{pmatrix} 0 & 0 & 0 & 0 \\ 0 & 1 & 1 & 0 \\ 0 & 1 & 0 & 0 \\ 0 & 0 & 0 & 1 \end{pmatrix}
\longleftrightarrow
\begin{pmatrix} 0 & 0 & 0 & 0 \\ 0 & 0 & 1 & 1 \\ 0 & 1 & 0 & 0 \\ 0 & 1 & 0 & 0 \end{pmatrix}
$$

$$
\begin{pmatrix} 0 & 0 & 1 & 0 \\ 1 & 1 & 0 & 0 \\ 0 & 0 & 0 & 2 \\ 0 & 0 & 0 & 0 \end{pmatrix}
\longleftrightarrow
\begin{pmatrix} 0 & 0 & 0 & 1 \\ 0 & 0 & 1 & 1 \\ 1 & 1 & 0 & 0 \\ 0 & 0 & 0 & 0 \end{pmatrix}
$$

The necessity of conditions (v) and (vi) is seen from the disconnected pairs

$$
\begin{pmatrix} n & n & 0 & n \\ 0 & 0 & 0 & n \\ n & 0 & 0 & 0 \\ n & 0 & n & n \end{pmatrix}
\longleftrightarrow
\begin{pmatrix} n & 0 & n & n \\ n & 0 & 0 & 0 \\ 0 & 0 & 0 & n \\ n & n & 0 & n \end{pmatrix}
$$

for any integer $n \geq 0$. Such minimally disconnected pairs of matrices are derived by computing witnesses for the relevant associated primes of $I_{\mathcal{B}}$.

Random walks arising from graphical models play a significant role in the statistical study of multi-dimensional contingency tables. A noteworthy real-world application of these techniques is the work on the U.S. census data by Stephen Fienberg (see e.g. [**DF00**]) and his collaborators at the National Institute of Statistical Sciences (http://www.niss.org/). Studying the connectivity problems of these random walks is precisely the issue of Problems 8.5 and 8.6. Namely, given a graph G, each of the three sets of independence facts in (8.8) translates into a set of quadratic binomials and hence into a random walk on all tables with margins in the graphical model G. The primary decompositions of the binomial ideals $I_{\text{pairwise}}(G)$, $I_{\text{local}}(G)$ and $I_{\text{global}}(G)$ will furnish us with conditions under which two multi-dimensional tables are connected in under the random walk. Example 8.8 is a good place to start; see Exercise (3) below.

We conclude with the family of *circuit walks* which is very natural from a mathematical perspective. Let A be a $d \times n$-integer matrix and $\mathcal{L} = \ker_{\mathbb{Z}}(A) \subset \mathbb{Z}^n$ as before. The ideal $I_{\mathcal{L}}$ is prime; it is the toric ideal associated with A. A non-zero vector $u = (u_1, \ldots, u_n)$ in $\mathcal{L}$ is called a *circuit* if its coordinates u_i are relatively prime and its support $\text{supp}(u) = \{ i : u_i \neq 0 \}$ is minimal with respect to inclusion. We shall consider the walk defined by the set $\mathcal{C}$ of all circuits in $\mathcal{L}$. This makes sense for two reasons:

- The lattice $\mathcal{L}$ is generated by the circuits, i.e., $\mathbb{Z}\mathcal{C} = \mathcal{L}$.
- The circuits can be computed easily from the matrix A.

Here is a simple algorithm for computing $\mathcal{C}$. Initialize $\mathcal{C} := \emptyset$. For any $(d+1)$-subset $\tau = \{\tau_1, \ldots, \tau_{d+1}\}$ of $\{1, \ldots, n\}$ form the vector

$$C_\tau = \sum_{i=1}^{d+1} (-1)^i \cdot det(A_{\tau \setminus \{\tau_i\}}) \cdot e_{\tau_i},$$

where e_j is the jth unit vector and A_σ is the submatrix of A with column indices σ. If C_τ is non-zero then remove common factors from its coordinates. The resulting vector is a circuit and all circuits are obtained in this manner.

EXAMPLE 8.16. Let $d = 2, n = 4$ and $A = \begin{pmatrix} 0 & 2 & 5 & 7 \\ 7 & 5 & 2 & 0 \end{pmatrix}$. Then

$$\mathcal{C} = \pm\big\{ (3, -5, 2, 0), (5, -7, 0, 2), (2, 0, -7, 5), (0, 2, -5, 3) \big\}.$$

It is instructive – for Exercise (4) below – to check that the $\mathbb{Z}$-span of $\mathcal{C}$ equals $\mathcal{L} = \ker_{\mathbb{Z}}(A)$. (For instance, try to write $(1, -1, -1, 1) \in \mathcal{L}$ as a $\mathbb{Z}$-linear combination of $\mathcal{C}$). We shall derive the following result: *Two $\mathcal{L}$-equivalent non-negative integer vectors (A, B, C, D) and (A', B', C', D') can be connected by the circuits if both of them satisfy the following inequality*

$$\min\Big\{ \max\{A, B, C, D\}, \max\{B, \tfrac{9}{4}C, \tfrac{9}{4}D\}, \max\{\tfrac{9}{4}A, \tfrac{9}{4}B, C\} \Big\} \geq 9.$$

The following two $\mathcal{L}$-equivalent pairs are not connected in the circuit walk:

(8.14) $(4, 9, 0, 2) \leftrightarrow (5, 8, 1, 1)$ and $(1, 6, 6, 1) \leftrightarrow (3, 4, 4, 3)$.

To analyze circuit walks in general, we consider the *circuit ideal* $I_\mathcal{C}$ generated by the binomials $x^{u_+} - x^{u_-}$ where $u = u_+ - u_-$ runs over all circuits in $\mathcal{L}$. The primary decomposition of circuit ideals was studied in Section 8 of [**ES96**]. We summarize the relevant results. Let $\text{pos}(A)$ denote the d-dimensional convex polyhedral cone in $\mathbb{R}^d$ spanned by the column vectors of A. Each face of $\text{pos}(A)$ is identified with the subset $\sigma \subset \{1, \ldots, n\}$ consisting of all indices i such that the ith column of A lies on that face. If σ is a face of $\text{pos}(A)$ then the ideal $I_\sigma := \langle x_i : i \notin \sigma \rangle + I_\mathcal{L}$ is prime. Note that $I_{\{1,\ldots,n\}} = I_\mathcal{L}$ and $I_{\{\}} = \langle x_1, x_2, \ldots, x_n \rangle$.

THEOREM 8.17. (**Decomposition of Circuit Ideals [ES96**, Section 8])

$$\text{Rad}(I_\mathcal{C}) = I_\mathcal{L} \quad \text{and} \quad \text{Ass}(I_\mathcal{C}) \subseteq \big\{ I_\sigma : \sigma \text{ is a face of } \text{pos}(A) \big\}.$$

Applying the techniques of binomial primary decomposition to the circuit ideal $I_\mathcal{C}$ gives connectivity properties of the circuit walk in terms of the faces of the polyhedral cone $\text{pos}(A)$. Let us see how this works for Example 8.16. We choose variables a, b, c, d for the four columns of A. The cone $\text{pos}(A) = \text{pos}\{(7, 0), (5, 2), (2, 5), (0, 7)\}$ equals the nonnegative quadrant in $\mathbb{R}^2$. It has one 2-dimensional face, labeled $\{a, b, c, d\}$, two 1-dimensional faces, labeled $\{a\}$ and $\{d\}$, and one 0-dimensional face, labeled $\{\}$. The toric ideal is

(8.15) $I_\mathcal{L} = \langle ad - bc, ac^4 - b^3d^2, a^3c^2 - b^5, b^2d^3 - c^5, a^2c^3 - b^4d \rangle.$

The circuit ideal equals

$$I_\mathcal{C} = \langle a^3c^2 - b^5, a^5d^2 - b^7, a^2d^5 - c^7, b^2d^3 - c^5 \rangle.$$

It has the minimal primary decomposition

$$I_\mathcal{C} \quad = \quad I_\mathcal{L} \quad \cap \; \langle\, b^9,\, c^4,\, d^4,\, b^2 d^2,\, c^2 d^2,\, b^2 c^2 - a^2 d^2,\, b^5 - a^3 c^2 \,\rangle$$
$$\cap \; \langle\, a^4,\, b^4,\, c^9,\, a^2 b^2,\, a^2 c^2,\, b^2 c^2 - a^2 d^2,\, c^5 - b^2 d^3 \,\rangle$$
$$\cap \; (\langle a^9, b^9, c^9, d^9 \rangle + I_\mathcal{C}).$$

The second and third ideals are primary to $I_{\{a\}} = \langle b, c, d \rangle$ and to $I_{\{d\}} = \langle a, b, c \rangle$. This primary decomposition implies the inequality in (8.16) because

$$\langle a^9, b^9, c^9, d^9 \rangle \;\cap\; \langle b^9,\, c^4,\, d^4 \rangle \;\cap\; \langle a^4,\, b^4,\, c^9 \rangle \;\cap\; I_\mathcal{L} \quad \subset \quad I_\mathcal{C}.$$

Returning to our general discussion, Theorem 8.17 implies that for each face σ of the polyhedral cone $\mathrm{pos}(A)$ there exists a non-negative integer M_σ such that

$$I_\mathcal{L} \;\cap\; \bigcap_{\sigma \text{ face}} \langle\, x_i : i \notin \sigma \,\rangle^{M_\sigma} \quad \subset \quad I_\mathcal{C}.$$

COROLLARY 8.18. *For each proper face σ of $\mathrm{pos}(A)$ there is an integer M_σ such that any two $\mathcal{L}$-equivalent vectors $(a_1, \ldots, a_n)$ and $(b_1, \ldots, b_n)$ in $\mathbb{N}^n$ with*

$$\sum_{i \notin \sigma} a_i \geq M_\sigma \quad and \quad \sum_{i \notin \sigma} b_i \geq M_\sigma \quad \text{for all proper faces } \sigma \text{ of } \mathrm{pos}(A)$$

can be connected in the circuit walk.

This suggests the following research problem.

PROBLEM 8.19. *Find bounds for the integers M_σ in terms of the matrix A.*

The optimal value of M_σ seems to be related to the singularity of the toric variety defined by $I_\mathcal{L}$ along the torus orbit labeled σ: The worse the singularity is, the higher the value of M_σ. It would be very interesting to understand these geometric aspects. In Example 8.16 the optimal values are

$$M_{\{\}} \;=\; 15 \quad and \quad M_{\{a\}} \;=\; 11 \quad and \quad M_{\{d\}} \;=\; 11.$$

Optimality is seen from the pairs of disconnected vectors in (8.14).

8.4. Maximum Likelihood Equations

We fix a $d \times n$-integer matrix $A = (a_{ij})$ with the property that all column sums of A are equal. As before we consider the polyhedral cone $\mathrm{pos}(A)$ and the sublattice $\mathcal{L} = \ker_\mathbb{Z}(A)$ of $\mathbb{Z}^n$. The toric ideal $I_\mathcal{L}$ is the prime ideal in $\mathbb{Q}[x_1, \ldots, x_n]$ generated by all binomials $x^{u^+} - x^{u^-}$ where u runs over $\mathcal{L}$. We write $\mathcal{V}_\mathcal{L}^+$ for the set of zeros of $I_\mathcal{L}$ in the non-negative orthant $\mathbb{R}_{\geq 0}^n$. This set is the *log-linear model* associated with A. Log-linear models include undirected graphical models and other statistical models defined by saturated independence facts. For instance, the graphical model for a four-chain of binary random variables corresponds to the 12×16-matrix A in Example 8.8. If an element p of $\mathbb{R}_{\geq 0}^n$ has coordinate sum 1 then we regard p as a probability distribution. The coordinates of the vector $A \cdot p$ in $\mathbb{R}^d$ are the *linear invariants* of p. If $\mathbf{n}$ is a non-negative integer vector (representing data) of length d then the vector $A \cdot \mathbf{n}$ is the *sufficient statistic* for the log-linear model associated to A. A probability vector p belongs to this log-linear model if and only if $p \in \mathcal{V}_\mathcal{L}^+$. The following result is fundamental both for statistics and for toric geometry.

THEOREM 8.20. **(Birch's Theorem)** *For any vector $p \in \mathbb{R}_{\geq 0}^n$ there exists a unique vector $\hat{p} \in \mathcal{V}_\mathcal{L}^+$ with the same linear invariants as p, i.e., $A \cdot \hat{p} = A \cdot p$.*

The vector $\hat{p}$ is called the *maximum likelihood estimate* for p in the model A. Computing the maximum likelihood estimate amounts to solving a system of polynomial equations. We write $\langle Ax - Ap \rangle$ for the ideal generated by the d linear polynomial $\sum_{j=1}^{n} a_{ij}(x_j - p_j)$ for $i = 1, 2, \ldots, d$. The *maximum likelihood ideal* for the non-negative vector p in the log-linear model A is

$$(8.16) \qquad I_{\mathcal{L}} + \langle Ax - Ap \rangle \qquad \subset \qquad \mathbb{Q}[x_1, \ldots, x_n].$$

We wish to find the zero $x = \hat{p}$. Theorem 8.20 can be reworded as follows.

COROLLARY 8.21. *Each maximum likelihood ideal (8.16) has precisely one non-negative real root.*

Theorem 8.20 is known as Birch's Theorem in statistics. A standard reference is Agresti's book [**Agr90**, page 168]. Proofs of Theorem 8.20 and Corollary 8.21 appearing in the geometry books are based on convexity considerations. One such proof can be found in Chapter 4 of Fulton [**Ful93**]. In toric geometry, the matrix A represents the *moment map* from $\mathcal{V}_{\mathcal{L}}^{+}$, the non-negative part of the toric variety, onto the polyhedral cone $\mathrm{pos}(A)$. The version of Theorem 8.20 appearing in [**Ful93**] states that the moment map defines a homeomorphism from $\mathcal{V}_{\mathcal{L}}^{+}$ onto $\mathrm{pos}(A)$.

As an example consider the log-linear model discussed in Example 8.16. Let us compute the maximum likelihood estimate for the probability distribution $p = (3/7, 0, 0, 4/7)$. The maximum likelihood ideal is given by the two coordinates of $Ax = Ap$ and the five binomial generators of (8.15). More precisely, the maximum likelihood ideal (8.16) for this example equals

$$\langle\, x_2 x_3 - x_1 x_4, x_3^5 - x_2^2 x_4^3, x_2^5 - x_1^3 x_3^2, x_1 x_3^4 - x_2^3 x_4^2, x_1^2 x_3^3 - x_2^4 x_4,$$
$$0x_1 + 2x_2 + 5x_3 + 7x_4 - b_1\,,\ 7x_1 + 5x_2 + 2x_3 + 0x_4 - b_2\,\rangle$$

with $b_1 = 4$ and $b_2 = 3$. This ideal has exactly one real zero $x = \hat{p}$, which is necessarily non-negative by Corollary 8.21. We find numerically

$$(8.17) \quad \hat{p} \;=\; \bigl(\, 0.3134107644,\, 0.2726959080,\, 0.2213225526,\, 0.1925707745\,\bigr).$$

There are other parameter values, for instance $b_1 = 1, b_2 = 50$, for which the above ideal has three real zeros. But always only of them is non-negative.

The maximum likelihood ideal deserves further study from an algebraic point of view. First, for special points p in $\mathbb{R}_{\geq 0}^n$, it can happen that the ideal (8.16) is not zero-dimensional. It would be interesting to characterize those special values of p. For generic values of p, the ideal (8.16) is always zero-dimensional and radical, and it is natural to ask how many complex zeros it has. This number is bounded above by the degree of the toric ideal $I_{\mathcal{L}}$, and for many matrices A these two numbers are equal. For instance, in the above example, the degree of $I_{\mathcal{L}}$ is seven and the maximum likelihood equations have seven complex zeros.

Interestingly, these two numbers are not equal for most of the toric ideals which actually arise in statistics applications. For instance, for the four-chain model in Example 8.8, the degree of $I_{\mathcal{L}}$ is 34 but the degree of the ideal (8.16) is 1; see Exercise (7) below. An explanation is offered by Proposition 4.18 in [**Lau96**] which gives a rational formula for maximum likelihood estimation in a decomposable graphical model. This raises the following question for nondecomposable graphical models.

PROBLEM 8.22. *What is the number of isolated complex zeros of the maximum likelihood equations for a nondecomposable graphical model G?*

Geiger, Meek and Sturmfels [**GMS02**] proved that this number is always greater than one. It would be nice to identify log-linear models other than decomposable graphical models whose maximum likelihood estimator is rational. Equivalently, which toric varieties have the property that the inverse of the moment map is given by a rational function? Let us phrase this question as follows:

PROBLEM 8.23. *Characterize the integer matrices A whose maximum likelihood ideal (8.16) has exactly one complex solution, for each generic p.*

Statisticians use a numerical algorithm called *iterative proportional scaling* to find the unique positive real solution of the maximum equations. One standard reference is a paper by Darroch and Ratcliff [**DR72**]. Iterative Proportional Scaling is extremely easy to describe and equally easy to implement. Here are a few lines of a generic `maple` program which works for any log-linear model. The data A and B are set up to compute the numerical vector (8.17) above:

```
A  := array([     [0,2,5,7],
                  [7,5,2,0]]);
B  := array([[ 4 ] ,
             [ 3 ]  ]):
epsilon := 10^(-6): Digits := 12:

with(linalg): d := rowdim(A): n := coldim(A):
a := sum(A[i,1], i=1..d):  b := sum(B[i,1], i=1..d):
P := []: for j from 1 to n do P := [P[],evalf(1/n)]: od:
C := multiply(scalarmul(A,1/a), transpose(array([P]))):

while (norm(matadd(scalarmul(B,-1/b),C)) > epsilon) do
 for j from 1 to n do
  P[j] := P[j]*product((B[i,1]/(b*C[i,1]))^(A[i,j]/a),i=1..d):
 od:
 C := multiply( scalarmul(A,1/a), transpose(array([P])) ):
od:
print(b/a*P);
```

The same code can be used for any non-negative integer $d \times n$-matrix A whose column sums all have the same sum $a > 0$. The user specifies a column d-vector B which is a positive linear combination of the columns of A, and we set $b > 0$ to be the coordinate sum of B. The goal is to find a probability n-vector P in the toric variety of A such that $A \cdot (\frac{b}{a} \cdot P) = B$, or, equivalently $\frac{1}{a} A \cdot P = \frac{1}{b} \cdot B$. We start our iterative procedure with the uniform distribution $P = (\frac{1}{n}, \frac{1}{n}, \ldots, \frac{1}{n})$. We always set

$$C = \frac{1}{a} A \cdot P.$$

If the norm of the d-column vector

$$C - \frac{1}{b} \cdot B$$

is less than our chosen $\epsilon > 0$, we are done and we output $\frac{b}{a} \cdot P$. Otherwise we update the probability vector P by the following simple rule:

$$(8.18) \qquad P \quad \longleftarrow \quad P \times (\frac{1}{b}B)^{\frac{1}{a}A} \times C^{-\frac{1}{a}A}.$$

Here the product "$\times$" is the product of elements in the multiplicative abelian group $(\mathbb{R}_+)^n$. All three factors lie in subgroup $\mathcal{V}(I_{\mathcal{L}}) \cap (\mathbb{R}_+)^n$, so, throughout the computation, P will always lie in the toric variety $\mathcal{V}(I_{\mathcal{L}})$. The two factors on right are understood as follows. If $A = (a_{ij})$ and $Y = (y_1, \dots, y_d)$ is any positive real d-vector then $Y^{\frac{1}{a}A}$ denotes the positive real n-vector whose ith coordinate is $y_1^{a_{1i}/a} y_2^{a_{2i}/a} \cdots y_d^{a_{di}/a}$. Darroch and Ratcliff [**DR72**] prove that this process always converges to the desired solution $\hat{P}$ provided B is a strictly positive combination of the columns of A. This hypothesis is equivalent to saying that $\hat{P}$ is strictly positive.

8.5. Exercises

(1) Let X_1, X_2, X_3, X_4 be binary random variables and consider the model

$$\mathcal{M} = \{ X_1 \perp X_2 | X_3, \; X_2 \perp X_3 | X_4, \; X_3 \perp X_4 | X_1, \; X_4 \perp X_1 | X_2 \}.$$

Compute the ideal $I_{\mathcal{M}}$ and find the irreducible decomposition of the variety $V_{\mathcal{M}}$. Does every component meet the probability simplex?

(2) Let G be the cycle on five binary random variables. List the generators of the binomial ideal $I_{\text{pairwise}}(G)$ and compute its minimal primes.

(3) Give a necessary and sufficient condition for two $2 \times 2 \times 2 \times 2$-contingency tables with the same margins in the four-chain model to be connected by pairwise Markov moves. In other words, use the primary decomposition of Example 8.8 to analyze the associated random walk.

(4) Prove that each sublattice $\mathcal{L}$ of $\mathbb{Z}^n$ is spanned by its subset $\mathcal{C}$ of circuits.

(5) Determine and interpret the three numbers $M_{\{\}}$, $M_{\{a\}}$ and $M_{\{d\}}$ for circuit walk defined by the matrix $A = \begin{pmatrix} 0 & 3 & 7 & 10 \\ 10 & 7 & 3 & 0 \end{pmatrix}$.

(6) Compute the maximum likelihood estimate $\hat{p}$ for the probability distribution $p = (1/11, 2/11, 3/11, 5/11)$ in the log-linear model specified by the 2×4-matrix A in the previous exercise.

(7) Write the maximum likelihood equations for the four-chain model in Example 8.8 and show that it has only one complex solution $x = p^*$.

(8) Let $X = (x_{ijk})$ be a $3 \times 3 \times 3$-matrix of indeterminates. Describe the solution set of the 27 quartic binomial equations of the form

$$x_{ijk} x_{imn} x_{ljn} x_{lmk} \quad = \quad x_{lmn} x_{ljk} x_{imk} x_{ijn}.$$

Interpret your result in terms of a random walk on $3 \times 3 \times 3$-tables.

(9) Pick an acyclic directed graph G with 5 vertices and 8 edges, where the vertices represent binary random variables. Compute the ideals $I_{\text{local}(G)}$ and $T_{\text{local}(G)}$ in the polynomial ring $\mathbb{R}[p_{11111}, p_{11112}, \dots, p_{22222}]$.

CHAPTER 9

Tropical Algebraic Geometry

The *tropical semiring* is the extended real line $\mathbb{R} \cup \{-\infty\}$ with two arithmetic operations called *tropical addition* and *tropical multiplication*. The tropical sum of two numbers is their maximum and the tropical product of two numbers is their sum. We use the familiar symbols "+" and "×" to denote these operations as well. The tropical semiring $(\mathbb{R} \cup \{-\infty\}, +, \times)$ satisfies many of the usual axioms of arithmetic such as $(a + b) \times c = (a \times c) + (b \times c)$. The additive unit is $-\infty$, the multiplicative unit is the real number 0, and x^2 denotes $x \times x$. Tropical polynomials make perfect sense. Consider the cubic $f(x) = 5 + (1) \times x + (0) \times x^2 + (-4) \times x^3$. Then, tropically, $f(3) = 6$. For background on tropical semirings see the article of Pin [**Pin98**]. We learned there that the adjective "tropical" originated when French computer scientists gave reference to the work of a Brazilian mathematician. In the Russian literature, the tropical calculus is known as *idempotent analysis* or as *Maslov dequantization*, in the honor of V.I. Maslov and his collaborators [**MK94**].

In this chapter we study the problem of solving systems of polynomial equations in the tropical semiring. The relationship to classical polynomial equations is given by valuation theory, specifically by considering Puiseux series solutions. This is made precise in Theorems 9.16 and 9.17. These two results are an extension of Misha Kapranov's note on amoebas over non-archimedean fields [**Kap00**].

Indeed, the material in this chapter offers a glimpse of the beautiful emerging subject of amoebas [**Mik01**] from the point of view of polynomial systems solving; see also [**FPT00**], [**The02**]. It is partly based on discussions with Grisha Mikhalkin, with whom the author shares a common passion for tropical algebraic geometry.

Gregorio Malajovich pointed out that the material in this chapter is related to the classical method of *Graeffe iteration* for numerical root finding [**MZ01**]. It would be fascinating to explore this further and to develop a truly multidimensional Graeffe iteration based on amoebas and tropical algebraic geometry.

9.1. Tropical Geometry in the Plane

A tropical polynomial $f(x)$ in n unknowns $x = (x_1, \dots, x_n)$ is the maximum of a finite set of linear functions with $\mathbb{N}$-coefficients. Hence the graph of $f(x)$ is piecewise linear and convex. We define the *variety* of $f(x)$ as the set of points $x \in \mathbb{R}^n$ at which $f(x)$ is not differentiable. This is consistent with the intuitive idea that we are trying to solve $f(x) = -\infty$, given that $-\infty$ is the additive unit. Equivalently, the variety of $f(x)$ is the set of all points x at which the maximum of the linear functions in $f(x)$ is attained at least twice.

Let us begin by deriving the solution to the general quadratic equation

(9.1)
$$ax^2 + bx + c \qquad \text{``} = 0 \text{''}$$

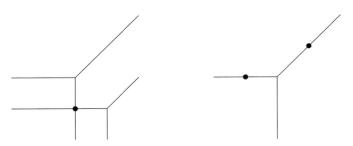

FIGURE 9.1. Tropical Lines

Here a, b, c are arbitrary real numbers. We wish to compute the tropical variety of (9.1). In ordinary arithmetic, this amounts to solving the equation

(9.2) $\max\{\, a + 2x,\, b + x,\, c \,\}$ is attained twice.

This is equivalent to

$$a + 2x = b + x \geq c \quad \text{or} \quad a + 2x = c \geq b + x \quad \text{or} \quad b + x = c \geq a + 2x.$$

From this we conclude: *The tropical solution set to the quadratic equation (9.1) equals $\{b - a, c - b\}$ if $a + c \leq 2b$, and it equals $\{(c - a)/2\}$ if $a + c \geq 2b$.*

Our next step is the study of tropical lines in the plane. A *tropical line* is the tropical variety defined by a polynomial

$$f(x, y) \quad = \quad ax + by + c,$$

where a, b, c are fixed real numbers. The tropical line is a star with three rays emanating in the directions west, south and northeast. The midpoint of the star is the point $(x, y) = (c - a, c - b)$. This is the unique solution of $a + x = b + y = c$, meaning that the maximum involved in $f(x, y)$ is attained not just twice but three times. The following result is easily seen in Figure 9.1.

PROPOSITION 9.1. *Two general tropical lines intersect in a unique point. Two general points lie on a unique tropical line.*

Consider now an arbitrary tropical polynomial in two variables

$$f(x, y) \quad = \quad \sum_{(i,j) \in \mathcal{A}} \omega_{ij} x^i y^j.$$

Here $\mathcal{A}$ is a finite subset of $\mathbb{Z}^2$. Note that it is important to specify the support set $\mathcal{A}$ because the term $\omega_{ij} x^i y^j$ is present even if $\omega_{ij} = 0$. For any two points (i', j'), (i'', j'') in $\mathcal{A}$, we consider the system of linear inequalities

(9.3)
$$\omega_{i'j'} + i'x + j'y \ = \ \omega_{i''j''} + i''x + j''y \ \geq \ \omega_{ij} + ix + jy \quad \text{for } (i,j) \in \mathcal{A}.$$

The solution set of (9.3) is either empty, or a point, or a line segment, or a ray in $\mathbb{R}^2$. The union of these solution sets, as (i', j'), (i'', j'') range over distinct points in $\mathcal{A}$, is the tropical curve defined by $f(x, y)$.

We use the following method to compute and draw this curve. For each point (i, j) in $\mathcal{A}$, plot the point (i, j, ω_{ij}) in 3-space. The convex hull of these points is a 3-dimensional polytope. Consider the set of upper faces of this polytope. These are the faces which have an upward pointing outer normal. The collection of these faces

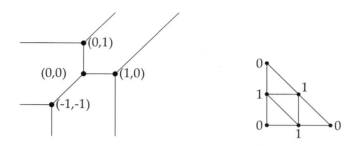

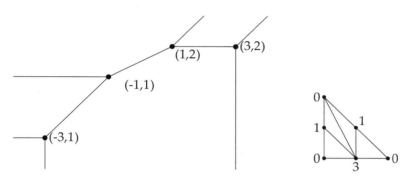

FIGURE 9.2. A quadratic curve

FIGURE 9.3. Another quadratic curve

maps bijectively onto the convex hull of $\mathcal{A}$ under deleting the third coordinates. It defines a *regular subdivision* Δ_ω of $\mathcal{A}$.

PROPOSITION 9.2. *The solution set to (9.3) is a segment if and only if (i', j') and (i'', j'') are connected by an interior edge in the regular subdivision Δ_ω, and it is a ray if and only if they are connected by a boundary edge of Δ_ω. The tropical curve of $f(x, y)$ is the union of these segments and rays.*

An analogous statement holds in higher dimensions: The tropical hypersurface of a multivariate polynomial $f(x_1, \dots, x_n)$ is an unbounded polyhedral complex geometrically dual to the regular subdivision Δ_ω of the support of f. If the coefficients of the tropical polynomial f are sufficiently generic, then Δ_ω is a regular triangulation. If, in addition, every simplex in Δ_ω has unit volume then the hypersurface is said to be *smooth*.

Returning to the case $n = 2$, here are a few examples of smooth curves.

EXAMPLE 9.3. *(Two Quadratic Curves)* A smooth quadratic curve in the plane is a trivalent graph with four vertices, connected by three bounded edges and six unbounded edges. These six rays come in three pairs which go off in directions west, south and northeast. The primitive vectors on the three edges emanating from any vertex always sum to zero. Our first example is

$$f_1(x, y) \quad = \quad 0x^2 + 1xy + 0y^2 + 1x + 1y + 0.$$

The curve of $f_1(x, y)$ has the four vertices $(0, 0)$, $(1, 0)$, $(0, 1)$ and $(-1, -1)$. It is depicted in Figure 9.2.

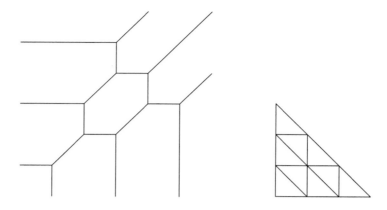

FIGURE 9.4. A cubic curve

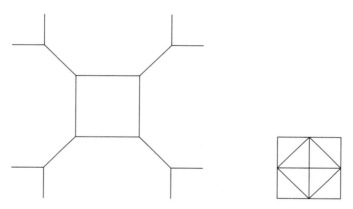

FIGURE 9.5. A biquadratic curve

We now gradually increase the coefficient of x from 1 to 3 and we observe what happens to our curve during this homotopy. The final curve is

$$f_3(x, y) \quad = \quad 0x^2 + 1xy + 0y^2 + 3x + 1y + 0.$$

This curve has the four vertices $(-3, -1)$, $(-1, 1)$, $(1, 2)$ and $(3, 2)$. It is depicted in Figure 9.3.

EXAMPLE 9.4. (*Two Elliptic Curves*) The *genus* of a smooth tropical curve is the number of bounded regions in its complement. The two quadratic curves divide the plane into six regions, all of them unbounded, so their genus is zero. A tropical elliptic curve has precisely one bounded region in its complement. A smooth cubic curve in the projective plane has this property, as seen in Figure 9.4.

Of course, we can also pick a different support set whose convex hull has exactly one interior lattice point. An example is the square of side length 2. It corresponds to a curve of bidegree $(2, 2)$ in the product of two projective lines $\mathbb{P}^1 \times \mathbb{P}^1$. Such curves are elliptic, as seen in Figure 9.5.

The result of Proposition 9.1 can be extended from tropical lines to tropical curves of any degree, and, in fact, to tropical hypersurfaces in any dimension. In

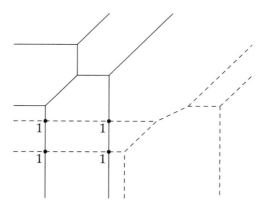

FIGURE 9.6. The Tropical Bézout theorem

particular, any two general quadratic curves in the plane meet in four points. An example is shown in Figure 9.6.

THEOREM 9.5. **(Tropical Bézout-Bernstein Theorem)** *Two general tropical curves of degrees d and e intersect in $d \cdot e$ points, counting multiplicities as explained below. More generally, the number of intersection points of two tropical curves with prescribed Newton polygons equals the mixed area of these polygons.*

We need to explain the multiplicities arising when intersecting two tropical curves. Consider two lines with rational slopes in the plane, where the primitive lattice vectors along the lines are (u_1, v_1) and (u_2, v_2). The two lines meet in exactly one point if and only if the determinant $u_1 v_2 - u_2 v_1$ is nonzero. The *multiplicity* of this intersection point is defined as $|u_1 v_2 - u_2 v_1|$.

This definition of multiplicity ensures that the total count of the intersection points is invariant under parallel displacement of the tropical curves. For instance, in the case of two curves in the tropical projective plane, we can displace the curves of degree d and e in such a way that all intersection points are gotten by intersecting the southern rays of the first curve with the eastern rays of the second curve, as in Figure 9.6. Clearly, there are precisely $d \cdot e$ such intersection points, and their local multiplicities are all one.

To prove the tropical Bernstein theorem, we use exactly the same method as in Chapter 3. Namely, we observe that the union of the two curves is the geometric dual of a mixed subdivision of the Minkowski sum of the two Newton polygons. The mixed cells in this mixed subdivision correspond to the intersection points of the two curves. The local intersection multiplicity at such a point, $|u_1 v_2 - u_2 v_1|$, is the area of the corresponding mixed cell. Hence the mixed area, which is the total area of all mixed cells, coincides with the number of intersection points, counting multiplicity. Figure 9.7 demonstrates this reasoning for the intersection of two quadratic curves.

9.2. Amoebas and their Tentacles

Let X be any subvariety of the n-dimensional algebraic torus $(\mathbb{C}^*)^n$. The *amoeba* of X is defined to be the image $\log(X)$ of X under the componentwise

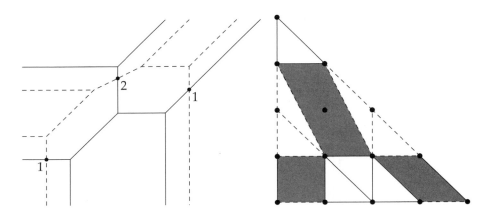

FIGURE 9.7. The Tropical Bernstein theorem

logarithm map from $(\mathbb{C}^*)^n$ into $\mathbb{R}^n$:

$$(9.4) \qquad \log : (\mathbb{C}^*)^n \to \mathbb{R}^n, \quad (z_1, \ldots, z_n) \mapsto \big(\log|z_1|, \log|z_2|, \ldots, \log|z_n|\big)$$

The computational study of amoebas is an important new direction in the general field of "Solving Polynomial Equations". Even testing membership in the amoeba is a non-trivial problem. Consider the question whether or not the origin $(0, 0, \ldots, 0)$ lies in $\log(X)$, where X is given by its vanishing ideal of Laurent polynomials. This problem is equivalent to the following: *Given a system of polynomial equations over the complex numbers, does there exist a solution all of whose coordinates are complex numbers of unit length?*

We shall not pursue this question any further here. Instead, we shall take a closer look at the tentacles of the amoeba. The term *amoeba* was coined by Gel'fand, Kapranov and Zelevinsky [**GKZ94**, Chapter 11.5]. In the case when X is a hypersurface, the complement of X in $\mathbb{R}^n$ is a union of finitely many open convex regions, at most one for each lattice point in the Newton polytope of the defining polynomial of X; see [**FPT00**]. For $n = 2$, the amoeba does look like one of these biological organisms, with unbounded tentacles going off to infinity. These tentacle directions are normal to the edges of the Newton polygon, just like the tentacles of a tropical curve. We shall see that this is no coincidence.

Given any variety X in $(\mathbb{C}^*)^n$ we define a subset $\mathcal{B}(X)$ of the unit $(n-1)$-sphere S^{n-1} in $\mathbb{R}^n$ as follows. A point $p \in S^{n-1}$ lies in $\mathcal{B}(X)$ if and only if there exists a sequence of vectors $p^{(1)}, p^{(2)}, p^{(3)}, \ldots$ in $\mathbb{R}^n$ such that

$$p^{(r)} \in \log(X) \cap r \cdot S^{n-1} \text{ for all } r \geq 1 \quad \text{and} \quad \lim_{r \to \infty} \frac{1}{r} \cdot p^{(r)} = p.$$

The set $\mathcal{B}(X)$ was first introduced by George Bergman [**Ber71**] who called it the *logarithmic limit set* of the variety X. We write $\tilde{\mathcal{B}}(X)$ for the subset of all vectors p in $\mathbb{R}^n$ such that either $p = 0$ or $\frac{1}{||p||} \cdot p$ lies in $\mathcal{B}(X)$. We refer to $\mathcal{B}(X)$ as the *Bergman complex* of X and to $\tilde{\mathcal{B}}(X)$ as the *Bergman fan* of X. These objects are polyhedral by the following result due to Bieri and Groves [**BG84**].

THEOREM 9.6. *The Bergman fan $\tilde{\mathcal{B}}(X)$ of a d-dimensional irreducible subvariety X of $(\mathbb{C}^*)^n$ is a finite union of rational d-dimensional convex polyhedral cones* *with apex at the origin. The intersection of any two cones is a common face of each. Hence $\mathcal{B}(X)$ is a pure $(d-1)$-dimensional polyhedral complex.*

Before discussing the proof of this theorem, let us to consider some special cases of low dimension or low codimension. Clearly, if $X = X_1 \cup X_2 \cup \cdots \cup X_r$ is a reducible variety then its Bergman complex equals $\mathcal{B}(X) = \mathcal{B}(X_1) \cup \mathcal{B}(X_2) \cup \cdots \cup \mathcal{B}(X_r)$. We start out with the case when each X_i is a point.

- $d = 0$: If X is a finite subset of $(\mathbb{C}^*)^n$ then $\mathcal{B}(X)$ is the empty set.
- $d = 1$: If X is a curve then $\mathcal{B}(X)$ is a finite subset of the unit sphere. The directions in $\mathcal{B}(X)$ are called *critical tropisms* in singularity theory.
- $d = 2$: If X is a surface then $\mathcal{B}(X)$ is a graph embedded in the unit sphere S^{n-1}. This geometric graph retains all the symmetries of X.
- $d = n - 1$: If X is a hypersurface whose defining polynomial has the Newton polytope P then $\mathcal{B}(X)$ is the intersection of S^{n-1} with the collection of proper faces in the normal fan of P. Thus $\mathcal{B}(X)$ is a radial projection of the $(n-1)$-skeleton of the dual polytope P^*.

Bergman [**Ber71**] showed that $\mathcal{B}(X)$ is a discrete union of spherical polytopes, and he conjectured that this union is finite and equidimensional. This conjecture was proved using valuation theory by Bieri and Groves [**BG84**]. In what follows we shall outline a simpler proof of Theorem 9.6 using Gröbner bases.

Let I be any ideal in the polynomial ring $R = \mathbb{C}[x_1^{\pm 1}, \ldots, x_n^{\pm 1}]$. For instance, I could be the prime ideal defining our irreducible variety X.

For a fixed weight vector $\omega \in \mathbb{R}^n$, we use the following notation. For any Laurent polynomial $f = \sum c_\alpha x^\alpha$, the initial form $in_\omega(f)$ is the sum of all terms $c_\alpha x^\alpha$ such that the inner product $\omega\alpha$ is maximal. The *initial ideal* $in_\omega(I)$ is the ideal generated by the initial forms $in_\omega(f)$ where f runs over I. Note that $in_\omega(I)$ will be the unit ideal in R if ω is chosen sufficiently generic. We are interested in the set of exceptional ω for which $in_\omega(I)$ does not contain any monomials (i.e. units). This is precisely the Bergman fan.

LEMMA 9.7. *Let X be any variety in $(\mathbb{C}^*)^n$ and I its vanishing ideal. Then*

$$\tilde{\mathcal{B}}(X) \;=\; \{\, \omega \in \mathbb{R}^n : in_\omega(I) \text{ does not contain a monomial} \,\}.$$

We sometimes use the notation $\tilde{\mathcal{B}}(I)$ for the Bergman fan of an ideal I, defined by the above formula, and similarly $\mathcal{B}(I)$ for the Bergman complex.

Consider the closure of X in n-dimensional complex projective space $\mathbb{P}^n$ and let J denote the homogeneous ideal in $S = \mathbb{C}[x_0, x_1, \ldots, x_n]$ which defines this closure. The ideal J is computed from I by homogenizing the given generators and saturating with respect to the ideal $\langle x_0 \rangle$. For any $\omega \in \mathbb{R}^n$, the initial ideal $in_\omega(I)$ is computed as follows: form the vector $(0, \omega)$ in $\mathbb{R}^{n+1}$, compute the initial ideal $in_{(0,\omega)}(J)$, and then replace x_0 by 1.

COROLLARY 9.8. $\tilde{\mathcal{B}}(X) = \{\, \omega \in \mathbb{R}^n : in_{(0,\omega)}(J) \text{ contains no monomial in } S \,\}.$

Proof of Theorem 9.6: Two vectors ω and ω' in $\mathbb{R}^n$ are considered equivalent for J if $in_{(0,\omega)}(J) = in_{(0,\omega')}(J)$. The equivalence classes are the relatively open cones in a complete fan in $\mathbb{R}^n$ called the *Gröbner fan* of J. This fan is the outer normal fan of the *state polytope* of J. See Chapter 2 in [**Stu95**]. If C is any cone in the Gröbner fan then we write $in_C(J)$ for $in_\omega(J)$ where ω is any vector in the relative interior of C.

The finiteness and completeness of the Gröbner fan together with Corollary 9.8 imply that $\tilde{\mathcal{B}}(X)$ is a finite union of rational polyhedral cones in $\mathbb{R}^n$. Indeed, $\tilde{\mathcal{B}}(X)$ is the support of the subfan of the Gröbner fan of J consisting of all Gröbner cones C such that $in_C(J)$ contains no monomial. Note that if C is any such cone then the Bergman fan of the zero set X_C of the initial ideal $in_C(J)$ in $(\mathbb{C}^*)^n$ equals

$$(9.5) \qquad\qquad \tilde{\mathcal{B}}(X_C) \quad = \quad star_C \tilde{\mathcal{B}}(X) + \mathbb{R} \cdot C,$$

where $star_C \tilde{\mathcal{B}}(X)$ is the fan consisting of all cones in $\tilde{\mathcal{B}}(X)$ which contain C. What remains to be proved is that the maximal Gröbner cones C which lie in $\tilde{\mathcal{B}}(X)$ all have the same dimension d. For that we need the following lemma.

LEMMA 9.9. *Let L be a homogeneous ideal in the polynomial ring S, containing no monomials and $X(L)$ its zero set in the algebraic torus $(\mathbb{C}^*)^n$. Then the following are equivalent:*

(1) *Every proper initial ideal of L contains a monomial.*
(2) *There exists a subtorus T of $(\mathbb{C}^*)^n$ such that $X(L)$ consists of finitely many T-orbits.*
(3) *The Bergman fan $\tilde{\mathcal{B}}(X(L))$ is a linear subspace of $\mathbb{R}^n$.*

Proof of Theorem 9.6 (continued): Let C be a cone in the Gröbner fan of J which is maximal with respect to containment in $\tilde{\mathcal{B}}(X)$. The ideal $L = in_C(J)$ satisfies the three equivalent properties in Lemma 9.9. The projective variety defined by L is equidimensional of the same dimension as the irreducible projective variety defined by J. Equidimensionality follows, for instance, from [**KS95**]. We conclude that $dim(X(L)) = dim(X) = d$. Hence the subtorus T in property (2) and the subspace in property (3) of Lemma 9.9 both have dimension d. It follows from (9.5) that

$$\tilde{\mathcal{B}}(X(L)) \quad = \quad \tilde{\mathcal{B}}(X_C) \quad = \quad \mathbb{R} \cdot C,$$

and we conclude that the Gröbner cone C has dimension d, as desired. $\square$

Proof of Lemma 9.9: Let $\mathcal{L}$ denote the linear subspace of $\mathbb{R}^n$ consisting of all vectors ω such that $in_\omega(L) = L$. In other words, $\mathcal{L}$ is the common lineality space of all cones in the Gröbner fan of L. A non-zero vector $(\omega_1, \dots, \omega_n)$ lies in $\mathcal{L}$ if and only if the one-parameter subgroup $\{ (t^{\omega_1}, \dots, t^{\omega_n}) : t \in \mathbb{C}^* \}$ fixes L. The subtorus T generated by these one-parameter subgroups of $(\mathbb{C}^*)^n$ has the same dimension as $\mathcal{L}$, and it fixes the variety $X(L)$. We now replace $(\mathbb{C}^*)^n$ by its quotient $(\mathbb{C}^*)^n/T$, and we replace $\mathbb{R}^n$ by its quotient $\mathbb{R}^n/\mathcal{L}$. This reduces our lemma to the following easier assertion: *For a homogeneous ideal L which contains no monomial the following are equivalent:*

(1') *For any non-zero vector ω, the initial ideal $in_\omega(L)$ contains a monomial.*
(2') *$X(L)$ is finite.*
(3') *$\tilde{\mathcal{B}}(X(L)) = \{0\}$.*

The equivalence of (1') and (3') is immediate from Corollary 9.8, and the equivalence of (2') and (3') follows from Theorem 3 in [**Ber71**]. It can also be derived from the well-known fact that a subvariety of $(\mathbb{C}^*)^n$ is compact if and only if it is finite. $\square$

Our proof suggests the following algorithm for computing the Bergman complex of an algebraic variety. First compute the Gröbner fan, or the state polytope, of the homogenization of its defining ideal. See Chapter 3 of [**Stu95**] for details. For certain nice varieties we might know a *universal Gröbner basis* and from this one can read off the Gröbner fan more easily. We then check all d-dimensional cones C in the Gröbner fan, or equivalently, all $(n-d)$-dimensional faces of the state polytope, and for each of them we determine whether or not $in_C(I)$ contains a monomial. This happens if and only if the reduced Gröbner basis of $in_C(I)$ in any term order contains a monomial. Here is an example to demonstrate these methods.

EXAMPLE 9.10. The Bergman complex of the Grassmannian $G_{2,5}$ of lines in $\mathbb{P}^4$ is the Petersen graph. The Grassmannian $G_{2,5}$ is the subvariety of $\mathbb{P}^9$ whose prime ideal is generated by the following five quadratic polynomials:

(9.6)
$$p_{03}p_{12} - p_{02}p_{13} + \underline{p_{01}p_{23}}, \ p_{04}p_{12} - p_{02}p_{14} + \underline{p_{01}p_{24}},$$
$$p_{04}p_{13} - p_{03}p_{14} + \underline{p_{01}p_{34}}, \ p_{04}p_{23} - p_{03}p_{24} + \underline{p_{02}p_{34}},$$
$$p_{14}p_{23} - p_{13}p_{24} + p_{12}\underline{p_{34}}.$$

A universal Gröbner basis consists of these five quadrics together with fifteen cubics such as $p_{01}p_{02}p_{34} - p_{02}p_{03}p_{14} + p_{03}p_{04}p_{12} + p_{04}p_{01}p_{23}$. The ideal of $G_{2,5}$ has 132 initial monomial ideals. They come in three symmetry classes:

$$
\begin{array}{ll}
\langle p_{02}p_{13}, p_{02}p_{14}, p_{04}p_{13}, p_{04}p_{23}, p_{14}p_{23}\rangle & \text{12 ideals}, \\
\langle p_{02}p_{14}, p_{04}p_{13}, p_{04}p_{23}, p_{14}p_{23}, p_{01}p_{23}\rangle & \text{60 ideals}, \\
\langle p_{01}p_{14}p_{23}, p_{01}p_{24}, p_{03}p_{12}, p_{03}p_{14}, p_{03}p_{24}, p_{13}p_{24}\rangle & \text{60 ideals}.
\end{array}
$$

We regard $G_{2,5}$ as the 7-dimensional variety in $(\mathbb{C}^*)^{10}$ consisting of all nonzero vectors $(p_{01}, \ldots, p_{34})$ formed by the 2×2-minors of any complex 2×5-matrix. Hence $n = 10$ and $d = 7$. The common lineality space $\mathcal{L}$ of all Gröbner cones has dimension 5; hence the state polytope of $G_{2,5}$ is 5-dimensional as well. Working modulo $\mathcal{L}$ as in the proof of Lemma 9.9, we conclude that $\tilde{\mathcal{B}}(G_{2,5})$ is a finite union of 2-dimensional cones in a 5-dimensional space. Equivalently, it is a finite union of spherical line segments on the 4-dimension sphere. We consider $\mathcal{B}(G_{2,5})$ in this embedding as a graph in the 4-sphere.

By doing a local computation for the Gröbner cones of the three distinct reduced Gröbner bases (modulo symmetry), we found that this graph has 10 vertices and 15 edges. The vertices are the rays spanned by the vectors $-e_{ij}$, the images modulo $\mathcal{L}$ of the negated unit vectors in $\mathbb{R}^{10}$. The corresponding initial ideal is gotten by erasing those monomials which contain variable p_{ij}. It is generated by three quadratic binomials and two quadratic trinomials.

Two vertices are connected by an edge if and only if the index sets of the two unit vectors are disjoint. Hence the graph $\tilde{\mathcal{B}}(G_{2,5})$ is isomorphic to the graph whose vertices are the 2-subsets of $\{0, 1, 2, 3, 4\}$ and whose edges are disjoint pairs. This is the Petersen graph. The edges correspond to the fifteen deformations of $G_{2,5}$ to a toric variety. See Example 11.9 in [**Stu95**]. For instance, the initial ideal corresponding to the disjoint pair $(\{0, 1\}, \{3, 4\})$ is gotten by setting the two underlined variables to zero in (9.6). □

9.3. The Bergman Complex of a Linear Space

We next compute the Bergman complex of an arbitrary linear subspace in terms of matroid theory. Let I be an ideal in $\mathbb{Q}[x_1, \ldots, x_n]$ generated by (homogeneous) linear forms. Let d be the dimension of the space of linear forms in I. A d-subset $\{i_1, \ldots, i_d\}$ of $\{1, \ldots, n\}$ is a *basis* if there does not exist a non-zero linear form in I

depending only on $\{x_1, \ldots, x_n\} \setminus \{x_{i_1}, \ldots, x_{i_d}\}$. The collection of bases is denoted M and called the *matroid* of I.

In the following, we investigate the Bergman complex of an *arbitrary* matroid M of rank d on the ground set $\{1, 2, \ldots, n\}$. We do not even require the matroid M to be representable over any field. One of many axiomatization of abstract matroids goes like this: take any collection M of $(n-d)$-subsets σ of $\{1, 2, \ldots, n\}$ and form the convex hull of the points $\sum_{i \in \sigma} e_i$ in $\mathbb{R}^n$. Then M is a matroid if and only if every edge of this convex hull is a parallel translate of the difference $e_i - e_j$ of two unit vectors. In this case, we call the above convex hull the *matroid polytope* of M.

Fix any vector $\omega \in \mathbb{R}^n$. We are interested in all the bases of M having *minimum* ω-cost. The set of these optimal bases is itself the set of bases of a matroid M_ω of rank d on $\{1, \ldots, n\}$. The matroid polytope of M_ω is the face of the matroid polytope of M at which the linear functional ω is minimized. An element of the matroid is a *loop* if it does not occur in any basis.

In the amoeba framework the correspondence between the tentacle characterization and the matroid characterization can be stated as follows.

LEMMA 9.11. *Let I be an ideal generated by linear forms, M be the associated matroid and $\omega \in \mathbb{R}^n$. Then the ideal $\mathrm{in}_\omega(I)$ does not contain any variable x_i if and only if the matroid M_ω does not have a loop.*

We may assume without loss of generality that ω is a vector of unit length having coordinate sum zero. The set of these vectors is

$$S^{n-2} \quad = \quad \{\, \omega \in \mathbb{R}^n : \omega_1 + \omega_2 + \cdots + \omega_n = 0 \text{ and } \omega_1^2 + \omega_2^2 + \cdots + \omega_n^2 = 1 \,\}.$$

The *Bergman complex* of an arbitrary matroid M is defined as the set

$$\mathcal{B}(M) \quad := \quad \{\, \omega \in S^{n-2} : M_\omega \text{ has no loops} \,\}.$$

THEOREM 9.12. *The Bergman complex $\mathcal{B}(M)$ of a rank d matroid M is a pure $(d-2)$-dimensional polyhedral complex embedded in the $(n-2)$-sphere.*

Clearly, $\mathcal{B}(M)$ is a subcomplex in the spherical polar to the matroid polytope of M. The content of this theorem is that each face of the matroid polytope of M whose matroid M_ω has no loops, and is minimal with this property, has codimension $n - d + 1$. If M is represented by a linear ideal I then $\mathcal{B}(M)$ coincides with $\mathcal{B}(X)$ where X is the variety of I in $(\mathbb{C}^*)^n$. In this case, Theorem 9.12 is simply a special case of Theorem 9.6. However, when M is not representable, then we need to give a new proof of Theorem 9.12. This can be done using an inductive argument involving the matroidal operations of *contraction* and *deletion*.

We wish to propose the combinatorial problem of studying the complex $\mathcal{B}(M)$ for various classes of matroids M. For instance, for $rank(M) = 3$ we always get a subgraph of the ridge graph of the matroid polytope, and for $rank(M) = 4$ we get a two-dimensional complex. What kind of extremal behavior, in terms of face numbers, homology etc...etc... can we expect? What is the most practical algorithm for computing $\mathcal{B}(M)$ from M?

EXAMPLE 9.13. Let M be the uniform matroid of rank d on $\{1, 2, \ldots, n\}$. Then $\mathcal{B}(M)$ is the set of all vectors ω in S^{n-2} whose largest $n - d + 1$ coordinates are all equal. This set can be identified with the $(d-2)$-skeleton of the $(n-1)$-simplex. For instance, let M be the uniform rank 3 matroid on $\{1, 2, 3, 4, 5\}$. Then $\mathcal{B}(M)$

is the complete graph K_5, which has ten edges, embedded in the 3-sphere S^3 with vertices

$$\Big(\frac{1}{2\sqrt{5}}, \frac{1}{2\sqrt{5}}, \frac{1}{2\sqrt{5}}, \frac{1}{2\sqrt{5}}, -\frac{2}{\sqrt{5}}\Big), \Big(\frac{1}{2\sqrt{5}}, \frac{1}{2\sqrt{5}}, \frac{1}{2\sqrt{5}}, -\frac{2}{\sqrt{5}}, \frac{1}{2\sqrt{5}}\Big), \dots$$

These vectors are normal to the ten facets of the second hypersimplex in $\mathbb{R}^5$, which is the polytope $\mathrm{conv}\{\, e_i + e_j \,:\, 1 \leq i < j \leq 5 \,\}$.

EXAMPLE 9.14. Let M be the rank 3 matroid on $\{1, 2, 3, 4, 5\}$ which has eight bases and two non-bases $\{1, 2, 3\}$ and $\{1, 4, 5\}$. Then $\mathcal{B}(M)$ is the complete bipartite graph $K_{3,3}$, given with a canonical embedding in the 3-sphere S^3.

EXAMPLE 9.15. Consider the codimension two subvariety X of $(\mathbb{C}^*)^6$ defined by the following two linear equations:

$$x_1 + x_2 - x_4 - x_5 \quad = \quad x_2 + x_3 - x_5 - x_6 \quad = \quad 0.$$

We wish to describe its Bergman complex $\mathcal{B}(X)$, or, equivalently, by Theorem 9.16 below, we wish to solve these two linear equations tropically. This amounts to finding all initial ideals of the ideal of these two linear forms which contain no variable, or equivalently, we are interested in all faces of the polar of the matroid polytope which correspond to loopless matroids.

We can think of $x_1, x_2, \dots, x_6$ as the vertices of a regular octahedron, where the affine dependencies are precisely given by our equations. The Bergman complex $\mathcal{B}(X)$ has 9 vertices, 24 edges, 20 triangles and 3 quadrangles. The 9 vertices come in two symmetry classes. There are six vertices which we identify with the vertices x_i of the octahedron. The other three vertices are drawn in the inside of the octahedron: they correspond to the three symmetry planes. We then take the boundary complex of the octahedron plus certain natural connection to the three inside points.

9.4. The Tropical Variety of an Ideal

We now connect tropical geometry with algebraic geometry in the usual sense. The basic idea is to introduce an auxiliary variable t and to take exponents of t as the coefficients in a tropical polynomial. More precisely, let f be any polynomial in $\mathbb{Q}[t, x_1, x_2, \dots, x_n]$, written as a polynomial in $x_1, \dots, x_n$,

$$f \quad = \quad \sum_{a \in \mathcal{A}} p_a(t) \cdot x_1^{a_1} x_2^{a_2} \cdots x_n^{a_n}.$$

We define the *tropicalization* of f to be the polynomial

$$\mathrm{trop}(f) \quad = \quad \sum_{a \in \mathcal{A}} (-\mathrm{lowdeg}(p_a)) \cdot x_1^{a_1} x_2^{a_2} \cdots x_n^{a_n} \quad \in \mathbb{N}[x_1, \dots, x_n],$$

where $\mathrm{lowdeg}(p_a)$ is the largest integer u such that t^u divides $p_a(t)$. For instance, for any non-zero rational numbers a, b and c, the polynomial

$$f \quad = \quad a \cdot t^3 x_1^5 + b \cdot t^7 x_1^5 + c \cdot t^2 x_1 x_2^4.$$

has the tropicalization

$$\mathrm{trop}(f) \quad = \quad (-3) \cdot x_1^5 + (-2) \cdot x_1 x_2^4.$$

The negation in the definition of $\mathrm{trop}(f)$ is necessary because we are taking the *maximum* of linear forms when we evaluate a tropical polynomial. On the other hand, when working with Puiseux series, as in the definition of $\log(X)$ below, we always take the *minimum* of the occurring exponents.

Given any ideal I in $\mathbb{Q}[t, x_1, \dots, x_n]$, we defined its *tropical variety* to be the tropical variety in $\mathbb{R}^n$ defined by the tropical polynomials $\text{trop}(f)$ as f runs over all polynomials in I. If the auxiliary variable t does not appear in any of the generators of I then I can be regarded as an ideal in $\mathbb{Q}[x_1, \dots, x_n]$. In this case we recover the Bergman complex.

THEOREM 9.16. *Let I be an ideal in $\mathbb{Q}[x_1, \dots, x_n]$ and X the variety it defines in $(\mathbb{C}^*)^n$. Then the tropical variety $\text{trop}(I)$ equals the Bergman fan $\mathcal{B}(X)$.*

In the more general case when t does appear in I, the tropical variety $\text{trop}(I)$ is not a fan, but it is a polyhedral complex with possibly many bounded faces. We have seen many examples of tropical curves at the beginning of this chapter. In those cases, I is a principal ideal in $\mathbb{Q}[x, y]$.

Consider the algebraically closed field $K = \mathbb{C}\{\{t\}\}$ of Puiseux series. Every Puiseux series $x(t)$ has a unique lowest term $a \cdot t^u$ where $a \in \mathbb{C}^*$ and $u \in \mathbb{Q}$. Setting $\text{val}(f) = u$, this defines the canonical *valuation map*

$$\text{val} : (K^*)^n \to \mathbb{Q}^n, \ (x_1, x_2, \dots, x_n) \mapsto \big(\text{val}(x_1), \text{val}(x_2), \dots, \text{val}(x_n)\big).$$

If X is any subvariety of $(K^*)^n$ then we can consider its image $\text{val}(X)$ in $\mathbb{Q}^n$. The closure of $\text{val}(X)$ in $\mathbb{R}^n$ is called the *non-archimedean amoeba* of X.

The following is our main theorem. It identifies all the piecewise-linear objects introduced in this chapter. The algorithmic importance of this theorem lies in the fact that we can compute arbitrary tropical varieties using Gröbner basis methods.

THEOREM 9.17. *Let I be any ideal in $\mathbb{Q}[t, x_1, \dots, x_n]$ and X its variety in $(K^*)^n$. Then the following three subsets of $\mathbb{R}^n$ coincide:*

- *The negative $-\text{val}(X)$ of the non-archimedean amoeba of the variety $X \subset (K^*)^n$,*
- *the tropical variety $\text{trop}(I)$ of I,*
- *the intersection of the Bergman complex $\mathcal{B}(I)$ in S^n with the southern hemisphere $\{t < 0\}$, identified with $\mathbb{R}^n$ via stereographic projection.*

Theorem 9.17 implies Theorem 9.16. The proof of Theorem 9.17 is not given here. It is based on reduction to the zero-dimensional case, by examining monomial curves and then applying Puiseux's theorem. This method was introduced by Kapranov [**Kap00**] who proved Theorem 9.17 in the case when X is a hypersurface.

Let us illustrate Theorem 9.17 for our most basic example, the solution to the quadratic equation. Suppose $n = 1$ and consider an ideal of the form

$$I = \langle \alpha t^a x^2 + \beta t^b x + \gamma t^c \rangle,$$

where α, β, γ are non-zero rationals and a, b, c are integers with $a + c \geq 2b$. Then $\text{trop}(I)$ is the variety of the tropicalization $(-a)x^2 + (-b)x + (-c)$ of the ideal generator. Since $(-a) + (-c) \leq 2(-b)$, we have $\text{trop}(I) = \{a - b, b - c\}$. The variety of X in the affine line over $K = \mathbb{C}\{\{t\}\}$ equals

$$X = \left\{ -\frac{\beta}{\alpha} t^{b-a} + \cdots, -\frac{\gamma}{\beta} t^{c-b} + \cdots \right\}.$$

Hence $\text{val}(X) = \{b - a, c - b\} = -\text{trop}(I)$. The Bergman fan $\tilde{\mathcal{B}}(I)$ of the bivariate ideal I is a one-dimensional fan in the (t, x)-plane $\mathbb{R}^2$, consisting of three rays.

These rays are generated by $(-1, a - b)$, $(-1, b - c)$ and $(2, c - a)$, and hence the intersection of $\tilde{\mathcal{B}}(I)$ with the line $t = -1$ is precisely trop(I).

9.5. Exercises

(1) Draw the graph and the variety of the tropical polynomial
$$f(x) \quad = \quad 10 + 9x + 7x^2 + 4x^3 + 0x^4.$$

(2) Draw the graph and the variety of the tropical polynomial
$$f(x, y) \quad = \quad 1x^2 + 2xy + 1y^2 + 3x + 3y + 1.$$

(3) Let I be the ideal of 3×3-minors of a 3×4-matrix of indeterminates. Compute the Bergman complex $\mathcal{B}(I)$ of this ideal.

(4) The Bergman complex $\mathcal{B}(M)$ of a rank 4 matroid M on $\{1, 2, 3, 4, 5, 6\}$ is a polyhedral surface embedded in the 4-sphere. What is the maximum number of vertices of $\mathcal{B}(M)$, as M ranges over all such matroids?

(5) Let I be a complete intersection ideal in $\mathbb{Q}[t, x_1, x_2, x_3]$ generated by two random polynomials of degree three. Describe trop(I) $\subset \mathbb{R}^3$.

(6) Prove that five general points in the plane determine a unique tropical quadric. What is the condition for six points in the plane to lie on a tropical quadric?

(7) Pick eight random points in the plane. Draw all tropical curves of degree three which pass through the eight points and which are not smooth.

(8) Determine the Bergman complex of the Grassmannian $G_{2,6}$ of lines in $\mathbb{P}^5$.

(9) Is there such a thing as a *tropical Buchberger algorithm*?

(10) On Tuesday, April 16, 2002, Maxim Kontsevich gave a lecture at Kansas State University in Manhattan, Kansas. What did he speak about?

CHAPTER 10

Linear Partial Differential Equations
with Constant Coefficients

Every system of polynomials translates naturally into a system of linear partial differential equations with constant coefficients. The equation

$$(10.1) \qquad \sum c_{i_1 i_2 \ldots i_n} x_1^{i_1} x_2^{i_2} \cdots x_n^{i_n} \quad = \quad 0$$

translates into the partial differential equation

$$(10.2) \qquad \sum c_{i_1 i_2 \ldots i_n} \frac{\partial^{i_1 + i_2 + \cdots + i_n} f}{\partial x_1^{i_1} \partial x_2^{i_2} \cdots \partial x_n^{i_n}} \quad = \quad 0$$

for an unknown function $f = f(x_1, \ldots, x_n)$. In this chapter we argue that it is advantageous to regard polynomials as linear PDEs, especially when the given polynomials have zeros with multiplicities or embedded components. This point of view was advocated by Wolfgang Gröbner, who frequently returned to this theme throughout his mathematical career, starting with his famous 1938 paper on the ideal-theoretic foundation of algebraic geometry [**Gro38**]; see also [**Gro39**].

The general theory was developed in the 1960's by Ehrenpreis and Palamodov, culminating in their *Fundamental Principle* which states that all solutions to a system of linear PDEs with constant coefficients have a certain integral representation over the underlying complex variety (Theorem 10.12). In the special case when I is a prime ideal, this representation was known to Gröbner in the 1930's. A good reference on the Fundamental Principle is the last chapter in Björk's book [**Bjö79**].

In the 1990's, Ulrich Oberst resumed Gröbner's tradition in Innsbruck, Tyrolia, with a sequence of important papers (specifically [**Obe95**] and [**Obe99**]) on this subject. These papers inspired the writing of this chapter. What follows is an introduction to the algebraic study of linear partial differential equations with constant coefficients, from the point of view of solving polynomial equations.

10.1. Why Differential Equations?

There are many good reasons for passing from polynomials to differential equations. The first reason is that we do not lose any information by doing so. The zeros of a polynomial system are recovered from the exponential solutions to the associated differential equations.

REMARK 10.1. A vector $p = (p_1, p_2, \ldots, p_n) \in \mathbb{C}^n$ is a solution to the polynomial equation (10.1) if and only if the exponential function $\exp(p \cdot x) = \exp(p_1 x_1 + p_2 x_2 + \cdots + p_n x_n)$ is a solution of the differential equation (10.2).

However, we wish to argue that the differential equations are somehow better. Let us illustrate this for one simple quadratic equation in one variable:

$$(10.3) \qquad x^2 \;=\; \alpha^2$$

where α is a real parameter. This equation has two distinct solutions, namely $x = \alpha$ and $x = -\alpha$, provided the parameter α is non-zero. For $\alpha = 0$, there is only one solution, namely $x = 0$, and conventional algebraic wisdom tells us that this solution is to be regarded as having multiplicity 2. In the design of homotopy methods for solving algebraic equations, such multiple points create considerable difficulties, both conceptually and numerically.

Consider the translation of (10.3) into an ordinary differential equation:

$$(10.4) \qquad f''(x) \;=\; \alpha^2 \cdot f(x).$$

The solution space V_α to (10.4) is always a two-dimensional complex vector space, for any value of α. For $\alpha \neq 0$, this space has a basis of exponentials,

$$V_\alpha \;=\; \mathbb{C}\left\{\, \exp(\alpha \cdot x),\, \exp(-\alpha \cdot x) \,\right\},$$

but for $\alpha = 0$ these two basis vectors become linearly dependent. However, there exists a better choice of a basis which works for all values of α, namely,

$$(10.5) \qquad V_\alpha \;=\; \mathbb{C}\left\{\, \exp(\alpha \cdot x),\, \frac{1}{2\alpha}\big(\exp(\alpha \cdot x) - \exp(-\alpha \cdot x)\big) \,\right\},$$

This new basis behaves gracefully when we take the limit $\alpha \to 0$:

$$V_0 \;=\; \mathbb{C}\left\{\, 1,\, x \,\right\}.$$

The representation (10.5) displays V_α as a rank 2 vector bundle on the affine α-line. There was really nothing special about the point $\alpha = 0$ after all. Perhaps this vector bundle point of view might be useful in developing new reliable homotopy algorithms for numerically computing the complicated scheme structure which is frequently hidden in a given non-radical ideal.

Our second example is the following system of three polynomial equations

$$(10.6) \qquad x^3 = yz, \quad y^3 = xz, \quad z^3 = xy.$$

These equations translate into the three differential equations

$$(10.7) \qquad \frac{\partial^3 f}{\partial x^3} = \frac{\partial^2 f}{\partial y \partial z}, \quad \frac{\partial^3 f}{\partial y^3} = \frac{\partial^2 f}{\partial x \partial z} \quad \text{and} \quad \frac{\partial^3 f}{\partial z^3} = \frac{\partial^2 f}{\partial x \partial y}.$$

The set of entire functions $f(x, y, z)$ which satisfy the differential equations (10.7) is a complex vector space. This vector space has dimension 27, the Bézout number of (10.6). A solution basis for (10.7) is given by

$$\begin{aligned}
&\big\{\, \exp(x+y+z),\, \exp(x-y-z),\, \exp(y-x-z),\, \exp(z-x-y), \\
&\quad \exp(x+iy-iz),\, \exp(x-iy+iz),\, \exp(y+ix-iz),\, \exp(y-ix+iz), \\
&\quad \exp(z+ix-iy),\, \exp(z-ix+iy),\, \exp(iy+iz-x),\, \exp(-iy-iz-x), \\
&\quad \exp(ix+iz-y),\, \exp(-ix-iz-y),\, \exp(ix+iy-z),\, \exp(-ix-iy-z), \\
&\quad 1,\, x,\, y,\, z,\, z^2,\, y^2,\, x^2,\, x^3+6yz,\, y^3+6xz,\, z^3+6xy,\, x^4+y^4+z^4+24xyz \,\big\}
\end{aligned}$$

Here $i = \sqrt{-1}$. Using Remark 10.1 and results to be stated in the next sections, we can read off the following facts about our equations from the solution basis above:

(a) The system (10.6) has 17 distinct complex zeros, of which 5 are real.

(b) A point (a, b, c) is a zero of (10.6) if and only if $\exp(ax + by + cz)$ is a solution to (10.7). All zeros other than the origin have multiplicity one.

(c) The multiplicity of the origin $(0, 0, 0)$ as a zero of (10.6) is eleven. This number is the dimension of the space of polynomial solutions to (10.7).

(d) Every polynomial solution to (10.7) is gotten from one specific solution, namely, from $x^4 + y^4 + z^4 + 24xyz$, by taking successive derivatives.

(e) The local ring of (10.6) at the origin is Gorenstein.

We conclude that our solution basis to (10.7) contains all the information one might want about the solutions to the polynomial system (10.6). The aim of this chapter is to extend this kind of reasoning to arbitrary polynomial systems, that is, to arbitrary systems of linear PDEs with constant coefficients.

Our third and final example is to reinforce the view that, in a sense, the PDE formulation reveals a lot more information than the polynomial formulation. Consider the problem of solving the following polynomial equations:

$$(10.8) \qquad x_1^i + x_2^i + x_3^i + x_4^i \;=\; 0 \qquad \text{for all integers } i \geq 1.$$

The only solution is the origin $(0, 0, 0, 0)$, and this zero has multiplicity 24. In the corresponding PDE formulation one seeks to identify the vector space of all functions $f(x_1, x_2, x_3, x_4)$, on a suitable subset of $\mathbb{R}^4$ or $\mathbb{C}^4$, such that

$$(10.9) \qquad \frac{\partial^i f}{\partial x_1{}^i} + \frac{\partial^i f}{\partial x_2{}^i} + \frac{\partial^i f}{\partial x_3{}^i} + \frac{\partial^i f}{\partial x_4{}^i} \;=\; 0 \qquad \text{for all integers } i \geq 1.$$

Such functions are called *harmonic*. The space of harmonic functions has dimension 24. It consists of all successive derivatives of the *discriminant*

$$\Delta(x_1, x_2, x_3, x_4) \;=\; (x_1 - x_2)(x_1 - x_3)(x_1 - x_4)(x_2 - x_3)(x_2 - x_4)(x_3 - x_4).$$

Thus the solution space to (10.9) is the cyclic $\mathbb{C}\left[\frac{\partial}{\partial x_1}, \frac{\partial}{\partial x_2}, \frac{\partial}{\partial x_3}, \frac{\partial}{\partial x_4}\right]$-module generated by $\Delta(x_1, x_2, x_3, x_4)$. This is what "solving (10.8)" should really mean.

10.2. Zero-dimensional Ideals

We fix the polynomial ring $\mathbb{Q}[\partial] = \mathbb{Q}[\partial_1, \dots, \partial_n]$. The variables have funny names but they are commuting variables just like $x_1, \dots, x_n$ in the previous chapters. We shall be interested finding the solutions of an ideal I in $\mathbb{Q}[\partial]$. The material in this section is well-known in the Gröbner basis community. It is sometimes referred to as *Gröbner duality*. Two relevant references are [**MMM96**] and [**Mou97**].

Let $\mathcal{F}$ be a class of C^∞-functions on $\mathbb{R}^n$ or on $\mathbb{C}^n$ or on some subset thereof. For instance $\mathcal{F}$ might be the class of entire functions on $\mathbb{C}^n$. Then $\mathcal{F}$ is a module over the ring $\mathbb{Q}[\partial]$: polynomials in $\mathbb{Q}[\partial]$ acts on $\mathcal{F}$ by differentiation. More precisely, if $p(\partial_1, \partial_2, \dots, \partial_n)$ is a polynomial then it acts on $\mathcal{F}$ by sending a function $f = f(x_1, \dots, x_n)$ in the class $\mathcal{F}$ to the result of applying the differential operator $p(\frac{\partial}{\partial x_1}, \frac{\partial}{\partial x_2}, \dots, \frac{\partial}{\partial x_n})$ to f.

The class of functions $\mathcal{F}$ in which we are solving should always be chosen large enough in the following sense. If I is any ideal in $\mathbb{Q}[\partial]$ and $\mathrm{Sol}(I)$ is its solution set in $\mathcal{F}$ then the set of all operators which annihilate all functions in $\mathrm{Sol}(I)$ should be precisely equal to I. What this means algebraically is that $\mathcal{F}$ is supposed to be an *injective cogenerator* for $\mathbb{Q}[\partial]$. See [**Obe95**] for a discussion of such injective cogenerators $\mathcal{F}$. In what follows we will consider functions which are gotten by integrating products of exponentials and polynomials. Any class $\mathcal{F}$ containing these functions will be large enough.

We start out by reviewing the case of one variable, abbreviated $\partial = \partial_1$, over the field $\mathbb{C}$ of complex numbers. Here $I = \langle p \rangle$ is a principal ideal in $\mathbb{C}[\partial]$, generated by one polynomial which factors completely:

$$
\begin{aligned}
p(\partial) &= a_d \partial^d + a_{d-1} \partial^{d-1} + \cdots + a_2 \partial^2 + a_1 \partial + a_0 \\
&= (\partial - u_1)^{e_1} (\partial - u_2)^{e_2} \cdots (\partial - u_r)^{e_r}
\end{aligned}
$$

We can take $\mathcal{F}$ to be the set of entire functions on the complex plane $\mathbb{C}$. The ideal I represents the ordinary differential equation

$$(10.10) \qquad a_d \cdot f^{(d)}(x) + \cdots + a_2 \cdot f''(x) + a_1 \cdot f'(x) + a_0 \cdot f(x) \;=\; 0.$$

The solution space $\mathrm{Sol}(I)$ consists of all entire functions $f(x)$ which satisfy the equation (10.10). This is a complex vector space of dimension $d = e_1 + e_2 + \cdots + e_r$. A canonical basis for this space is given as follows:

$$(10.11) \quad \mathrm{Sol}(I) \;=\; \mathbb{C}\{\, x^j \cdot \exp(u_i \cdot x) \;\mid\; i = 1, 2, \ldots, r, \; j = 0, 1, \ldots, e_i - 1 \,\}.$$

We see that $\mathrm{Sol}(I)$ encodes all the zeros together with their multiplicities.

We now generalize the formula (10.11) to PDEs in n unknowns which have a finite-dimensional solution space. Let I be any zero-dimensional ideal in $\mathbb{C}[\partial] = \mathbb{C}[\partial_1, \ldots, \partial_n]$. We work over the complex numbers $\mathbb{C}$ instead of the rational numbers $\mathbb{Q}$ to keep things simpler. The variety of I is a finite set

$$\mathcal{V}(I) \;=\; \{\, u^{(1)}, u^{(2)}, \ldots, u^{(r)} \,\} \;\subset\; \mathbb{C}^n,$$

where $u^{(i)} = (u_1^{(i)}, \ldots, u_n^{(i)})$. The ideal I has a unique primary decomposition

$$I \;=\; Q_1 \cap Q_2 \cap \cdots \cap Q_r,$$

where Q_i is primary to the maximal ideal of the point $u^{(i)}$,

$$\mathrm{Rad}(Q_i) \;=\; \langle\, \partial_1 - u_1^{(i)}, \, \partial_2 - u_2^{(i)}, \, \ldots, \, \partial_n - u_n^{(i)} \,\rangle.$$

Given any operator p in $\mathbb{C}[\partial]$, we write $p(\partial + u^{(i)})$ for the operator gotten from $p(\partial)$ by replacing the variable ∂_j with $\partial_j + u_j^{(i)}$ for all $j \in \{1, 2, \ldots, n\}$. The following shifted ideal is primary to the maximal ideal $\langle \partial_1, \ldots, \partial_n \rangle$:

$$\mathrm{shift}(Q_i) \;=\; \langle\, p(\partial + u^{(i)}) \;:\; p \in Q_i \,\rangle.$$

Let $\mathrm{shift}(Q_i)^{\perp}$ denote the complex vector space of all polynomials $f \in \mathbb{C}[x_1, \ldots, x_n]$ which are annihilated by all the operators in $\mathrm{shift}(Q_i)$.

LEMMA 10.2. *The vector spaces* $\mathrm{shift}(Q_i)^{\perp}$ *and* $\mathbb{C}[\partial]/Q_i$ *are isomorphic.*

PROOF. Writing $J = \mathrm{shift}(Q_i)$, we need to show the following. If J is a $\langle \partial_1, \ldots, \partial_n \rangle$-primary ideal, then $\mathbb{C}[\partial]/J$ is isomorphic to the space $J^{\perp}$ of polynomial solutions of J. By our hypothesis, there exists a positive integer m such that $\langle \partial_1, \ldots, \partial_n \rangle^m$ lies in J. Hence $J^{\perp}$ consists of polynomials all of whose terms have degree less than m. Consider the two complex vector spaces $\mathbb{C}[\partial]/\langle \partial_1, \ldots, \partial_n \rangle^m$ and $\mathbb{C}[x]_{<m} = \{$ polynomials of degree less than $m \}$. Both spaces have the same finite dimension, and there is a natural $\mathbb{C}$-bilinear map from their product to $\mathbb{C}$, given by differentiating polynomials. This pairing is *nondegenerate*, which means that any square matrix representing this bilinear map is non-singular. This implies that J equals the annihilator of $J^{\perp}$ in $\mathbb{C}[\partial]/\langle \partial_1, \ldots, \partial_n \rangle^m$, and hence $\mathbb{C}[\partial]/J$ and $J^{\perp}$ are complex vector spaces of the same dimension. $\qquad\square$

In the next section we will show how to compute all polynomial solutions of an ideal in $\mathbb{C}[\partial]$. Here we patch solutions from the points of $\mathcal{V}(I)$ together.

THEOREM 10.3. *The solution space* $\mathrm{Sol}(I)$ *of the zero-dimensional ideal* $I \subset \mathbb{C}[\partial]$ *is a finite-dimensional complex vector space isomorphic to* $\mathbb{C}[\partial]/I$. *It is spanned by the functions*

$$q(x) \cdot \exp(u^{(i)} \cdot x) \quad = \quad q(x_1, x_2, \ldots, x_n) \cdot \exp(u_1^{(i)} x_1 + u_2^{(i)} x_2 + \cdots + u_n^{(i)} x_n),$$

where $i = 1, 2, \ldots, r$ *and* $q(x) \in \mathrm{shift}(Q_i)^{\perp}$.

PROOF. An operator $p(\partial)$ annihilates the function $q(x) \cdot \exp(u^{(i)} \cdot x)$ if and only if the shifted operator $p(\partial + u^{(i)})$ annihilates the polynomial $q(x)$. Hence the given functions do lie in $\mathrm{Sol}(I)$. Moreover, if we let $q(x)$ range over a basis of $\mathrm{shift}(Q_i)^{\perp}$, then the resulting functions are $\mathbb{C}$-linearly independent. We conclude that the dimension of $\mathrm{Sol}(I)$ is at least the dimension of $\mathbb{C}[\partial]/I$. For the reverse direction, we assume that every function f in $\mathcal{F}$ is characterized by its Taylor expansion at the origin. Any set of such functions whose cardinality exceeds the number of standard monomials of I, in any term order, is easily seen to be linearly dependent over the ground field $\mathbb{C}$. $\square$

We have demonstrated that solving a zero-dimensional ideal in $\mathbb{C}[\partial]$ can be reduced, by means of primary decomposition, to finding all polynomial solutions of a system of linear PDEs with constant coefficients. In the next section we describe how to compute the polynomial solutions.

10.3. Computing Polynomial Solutions

In this section we switch back to our favorite ground field, the rational numbers $\mathbb{Q}$, and we address the following problem. Let J be any ideal in $\mathbb{Q}[\partial] = \mathbb{Q}[\partial_1, \ldots, \partial_n]$. We do not assume that J is zero-dimensional. We are interested in the space $\mathrm{Polysol}(J)$ of polynomial solutions to J. Thus $\mathrm{Polysol}(J)$ consists of all polynomials in $\mathbb{Q}[x] = \mathbb{Q}[x_1, \ldots, x_n]$ which are annihilated by all operators in J. Our problem is to decide whether $\mathrm{Polysol}(J)$ is finite-dimensional and, in the affirmative case, to give a vector space basis.

The first step in our computation is to find the ideal quotient

$$(10.12) \qquad J' \quad = \quad \left(J : \langle \partial_1, \partial_2, \ldots, \partial_n \rangle^{\infty} \right)$$

The ideal J' is the intersection of all primary components of J whose prime is not the maximal ideal $\langle \partial_1, \partial_2, \ldots, \partial_n \rangle$.

PROPOSITION 10.4. *The following three conditions are equivalent:*

- *The vector space* $\mathrm{Polysol}(J)$ *is finite-dimensional.*
- *The vector space* $\mathrm{Polysol}(J')$ *is zero.*
- *One of the generators of* J' *has a nonzero constant term.*

It is easy to test the last condition. If it is not satisfied then we stop. If it is satisfied then we test whether $J = J'$. In that case there are no nonzero polynomial solutions to J and we stop as well. Otherwise, we can conclude that $\langle \partial_1, \partial_2, \ldots, \partial_n \rangle$ is a minimal prime of J and we compute

$$(10.13) \qquad\qquad I \quad = \quad (J : J').$$

The ideal I is the primary component of J at $\langle \partial_1, \partial_2, \ldots, \partial_n \rangle$. We have

$$(10.14) \qquad \mathrm{Polysol}(J) \;\; = \;\; \mathrm{Polysol}(I).$$

Let $\mathcal{B}$ be the (finite) set of monomials in $\mathbb{Q}[x_1, \ldots, x_n]$ which are annihilated by $\mathrm{in}_{\prec}(I)$. These are precisely the $\prec$-standard monomials of I but written in the x-variables instead of the ∂-variables. Clearly, the set $\mathcal{B}$ is a $\mathbb{Q}$-basis of $\mathrm{Polysol}(\mathrm{in}_{\prec}(I))$. For every non-standard monomial ∂^α there is a unique polynomial

$$\partial^\alpha \;-\; \sum_{x^\beta \in \mathcal{B}} c_{\alpha,\beta} \cdot \partial^\beta$$

in the ideal I which is gotten by taking the normal form modulo $\mathcal{G}$. Here $c_{\alpha,\beta} \in \mathbb{Q}$.

Abbreviate $\beta! := \beta_1! \beta_2! \cdots \beta_n!$. For a standard monomial x^β, define

$$(10.15) \qquad f_\beta(x) \;\; = \;\; x^\beta + \sum_{x^\alpha \in \mathcal{N}} c_{\alpha,\beta} \frac{\beta!}{\alpha!} x^\alpha,$$

where $\mathcal{N}$ denotes the set of monomials in $\mathbb{Q}[x_1, \ldots, x_n] \backslash \mathcal{B}$. This sum is finite because I is $\langle \partial_1, \ldots, \partial_n \rangle$-primary, i.e., if $|\alpha| \gg 0$, then $\partial^\alpha \in I$ and hence $c_{\alpha,\beta} = 0$. We can also write it as a sum over all $\alpha \in \mathbb{N}^n$:

$$f_\beta(x) \;\; = \;\; \sum_\alpha c_{\alpha,\beta} \frac{\beta!}{\alpha!} x^\alpha.$$

THEOREM 10.5. *The polynomials f_β, where x^β runs over the set $\mathcal{B}$ of standard monomials, form a $\mathbb{Q}$-basis for the space $I^\perp = \mathrm{Sol}(I) = \mathrm{Polysol}(I)$.*

PROOF. The polynomials f_β are $\mathbb{Q}$-linearly independent. Therefore, it suffices to show $g(\partial) f_\beta(x) = 0$ for $g(\partial) = \sum_u C_u \partial^u \in I$.

$$
\begin{aligned}
g(\partial) f_\beta(x) \;\; &= \;\; \sum_\alpha \sum_u c_{\alpha,\beta} C_u \frac{\beta!}{\alpha!} (\partial^u x^\alpha) \\
&= \;\; \sum_\alpha \sum_{u \le \alpha} c_{\alpha,\beta} C_u \frac{\beta!}{(\alpha - u)!} x^{\alpha - u} \\
&= \;\; \sum_v \left(\sum_u c_{u+v,\beta} C_u \frac{\beta!}{v!} \right) x^v \quad \text{where } v = \alpha - u \\
&= \;\; \beta! \sum_v \frac{1}{v!} \left(\sum_u c_{u+v,\beta} C_u \right) x^v.
\end{aligned}
$$

The expression $\sum_u c_{u+v,\beta} C_u$ is the coefficient of ∂^β in the $\prec$-normal form of $\partial^v g(\partial)$. It is zero since $\partial^v g(\partial) \in I$. $\qquad\square$ $\qquad\qquad\square$

If I is homogeneous, then we can write

$$(10.16) \qquad f_\beta \;\; = \;\; x^\beta \;+\; \sum_{x^\alpha \in \mathcal{N}_d} c_{\alpha,\beta} \cdot \frac{\beta!}{\alpha!} \cdot x^\alpha$$

where the degree of x^β is d and $\mathcal{N}_d$ denotes the degree d elements in the set $\mathcal{N}$ of non-standard monomials.

We summarize our algorithm for finding all polynomial solutions to a system of linear partial differential equations with constant coefficients.

Input: An ideal $J \in \mathbb{Q}[\partial]$.
Output: A basis for the space of polynomial solutions of J.

1. Compute the colon ideal I using formulas (10.12) and (10.13).
2. Compute the reduced Gröbner basis of I for a term order $\prec$.
3. Let $\mathcal{B}$ be the set of standard monomials for I.
4. Output $f_\beta(x_1, \ldots, x_n)$ for f_β in (10.15), for all $x^\beta \in \mathcal{B}$.

The following special case deserves particular attention. A homogeneous zero-dimensional ideal I is called *Gorenstein* if there is a homogeneous polynomial $V(x)$ such that $I = \{ p \in \mathbb{Q}[\partial] : p(\partial)V(x) = 0 \}$. In this case $I^\perp$ consists precisely of all polynomials which are gotten by taking successive partial derivatives of $V(x)$. For example, the ideal I generated by the elementary symmetric polynomials is Gorenstein. Here $V(x) = \prod_{1 \leq i < j \leq n}(x_i - x_j)$, the *discriminant*, and $I^\perp$ is the space of *harmonic polynomials*.

Suppose we wish to decide whether or not an ideal I is Gorenstein. We first compute a Gröbner basis $\mathcal{G}$ of I with respect to some term order $\prec$. A necessary condition is that there exists a unique standard monomial x^β of maximum degree, say t. For every monomial x^α of degree t there exists a unique constant $c_\alpha \in \mathbb{Q}$ such that $x^\alpha - c_\alpha \cdot x^\beta \in I$. We can find the c_α's by normal form reduction modulo $\mathcal{G}$. Define $V := \sum_{\alpha:|\alpha|=t}(c_\alpha/\alpha\,!) \cdot x^\alpha$, and let $\mathbb{Q}[\partial]V$ be the $\mathbb{Q}$-vector space spanned by the polynomials

$$(10.17) \qquad \partial^u V \;=\; \sum_{\alpha:|\alpha|=t-|u|} (c_{\alpha+u}/\alpha\,!) \cdot x^\alpha,$$

where ∂^u runs over all monomials of degree at most t.

PROPOSITION 10.6. *The ideal I is Gorenstein if and only if $\mathbb{Q}[\partial]V = I^\perp$ if and only if $\dim_{\mathbb{Q}}(\mathbb{Q}[\partial]V)$ equals the number of standard monomials.*

The previous two propositions provide a practical method for solving linear systems with constant coefficients. We illustrate this in a small example.

EXAMPLE 10.7. For $n = 5$ consider the homogeneous ideal

$$I \;=\; \langle \partial_1\partial_3, \partial_1\partial_4, \partial_2\partial_4, \partial_2\partial_5, \partial_3\partial_5, \ \partial_1 + \partial_2 - \partial_4, \partial_2 + \partial_3 - \partial_5 \rangle.$$

Let $\prec$ be any term order with $\partial_5 \prec \partial_4 \prec \partial_3 \prec \partial_2 \prec \partial_1$. The reduced Gröbner basis of I with respect to $\prec$ equals

$$\mathcal{G} \;=\; \{ \underline{\partial_1} - \partial_3 - \partial_4 + \partial_5, \ \underline{\partial_2} + \partial_3 - \partial_5, \ \underline{\partial_3^2} + \partial_4\partial_5, \ \underline{\partial_3\partial_5}, \ \underline{\partial_4^2}, \ \underline{\partial_3\partial_4} - \partial_4\partial_5, \ \underline{\partial_5^2} \}.$$

The underlined monomials generate the initial ideal $\mathrm{in}_\prec(I)$. The space of polynomials annihilated by $\mathrm{in}_\prec(I)$ is spanned by the standard monomials

$$\mathcal{B} \;=\; \{ 1, x_3, x_4, x_5, x_4x_5 \}.$$

There exists a unique standard monomial of maximum degree $t = 2$, so it makes sense to check whether I is Gorenstein. For any quadratic monomial x_ix_j, the normal form of x_ix_j with respect to $\mathcal{G}$ equals $c_{ij} \cdot x_4x_5$ for some constant $c_{ij} \in \mathbb{Q}$. We collect these constants in the quadratic form

$$
\begin{aligned}
V \;&=\; \frac{1}{2}\sum_{i=1}^{5} c_{ii}x_i^2 + \sum_{1 \leq i < j \leq 5} c_{ij}x_ix_j \\
&=\; \underline{x_4x_5} + x_1x_5 + x_3x_4 + x_2x_3 + x_1x_2 - \frac{1}{2}x_3^2 - \frac{1}{2}x_2^2 - \frac{1}{2}x_1^2.
\end{aligned}
$$

This polynomial is annihilated by I, and its initial monomial is annihilated by $\mathrm{in}_{\prec}(I)$. We next compute the $\mathbb{Q}$-vector space $\mathbb{Q}[\partial]V$ of all partial derivatives of V. It turns out that this space is five-dimensional. Using Proposition 10.6 we conclude that I is Gorenstein and its solution space $I^{\perp}$ equals $\mathbb{Q}[\partial]V$.

10.4. How to Solve Monomial Equations

We consider an arbitrary monomial ideal $M = \langle \partial^{a^{(1)}}, \partial^{a^{(2)}}, \ldots, \partial^{a^{(r)}} \rangle$ in $\mathbb{Q}[\partial]$. The solution space $\mathrm{Sol}(M)$ consists of all functions $f(x_1, \ldots, x_n)$ for which a specified set of partial derivatives vanishes:

$$\frac{\partial^{|a^{(i)}|} f}{\partial x_1^{a_1^{(i)}} \cdots \partial x_r^{a_r^{(i)}}} = 0 \qquad \text{for } i = 1, 2, \ldots, r.$$

If M is zero-dimensional then $\mathrm{Sol}(M)$ is finite-dimensional with basis the standard monomials $\mathcal{B}$ as in the previous section. Otherwise, $\mathrm{Sol}(M)$ is an infinite-dimensional space. In what follows we offer a finite description.

We are interested in pairs (u, σ) consisting of a monomial x^u, with $u \in \mathbb{N}^n$, and a subset σ of $\{x_1, x_2, \ldots, x_n\}$ with the following three properties:

1. $u_i = 0$ for all $i \in \sigma$.
2. Every monomial of the form $x^u \cdot \prod_{i \in \sigma} x_i^{v_i}$ lies in $\mathrm{Sol}(M)$.
3. For each $j \notin \sigma$ there exists a monomial $\partial_j^{w_j} \cdot \prod_{i \in \sigma} \partial_i^{v_i}$ which lies in M.

The pairs (u, σ) with these three properties are called the *standard pairs* of the monomial ideal M. Computing the standard pairs of a monomial ideal is a standard task in combinatorial commutative algebra. See [**HS01**] for an implementation in `Macaulay 2`. This is important for us because the standard pairs are exactly what we want when solving a monomial ideal.

THEOREM 10.8. *A function $f(x)$ is a solution to the ideal M of monomial differential operators if and only if it can be written in the form*

$$f(x_1, \ldots, x_n) = \sum x_1^{u_1} \cdots x_n^{u_n} \cdot g_{(u,\sigma)}(x_i : i \in \sigma),$$

where the sum is over all standard pairs of M.

EXAMPLE 10.9. Let $n = 3$ and consider the monomial ideal

$$M = \langle \partial_1^2 \partial_2^3 \partial_3^4, \partial_1^2 \partial_2^4 \partial_3^3, \partial_1^3 \partial_2^2 \partial_3^4, \partial_1^3 \partial_2^4 \partial_3^2, \partial_1^4 \partial_2^2 \partial_3^3, \partial_1^4 \partial_2^3 \partial_3^2 \rangle.$$

Thus $\mathrm{Sol}(M)$ consists of all function $f(x_1, x_2, x_3)$ with the property

$$\frac{\partial^9 f}{\partial x_i^2 \partial x_j^3 \partial x_k^4} = 0 \qquad \text{for all permutations } (i, j, k) \text{ of } \{1, 2, 3\}.$$

The ideal M has precisely 13 standard pairs:

$$(x_3, \{x_1, x_2\}), \ (1, \{x_1, x_2\}), \ (x_2, \{x_1, x_3\}), \ (1, \{x_1, x_3\}),$$
$$(x_1, \{x_2, x_3\}), \ (1, \{x_2, x_3\}), \ (x_2^2 x_3^2, \{x_1\}), \ (x_3^2 x_1^2, \{x_2\}), \ (x_1^2 x_2^2, \{x_3\}),$$
$$(x_1^3 x_2^3 x_3^3, \emptyset), \ (x_1^2 x_2^3 x_3^3, \emptyset), \ (x_1^3 x_2^3 x_3^2, \emptyset), \ (x_1^3 x_2^2 x_3^3, \emptyset).$$

We conclude that the solutions to M are the functions of the following form

$$x_3 \cdot f_1(x_1, x_2) + f_2(x_1, x_2) + x_2 \cdot g_1(x_1, x_3) + g_2(x_1, x_3)$$
$$+ x_1 \cdot h_1(x_2, x_3) + h_2(x_2, x_3) + x_2^2 x_3^2 \cdot p(x_1) + x_1^2 x_3^2 \cdot q(x_2) + x_1^2 x_2^2 \cdot r(x_3)$$
$$+ a_1 \cdot x_1^3 x_2^3 x_3^3 + a_2 \cdot x_1^2 x_2^3 x_3^3 + a_3 \cdot x_1^3 x_2^2 x_3^3 + a_4 \cdot x_1^3 x_2^3 x_3^2.$$

10.5. The Ehrenpreis-Palamodov Theorem

We are seeking a finite representation of all the solutions to an arbitrary ideal I in $\mathbb{C}[\partial] = \mathbb{C}[\partial_1, \dots, \partial_n]$. This representation should generalize both the case of zero-dimensional ideals and the case of monomial ideals, and it should reveal all polynomial solutions. Let us present two simple examples, both for $n = 3$, which do not fall in the categories discussed so far.

EXAMPLE 10.10. Consider the principal prime ideal $I = \langle \partial_1\partial_3 - \partial_2 \rangle$. The variety of I is a surface in $\mathbb{C}^3$ parametrically given as (s, st, t) where s, t runs over all complex numbers. The PDE solutions to I are the functions $f(x_1, x_2, x_3)$ which satisfy the equation

$$\frac{\partial^2 f}{\partial x_1 \partial x_3} = \frac{\partial f}{\partial x_2}.$$

In the setting of Ehrenpreis and Palamodov, every solution to this differential equation can be expressed as a double integral of the form

$$(10.18) \qquad f(x_1, x_2, x_3) = \iint \exp\big(sx_1 + stx_2 + tx_3\big) d\mu(s, t),$$

where the integral is taken with respect to any measure μ on the complex (s, t)-plane $\mathbb{C}^2$. For instance, we might integrate with respect to a measure supported only at the two points (i, i) and $(0, 17)$. From this we get a solution like

$$g(x_1, x_2, x_3) = \exp(ix_1 - x_2 + ix_3) + \exp(17x_3).$$

EXAMPLE 10.11. Let us consider the previous example but now add the requirement that the second partials with respect to x_2 and x_3 should vanish as well. That is, we now consider the larger ideal $J = \langle \partial_1\partial_3 - \partial_2, \partial_2^2, \partial_3^2 \rangle$. The ideal J is primary to $\langle\partial_2, \partial_3\rangle$. It turns out that there are two kinds of solutions: The first class of solutions are functions in the first variable only:

$$f(x_1, x_2, x_3) = g(x_1),$$

The second class of solutions takes the following form:

$$f(x_1, x_2, x_3) = g(x_1) \cdot x_3 + g'(x_1) \cdot x_2.$$

In both cases, g is any differentiable function in one variable. It is instructive to derive the second class as a special case from the integral formula (10.18). □

We are now prepared to state the Ehrenpreis-Palamodov Theorem, in a form that emphasizes the algebraic aspects over the analytic aspects. For more analytic information and a proof of Theorem 10.12 see [**Bjö79**].

THEOREM 10.12. *Given any ideal I in $\mathbb{C}[\partial_1, \dots, \partial_n]$, there exist finitely many pairs (A_j, V_j) where $A_j(x_1, \dots, x_n, \xi_1, \dots, \xi_n)$ is a polynomial in $2n$ unknowns and $V_j \subset \mathbb{C}^n$ is the irreducible variety of an associated prime of I, such that the following holds. If $\mathcal{K}$ is any compact and convex subset of $\mathbb{R}^n$ and $f \in C^\infty(\mathcal{K})$ is any solution to I, then there exist measures μ_j on V_j such that*

$$(10.19) \qquad f(ix_1, \dots, ix_n) = \sum_j \int_{V_j} A_j(x, \xi) \exp(ix \cdot \xi) \, d\mu_j(\xi).$$

Here $i^2 = -1$. Theorem 10.12 gives a precise characterization of the scheme structure defined by I. Indeed, if I is a radical ideal then all A_j can be taken as the constant 1, and the pairs $(1, V_j)$ simply run over the irreducible components of I. The main point is that the polynomials $A_j(x, \xi)$ are independent of the space $\mathcal{F} = C^\infty(\mathcal{K})$ in which the solutions lie. In the opinion of the author, the true meaning of solving a polynomial system I is to exhibit the associated primes of I together with their multiplier polynomials $A_j(x, \xi)$.

Our earlier results on zero-dimensional ideals and monomial ideals can be interpreted as special cases of the Ehrenpreis-Palamodov Theorem. In both cases, the polynomials $A_j(x, \xi)$ only depend on x and not on the auxiliary variables ξ. In the zero-dimensional case, each V_j is a single point, say $V_j = \{u^{(j)}\}$. Specifying a measure μ_j on V_j means picking a constant multiplier for the function $\exp(x \cdot u^{(j)})$. Hence we recover Theorem 10.3. If I is a monomial ideal then each V_j is a coordinate subspace, indexed by a subset σ of the variables, and we can take monomials $x_1^{u_1} \cdots x_n^{u_n}$ for the A_j. Thus, in the monomial case, the pairs (A_j, V_j) are the standard pairs of Theorem 10.8.

For general ideals which are neither zero-dimensional nor monomials, one needs the appearance of the extra variables $\xi = (\xi_1, \ldots, \xi_n)$ is the polynomials $A_j(x, \xi)$. A small ideal where this is necessary appears in Example 10.11.

Suppose we are given an ideal I in $\mathbb{C}[\partial]$ and we wish to compute the list of pairs (A_j, V_j) described in the Ehrenpreis-Palamodov Theorem. It is conceptually easier to first compute a primary decomposition of I, and then compute multipliers A_j for each primary component separately. This leads to the idea of *Noetherian operators* associated to a primary ideal. In the literature, it is customary to Fourier-dualize the situation and to think of the $A_i(x, \xi)$ as differential operators. We shall sketch this in the next section.

10.6. Noetherian Operators

In this section we consider ideals in the polynomial ring $\mathbb{C}[x] = \mathbb{C}[x_1, \ldots, x_n]$. Let Q be a primary ideal in $\mathbb{C}[x]$ and V its irreducible variety in $\mathbb{C}^n$.

THEOREM 10.13. *There exist differential operators with polynomial coefficients,*

$$A_i(x, \partial) \;=\; \sum_j c_j^i \cdot p_j(x_1, \ldots, x_n) \cdot \partial_1^{j_1} \partial_2^{j_2} \cdots \partial_n^{j_n}, \qquad i = 1, 2, \ldots, t,$$

with the following property. A polynomial $f \in \mathbb{C}[x]$ lies in the ideal Q if and only if the result of applying $A_i(x, \partial)$ to $f(x)$ vanishes on V for $i = 1, 2, \ldots, t$.

The operators $A_1(x, \partial), \ldots, A_r(x, \partial)$ are said to be *Noetherian operators* for the primary ideal Q. Note that the Noetherian operators for Q are not unique. Our computational task is to go back and forth between the two presentations of a primary ideal Q. The first presentation is by means of ideal generators, the second presentation is by means of Noetherian operators. Solving the equations Q means to go from the first presentation to the second. The reverse process can be thought of as implicitization and is equally important.

An algorithm for computing Noetherian operators for a given primary ideal Q was given by Oberst [**Obe99**]. Just like the proof in [**Bjö79**], Oberst's approach is based on Noether normalization. We will not discuss this algorithm here.

EXAMPLE 10.14. We Fourier-dualize the primary ideal in Example 10.11 to get

$$Q \quad = \quad \langle\, x_1 x_3 - x_2,\, x_2^2,\, x_3^2 \,\rangle.$$

Here V is the x_1-axis in affine 3-space. There are two Noetherian operators:

$$A_1 \;=\; 1 \quad \text{and} \quad A_2 \;=\; \partial_3 + x_1 \partial_2.$$

A polynomial $f = f(x_1, x_2, x_3)$ lies in the primary ideal Q if and only if both $A_1(f) = f$ and $A_2(f) = \partial f / \partial x_3 + x_1 \cdot \partial f / \partial x_2$ vanish on the line V. □

If I is an arbitrary (not necessarily primary) ideal in $\mathbb{C}[x]$ then we can characterize the membership in I by Noetherian operators $A_j(x, \partial)$ attached to the various primary components of I. If we replace x_i by ξ_i and ∂_i by x_i in these A_j, then we obtain a description as in Theorem 10.12 of all solutions to the system of linear partial differential equations represented by the ideal I. The number of Noetherian operators needed to describe I is closely related to a quantity known in commutative algebra as the *arithmetic degree* of I.

We illustrate the process of solving a polynomial system by means of Noetherian operators for a non-trivial example. Consider the ideal

$$
\begin{aligned}
I \quad = \quad & \langle\, x_1^3 x_4^2 - x_2^5,\, x_1^2 x_4^3 - x_3^5,\, x_1 x_3^2 - x_2^3,\, x_2^2 x_4 - x_3^3 \,\rangle \\
= \quad & \langle\, x_1 x_4 - x_2 x_3,\, x_1 x_3^2 - x_2^3,\, x_2^2 x_4 - x_3^3 \,\rangle \\
& \cap \;\; \langle\, x_1^2,\, x_2^2,\, x_3^2 \,\rangle \;\; \cap \;\; \langle\, x_2^2,\, x_3^2,\, x_4^2 \,\rangle \\
& \cap \;\; \langle\, x_1^3,\, x_2^3,\, x_3^3,\, x_4^3,\, x_1 x_3^2,\, x_2^2 x_4 \,\rangle.
\end{aligned}
$$

This is the *circuit ideal* of the matrix $A = \begin{pmatrix} 0 & 2 & 3 & 5 \\ 5 & 3 & 2 & 0 \end{pmatrix}$. As predicted by Theorem 8.17, there are four associated primes, namely, the radicals of the primary ideals appearing in the intersection. The corresponding irreducible varieties are

- the toric surface $V^{(1)} = \{\, (s^5, s^3 t^2, s^2 t^3, t^5) \,:\, s, t \in \mathbb{C} \,\}$,
- the x_1-axis $V^{(2)} = \{\, (s, 0, 0, 0) \,:\, s \in \mathbb{C} \,\}$,
- the x_4-axis $V^{(3)} = \{\, (0, 0, 0, t) \,:\, t \in \mathbb{C} \,\}$,
- the origin $V^{(4)} = \{\, (0, 0, 0, 0) \,\}$.

The first primary ideal is prime: it consists precisely of those polynomials which vanish on V_1. The three embedded primary ideals are monomial. Membership in these ideals is easily characterized by standard pairs. Putting everything together we find the following list of 13 Noetherian operators:

$$A_1^{(1)} \;=\; 1,$$

$$A_2^{(2)} \;=\; \partial_2 \partial_3 \partial_4,\; A_3^{(2)} \;=\; \partial_2 \partial_3,\; A_4^{(2)} \;=\; \partial_2 \partial_4,\; A_5^{(2)} \;=\; \partial_3 \partial_4,$$

$$A_6^{(3)} \;=\; \partial_1 \partial_2 \partial_3,\; A_7^{(3)} \;=\; \partial_1 \partial_2,\; A_8^{(3)} \;=\; \partial_1 \partial_3,\; A_9^{(3)} \;=\; \partial_2 \partial_3,$$

$$A_{10}^{(4)} \;=\; \partial_1^2 \partial_4^2 + \partial_2^2 \partial_3^2,\; A_{11}^{(4)} \;=\; \partial_1^2 \partial_2 \partial_3 \partial_4^2,\; A_{12}^{(4)} \;=\; \partial_1^2 \partial_2 \partial_4^2,\; A_{13}^{(4)} \;=\; \partial_1^2 \partial_3 \partial_4^2.$$

This results in the following characterization: *A polynomial $f = f(x_1, x_2, x_3, x_4)$ lies in the ideal I if and only if $A_i^{(j)}(f)$ vanishes on $V^{(j)}$ for all i and j.*

We now translate this result into a corresponding result for solving differential equations. Here I is regarded as an ideal in $\mathbb{C}[\partial]$:

$$I \quad = \quad \langle\, \partial_1^3 \partial_4^2 - \partial_2^5,\, \partial_1^2 \partial_4^3 - \partial_3^5,\, \partial_1 \partial_3^2 - \partial_2^3,\, \partial_2^2 \partial_4 - \partial_3^3 \,\rangle.$$

Each of the 13 Noetherian operators translates into a class of functions which is a solution to I. For instance, the operator $A_1^{(1)} = 1$ associated to the toric surface $V^{(1)}$ gives rise to all the solutions $p(x_1, x_2, x_3, x_4)$ of the prime ideal

$$\text{Rad}(I) \quad = \quad \langle \partial_1 \partial_4 - \partial_2 \partial_3 \, , \, \partial_1 \partial_3^2 - \partial_2^3 \, , \, \partial_2^2 \partial_4 - \partial_3^3 \rangle.$$

Each of these solutions has an integral representation

$$(10.20) \quad f_1(x_1, x_2, x_3, x_4) \quad = \quad \iint \exp(s^5 x_1 + s^3 t^2 x_2 + s^2 t^3 x_3 + t^5 x_4) d\mu(s, t),$$

where $\mu(s, t)$ is a suitable measure. The second Noetherian operator $A_2^{(2)} = \partial_2 \partial_3 \partial_4$ is associated to the line $V^{(2)}$. It represents all the solutions

$$x_2 x_3 x_4 \cdot g_2(x_1) \quad = \quad x_2 x_3 x_4 \cdot \int \exp(s x_1) d\mu'(s).$$

Continuing in this manner, we reach the following final conclusion of this example: A function $p(x_1, x_2, x_3, x_4)$ satisfies the four differential equations

$$\frac{\partial^5 p}{\partial x_1^3 \partial x_4^2} = \frac{\partial^5 p}{\partial x_3^5}, \quad \frac{\partial^5 p}{\partial x_1^2 \partial x_4^3} = \frac{\partial^5 p}{\partial x_2^5}, \quad \frac{\partial^3 p}{\partial x_1 \partial x_3^2} = \frac{\partial^3 p}{\partial x_2^3}, \quad \frac{\partial^3 p}{\partial x_2^2 \partial x_4} = \frac{\partial^3 p}{\partial x_3^3}$$

if and only if it can be written in the following form

$$
\begin{aligned}
p \quad = \quad & f_1(x_1, x_2, x_3, x_4) \\
& + x_2 x_3 x_4 \cdot g_2(x_1) + x_2 x_3 \cdot g_3(x_1) + x_2 x_4 \cdot g_4(x_1) + x_3 x_4 \cdot g_5(x_1) \\
& + x_1 x_2 x_3 \cdot h_6(x_4) + x_1 x_2 \cdot h_7(x_4) + x_1 x_3 \cdot h_8(x_4) + x_2 x_3 \cdot h_9(x_4) \\
& + c_{10} \cdot (x_1^2 x_4^2 + x_2^2 x_3^2) + c_{11} \cdot x_1^2 x_2 x_3 x_4^2 + c_{12} \cdot x_1^2 x_2 x_4^2 + c_{13} \cdot x_1^2 x_3 x_4^2,
\end{aligned}
$$

where the c_i are constants, the g_i and h_i are arbitrary functions in one variable, and f_1 is any function which has an integral representation as in (10.20).

10.7. Exercises

(1) Let a, b, c be arbitrary positive integers. How many linearly independent (polynomial) functions $f(x, y, z)$ satisfy the differential equations

$$\frac{\partial^a f}{\partial x^a} = \frac{\partial^{b+c} f}{\partial y^b \partial z^c}, \quad \frac{\partial^a f}{\partial y^a} = \frac{\partial^{b+c} f}{\partial z^b \partial x^c} \quad \text{and} \quad \frac{\partial^a f}{\partial z^a} = \frac{\partial^{b+c} f}{\partial x^b \partial y^c}?$$

(2) Let $\alpha_1, \alpha_2, \alpha_3$ be parameters and consider the differential equations

$$\langle \partial_1 + \partial_2 + \partial_3 - \alpha_1, \ \partial_1 \partial_2 + \partial_1 \partial_3 + \partial_2 \partial_3 - \alpha_2, \ \partial_1 \partial_2 \partial_3 - \alpha_3 \rangle$$

Find a solution basis which works for all values of the three parameters α_1, α_2 and α_3. One of your basis elements should have the form

$$(x_1 - x_2)(x_1 - x_3)(x_2 - x_3) \ + \ O(\alpha_1, \alpha_2, \alpha_3).$$

(3) Describe all solutions to the differential equations $\langle \partial_1 \partial_3 - \partial_2^2 \, , \, \partial_2^3 \, , \, \partial_3^3 \rangle$.

(4) The mth *symbolic power* $P^{(m)}$ of a prime ideal P in a polynomial ring $\mathbb{C}[x_1, \dots, x_n]$ is the P-primary component in the ordinary power P^m. What are the Noetherian operators for $P^{(m)}$?

(5) Let P be any homogeneous prime ideal in $\mathbb{C}[x]$ and M an artinian monomial ideal in $\mathbb{C}[\partial]$, both given by generators. Let $P^{(M)}$ denote the set of all polynomials $f = f(x)$ such that, for every standard monomial ∂^a of M, the polynomial $\partial^a(f)$ lies in P. Show that $P^{(M)}$ is an ideal in $\mathbb{C}[x_1, \dots, x_n]$. How would you compute a generating set of this ideal?

(6) Revisit the circuit ideal in Example 8.16 from the Ehrenpreis-Palamodov perspective. Determine all solutions to the differential equations

$$\langle \partial_1^3 \partial_3^2 - \partial_2^5, \ \partial_1^5 \partial_4^2 - \partial_2^7, \ \partial_1^2 \partial_4^5 - \partial_3^7, \ \partial_2^2 \partial_4^3 - \partial_3^5 \rangle.$$

(7) Explain the commands `toDual` and `fromDual` in `Macaulay 2`. What are these commands good for, and how do they work?

(8) Let I be the ideal of all operators in $\mathbb{C}[\partial_1, \partial_2, \partial_3, \partial_4]$ which annihilate all functions in x_1, x_2, x_3, x_4 which have the special form

$$f(x_1 + x_2, x_3 + x_4) + g(x_1 + x_3, x_2 + x_4) + h(x_1 + x_4, x_2 + x_3).$$

Show that I is generated by three second-order operators. Find them.

(9) Let $\mathbb{C}[\partial]$ be the polynomial ring in the nine differential operators

$$\begin{pmatrix} \partial_{11} & \partial_{12} & \partial_{13} \\ \partial_{21} & \partial_{22} & \partial_{23} \\ \partial_{31} & \partial_{32} & \partial_{33} \end{pmatrix}$$

  - The ideal of 2×2-subpermanents of this 3×3-matrix is a system of nine second order operators. Describe all its solutions.
  - The ideal of adjacent 2×2-subdeterminants of this 3×3-matrix is a system of four second order operators. Describe all its solutions.

Bibliography

[Agr90]   A. Agresti, *Categorical Data Analysis*, Wiley Series in Probability and Mathematical Statistics, Wiley, New York.

[AG90]   E. Allgower and K. Georg, *Numerical Continuation Methods: An Introduction*, Springer Verlag, 1990. This book is out of print and can be downloaded at http://www.math.colostate.edu/~georg/Preprints/Publications.html.

[BR90]   R. Benedetti and J.-J. Risler, *Real Algebraic and Semi-algebraic Sets*, Actualités Mathematiques, Hermann, Paris, 1990.

[Ber71]   G. Bergman, *The logarithmic limit-set of an algebraic variety*, Trans. Amer. Math. Soc. **157** (1971) 459–469.

[Ber75]   D. Bernstein, *The number of roots of a system of equations*, Functional Analysis and its Applications **9** (1975) 183–185.

[BG84]   R. Bieri and J. Groves, *The geometry of the set of characters induced by valuations*, J. Reine Angew. Math. **347** (1984) 168–195.

[Bjö79]   J.-E. Björk, *Rings of Differential Operators*, North-Holland Mathematical Library, Vol. 21, Amsterdam-New York, 1979.

[CE00]   J. Canny and I. Emiris, *A subdivision-based algorithm for the sparse resultant*, Journal of the ACM **47** (2000) 417–451.

[CD02]   M. Chardin and C. D'Cruz, *Castelnuovo-Mumford regularity: Examples of curves and surfaces*, Preprint, March 2002, posted at http://www.math.jussieu.fr/~chardin/textes.html.

[CLO97]   D. Cox, J. Little and D. O'Shea, *Ideals, Varieties, and Algorithms. An Introduction to Computational Algebraic Geometry and Commutative Algebra*, Second edition. Undergraduate Texts in Mathematics. Springer-Verlag, New York, 1997.

[CLO98]   D. Cox, J. Little and D. O'Shea, *Using Algebraic Geometry*, Graduate Texts in Mathematics, Vol 185. Springer-Verlag, New York, 1998.

[DR72]   J. Darroch and D. Ratcliff, *Generalized iterative scaling for log-linear models*, The Annals of Mathematical Statitics **43** (1972) 1470–1480.

[DGP99]   W. Decker, G.-M. Greuel and G. Pfister, *Primary decomposition: algorithms and comparisons*. Algorithmic algebra and number theory (Heidelberg, 1997), 187–220, Springer, Berlin, 1999.

[DOS02]   J. De Loera, S. Onn and A. Sebo, *Characterization of graph properties via polynomial equations*, Preprint UC Davis, May 2002.

[DS98]   P. Diaconis and B. Sturmfels, *Algebraic algorithms for sampling from conditional distributions*, Annals of Statistics **26** (1998) 363–397.

[DES98]   P. Diaconis, D. Eisenbud and B. Sturmfels, *Lattice walks and primary decomposition*, in: B. Sagan and R. Stanley (eds), Mathematical Essays in Honor of Gian-Carlo Rota, Progress in Mathematics, Vol 161, Birkhäuser, Boston, 1998, pp. 173–193.

[DE02]   A. Dickenstein and I. Emiris, *Multihomogeneous resultant matrices*, ISSAC 2002, posted at http://mate.dm.uba.ar/~alidick.

[DF00]   A. Dobra and S. Fienberg, *Bounds for cell entries in contingency tables given marginal totals and decomposable graphs*, Proc. Natl. Acad. Sci. USA **97** (2000), 11885–11892.

[DS02]   A. Dobra and S. Sullivant, *A divide-and-conquer algorithm for generating Markov bases of multi-way tables*, Manuscript, 2002, posted at http://www.niss.org/adobra.html/.

[DvK98]   J. Duistermaat and W. van der Kallen, *Constant terms in powers of a Laurent polynomial*, Indag. Math. (N.S.) **9** (1998) 221–231.

[Eis95]   D. Eisenbud, *Commutative Algebra With A View Toward Algebraic Geometry*, Graduate Texts in Mathematics, Vol 150, Springer-Verlag, New York, 1995.

[EGSS01]   D. Eisenbud, D. Grayson, M. Stillman and B. Sturmfels, *Mathematical Computations with Macaulay 2*, Algorithms and Computation in Mathematics, Vol. 8, Springer Verlag, Heidelberg, 2001, see also `http://www.math.uiuc.edu/Macaulay2/`.

[EH00]   D. Eisenbud and J. Harris, *The Geometry of Schemes*, Graduate Texts in Mathematics, Vol 197, Springer-Verlag, New York, 2000.

[ES02]   D. Eisenbud and F. Schreyer, *Resultants and Chow forms via exterior syzygies*, Journal of the American Mathematical Society, to appear.

[ES96]   D. Eisenbud and B. Sturmfels, *Binomial ideals*, Duke Math. Journal **84** (1996) 1–45.

[FPT00]   M. Forsberg, M. Passare and A. Tsikh, *Laurent determinants and arrangements of hyperplane amoebas*, Advances in Mathematics **151** (2000) 45–70.

[Ful93]   W. Fulton, *Introduction to Toric Varieties*, Annals of Mathematics Studies, 131, Princeton University Press, Princeton, NJ, 1993.

[GMS02]   D. Geiger, C. Meek and B. Sturmfels, *On the toric algebra of graphical models*, Preprint, March 2002, posted at
           `http://research. microsoft.com/scripts/pubs/view.asp?TR_ID=MSR-TR-2002-47`

[GKZ94]   I. Gel'fand, M. Kapranov and A. Zelevinsky, *Discriminants, Resultants, and Multidimensional Determinants*, Birkhäuser, Boston, 1994.

[GPS01]   G.-M. Greuel, G. Pfister and H. Schönemann. SINGULAR 2.0. *A Computer Algebra System for Polynomial Computations*, Centre for Computer Algebra, University of Kaiserslautern (2001). `http://www.singular.uni-kl.de`.

[GP02]   G. Greuel and G. Pfister, *A* SINGULAR *Introduction to Commutative Algebra*, Springer Verlag, 2002.

[Gro38]   W. Gröbner, *Über eine neue idealtheoretische Grundlegung der algebraischen Geometrie*, Mathematische Annalen **115** (1938) 333–358.

[Gro39]   W. Gröbner, *Über die algebraischen Eigenschaften der Integrale von linearen Differentialgleichungen mit konstanten Koeffizienten*, Monatshefte für Mathematische Physik **47** (1939) 247–284.

[Haa02]   B. Haas, *A simple counterexample to Kouchnirenko's conjecture*, Beiträge zur Algebra und Geometrie **43** (2002) 1–8.

[HS00]   S. Hoşten and J. Shapiro, *Primary decomposition of lattice basis ideals*, Journal of Symbolic Computation **29** (2000) 625–639.

[HS01]   S. Hoşten and G. Smith, *Monomial ideals*, in Mathematical Computations with Macaulay 2, eds. D. Eisenbud, D. Grayson, M. Stillman and B. Sturmfels, Algorithms and Computation in Mathematics, Vol. 8, Springer Verlag, Heidelberg, 2001, pp. 73–100.

[Iar72]   A. Iarrobino, *Reducibility of the families of 0-dimensional schemes on a variety*, Invent. Math. **15** (1972) 72–77.

[Ily92]   N.V. Ilyushechkin, The discriminant of the characteristic polynomial of a normal matrix. *Mat. Zametki* **51** (1992), no. 3, 16–23; translation in *Math. Notes* **51** (1992), no. 3-4, 230–235.

[KS95]   M. Kalkbrener and B. Sturmfels, *Initial complexes of prime ideals*, Advances in Mathematics **116** (1995) 365–376.

[Kap00]   M. Kapranov, *Amoebas over non-archimedean fields*, Manuscript, 2000.

[KLS01]   M. Kearns, M. Littman and S. Singh, *Graphical models for game theory*, Proceedings of the 17th Conference on Uncertainty in Artificial Intelligence (UAI), 2001, pp. 253–260, posted at `http://www.cs.colorado.edu/~baveja/Papers/graphgames.pdf`

[Khe02]   A. Khetan, *Determinantal formula for the Chow form of a toric surface*, ISSAC 2002, posted at `http://math.berkeley.edu/~akhetan/`

[Kho80]   A. Khovanskii, *A class of systems of transcendental equations*, Dokl. Akad. Nauk SSSR **255** (1980), no. 4, 804–807.

[Kho91]   A. Khovanskii, *Fewnomials*, Translations of Mathematical Monographs, Vol 88. American Mathematical Society, Providence, RI, 1991.

[KR00]   M. Kreuzer and L. Robbiano, *Computational Commutative Algebra. 1*, Springer-Verlag, Berlin, 2000, see also `http://cocoa.dima.unige.it/`

[LR97]   J. Lagarias and T. Richardson, *Multivariate Descartes rule of signs and Sturmfels's challenge problem*, Math. Intelligencer **19** (1997) 9–15.

[LS00]   R. Laubenbacher and I. Swanson, *Permanental ideals*, J. Symbolic Comput. **30** (2000) 195–205.

[Lau96]   S. Lauritzen, *Graphical Models*. Oxford Statistical Science Series, 17, Oxford University Press, New York, 1996.

[Lax98]   P. Lax, *On the discriminant of real symmetric matrices*, Comm. Pure Appl. Math. **51** (1998) 1387–1396.

[LH64]   C. Lemke and J. Howson, Jr., *Equilibrium points of bimatrix games*, J. Soc. Indust. Appl. Math. **12** (1964) 413–423.

[Li97]   T.Y. Li, *Numerical solution of multivariate polynomial systems by homotopy continuation methods*, Acta numerica, 1997, 399–436, Acta Numer., Vol 6, Cambridge Univ. Press, Cambridge, 1997.

[LRW00]   T.Y. Li, J.M. Rojas and X. Wang, *Counting real connected components of trinomial curve intersections and m-nomial hypersurfaces*, submitted for publication, `math.CO/0008069`.

[LL01]   T.Y. Li and X. Li, *Finding mixed cells in the mixed volume computation*, Found. Comput. Math. **1** (2001) 161–181.

[MZ01]   G. Malajovich and J. Zubelli, *On the geometry of Graeffe iteration*, Journal of Complexity **17** (2001) 541–573.

[MMM96]   M.G. Marinari, H.M. Möller and T. Mora, *On multiplicities in polynomial system solving*, Trans. Amer. Math. Soc. **348** (1996) 3283–3321.

[MK94]   V.P. Maslov and V.N. Kolokoltsov, *Idempotent Analysis and its Application in Optimal Control*, (in Russian), VO "Nauka", Moscow, 1994.

[May37]   K. Mayer, *Über die Lösung algebraischer Gleichungssysteme durch hypergeometrische Funktionen*, Monatshefte Math. Phys. **45** (1937).

[McD95]   J. McDonald, *Fiber polytopes and fractional power series*, J. Pure Appl. Algebra **104** (1995) 213–233.

[McD02]   J. McDonald, *Fractional power series solutions for systems of equations*, Discrete and Computational Geometry **27** (2002) 501–529.

[MM97]   R.D. McKelvey and A. McLennan, *The maximal number of regular totally mixed Nash equilibria*, J. Economic Theory **72** (1997) 411–425.

[Mik01]   G. Mikhalkin, *Amoebas of algebraic varieties*, Real Algebraic and Analytic Geometry Congress, Rennes, June 2001, `math.AG/0108225`.

[Mou97]   B. Mourrain, *Isolated points, duality and residues*. Algorithms for algebra (Eindhoven, 1996). J. Pure Appl. Algebra **117/118** (1997) 469–493.

[Nas51]   J. Nash, *Non-cooperative games*, Annals of Math. **54** (1951) 286–295.

[NS50]   J. Nash and L. Shapley, *A simple three-person poker game*, Contributions to the Theory of Games, pp. 105–116. Annals of Mathematics Studies, no. 24. Princeton University Press, Princeton, NJ, 1950.

[Obe95]   U. Oberst, *Variations on the fundamental principle for linear systems of partial differential and difference equations with constant coefficients*, Appl. Algebra Engrg. Comm. Comput. **6** (1995) 211–243.

[Obe99]   U. Oberst, *The construction of Noetherian operators*, Journal of Algebra **222** (1999) 595–620.

[Par00]   P. Parrilo, *Structured Semidefinite Programs and Semialgebraic Geometry Methods in Robustness and Optimization*, Ph.D. thesis, California Institute of Technology, 2000, `http://www.aut.ee.ethz.ch/~parrilo/pubs/index.html`.

[PaS01]   P. Parrilo and B. Sturmfels, *Minimizing polynomial functions*, to appear in the Proceedings of the DIMACS Workshop on Algorithmic and Quantitative Aspects of Real Algebraic Geometry in Mathematics and Computer Science (March 2001), (eds. S. Basu and L. Gonzalez-Vega), American Mathematical Society, posted at `math.OC/0103170`.

[PeS93]   P. Pedersen and B. Sturmfels, *Product formulas for resultants and Chow forms*, Mathematische Zeitschrift **214** (1993) 377–396.

[Pin98]   J.-E. Pin, *Tropical semirings*. Idempotency (Bristol, 1994), 50–69, Publ. Newton Inst., 11, Cambridge Univ. Press, Cambridge, 1998.

[PRW01]   G. Pistone, E. Riccomagno and H.P. Wynn, *Algebraic Statistics: Computational Commutative Algebra in Statistics*, Chapman and Hall, Boca Raton, Florida, 2001.

[Rou99]   F. Roullier, *Solving zero-dimensional systems through the rational univariate representation*, Appl. Algebra Engrg. Comm. Comput. **9** (1999) 433–461.

[Roy01]   M.-F. Roy, Lecture at the DIMACS Workshop on Algorithmic and Quantitative Aspects of Real Algebraic Geometry in Mathematics and Computer Science (March 2001).

[SST99]   M. Saito, B. Sturmfels and N. Takayama, *Gröbner Deformations of Hypergeometric Differential Equations*, Algorithms and Computation in Mathematics **6**, Springer Verlag, Heidelberg, 1999.

[Sca73]   H. Scarf, *The computation of economic equilibria*, Cowles Foundation Monograph, No. 24, Yale University Press, New Haven, Conn.-London, 1973.

[Sha94]   I. Shafarevich, *Basic Algebraic Geometry. 1. Varieties in Projective Space*, Second edition. Translated from the 1988 Russian edition and with notes by Miles Reid. Springer-Verlag, Berlin, 1994.

[Sho98]   N. Shor, *Nondifferentiable Optimization and Polynomial Problems*, Nonconvex Optimization and its Applications, Volume 24. Kluwer Academic Publishers, Dordrecht, 1998.

[SVW01]   A. Sommese, J. Verschelde and C. Wampler, *Numerical decomposition of the solution sets of polynomial systems into irreducible components*, SIAM J. Numer. Anal. **38** (2001) 2022–2046.

[vSt99]   B. von Stengel, *New maximal numbers of equilibria in bimatrix games*, Discrete and Computational Geometry **21** (1999) 557–568.

[vSt02]   B. von Stengel, *Computing equilibria for two-person games*, Chapter 45, *Handbook of Game Theory*, Vol. 3, eds. R. J. Aumann and S. Hart, North-Holland, 2002.

[Ste74]   G. Stengle, *A nullstellensatz and a positivstellensatz in semialgebraic geometry*, Math. Ann. **207** (1974) 87–97.

[Stu94]   B. Sturmfels, *On the Newton polytope of the resultant*, Journal of Algebraic Combinatorics **3** (1994) 207–236.

[Stu95]   B. Sturmfels, *Gröbner Bases and Convex Polytopes*, American Mathematical Society, University Lectures Series, No. 8, Providence, Rhode Island, 1995.

[Stu00]   B. Sturmfels, *Solving algebraic equations in terms of $\mathcal{A}$-hypergeometric series*, Discrete Mathematics **210** (2000) 171-181.

[SZ94]   B. Sturmfels and A. Zelevinsky, *Multigraded resultants of Sylvester type*, Journal of Algebra **163** (1994) 115-127.

[Tak99]   A. Takken, *Monte Carlo Goodness-of-Fit Tests for Discrete Data*, PhD Dissertation, Department of Statistics, Stanford University, 1999.

[The02]   T. Theobald, *Computing amoebas*, Experimental Mathematics, to appear, posted at `http://www-m9.mathematik.tu-muenchen.de/dm/homepages/theobald/publications/`

[VB96]   L. Vandenberghe and S. Boyd, *Semidefinite programming*, SIAM Review **38** (1996) 49–95.

[Yu99]   Y. Yu, *The permanent rank of a matrix*, J. Combin. Theory Ser. A **85** (1999) 237–242.

Index